*22nd Edition 2002–2003*

# Grants *and* Awards *available to* American Writers

$£¥€$£¥€$£¥€$£¥€$£¥€$£¥€$£¥€$£¥€$£¥€$£¥€$£¥€$£¥€$£¥€$£¥€$£¥€$£¥€$£¥€$£¥€$£¥€$£¥€$£¥€$£¥€$£¥€$£¥€$£¥€$£¥€$£¥€$£¥€$£¥€

Series Editor: JOHN MORRONE

Principal Researcher: VICTORIA KUPCHINETSKY

Copy Editor: ANNA JARDINE

A Publication of the PEN American Center

Grants and Awards Available to American Writers
22nd Edition 2002-2003
© 2002 PEN American Center
Printed in the United States of America
ISBN: 0-934638-20-9

A publication of
PEN American Center
568 Broadway
New York, NY 10012-3225
www.pen.org

Cover: Erin Shigaki, Purple Gate Design

First printing: August 2002

# CONTENTS

### A Note on Using this Book

Because the term *writer* covers many categories, we have coded pertinent entries with the following designations, and as described further below:

| | |
|---|---|
| Fiction | Ⓕ |
| Poetry | Ⓟ |
| Drama | Ⓓ |
| Journalism | Ⓙ |
| General Nonfiction | Ⓝ |
| Children's Literature | Ⓒ |
| Translation | Ⓣ |
| Screenwriting | Ⓢ |

Most awards that apply to more than two of the eight categories above are designated by the symbol Ⓜ. These codes are located in the margin of each page, to the left of the award description.

Residences for writers are indicated by the symbol Ⓡ.

Awards for which individuals may not apply directly on their own behalf are designated in the margin with the symbol Ⓘ and in the text of the entry with *By Internal Nomination Only*.

The appendix provides a listing of state commissions and agencies for such programs as writers-in-residence and poets-in-the-schools, and for arts and humanities initiatives. Three indexes address awards, organizations, and categories. The category index uses the letter symbols described above.

Deadlines given are, for the most part, confirmed for 2002 and 2003. Writers should always confirm these dates before submitting applications or other materials.

# Editor's Note

The 2002-2003 edition of PEN's *Grants and Awards Available to American Writers* is the most comprehensive directory of domestic and foreign grants and awards for use by American writers in the United States and abroad. First published in 1969 as a pamphlet, and now updated as a book every two years by PEN American Center, the association of literary writers, *Grants and Awards* is a low-cost, one-volume directory for writers of all income brackets, at work in all genres and at various levels of achievement.

*Grants and Awards'* principal researcher, Victoria Kupchinesky, has listed primarily competitions that offer a cash stipend of $500 or more, and/or publication of a manuscript or production of a dramatic or performance work. Occasionally, an award is included even though its stipend is less than $500, because it confers a special distinction in the field it honors. Some of the prizes offered by established literary magazines are given only to authors of works that have appeared in those publications during the past year or season; therefore, no deadline is stated. Also listed are grants that are not exclusively for writers, but whose purposes are defined broadly enough that writers are among the pool of eligible applicants. Some of these are research grants or fellowships sponsored by foundations or academic institutions; the main criterion in deciding whether to list them is the likelihood that the grant will allow recipients to produce writing of a literary, rather than a purely technical, nature.

What's new in the 2002-2003 edition? In 1998, *Grants and Awards* began to give sponsoring organizations' fax numbers, e-mail addresses, and Web site addresses; many more appear this time around, as organizations frequently encourage applicants to fax or e-mail inquiries about their programs, and may even allow browsers to download application forms directly. (We have also begun to give many organizations' general telephone numbers, which frequently appear on their Web sites.) In most cases, however, formal applications are not accepted electronically. If you are obtaining documents electronically from the organizations named in this book, ascertain the method by which you are expected to file an application before you do so. New to this edition, it should be noted, are a number of on-line publishers that *expect* electronic submissions.

A total of 104 new awards from seventy-five organizations are described in this edition; forty-six discontinued programs have been dropped from the previous edition. As in the previous edition, the total number of grants and awards featured in this edition exceeds 1,000. In order to keep *Grants and Awards* to a manageable length, we no longer include award programs that are strictly for Canadian writers, and we mention only those Canadian awards for which U.S. writers may apply. Canadian nationals and landed immigrants should consult the informational booklets available from the Writers Union of Canada, 24 Ryerson Avenue, Toronto, Ontario M5T 2P3; www.writersunion.ca.

*Grants and Awards* continues to list programs in foreign countries for which American writers are eligible. These are found under the alphabetized name of the specific country or, if the scope of the prize encompasses more than one country, under INTERNATIONAL.

"A mark, a yen, a buck, or a pound" (as Sally Bowles sang in *Cabaret*)? The conversion of many, but not all, European currencies to the euro caused some uncertainty about the amounts of certain awards administered abroad. Where we were able to confirm the amount of the stipend in euros, that information is included. In cases where it was unclear, we have stated the amount most recently awarded in the former currency.

To assist readers in finding awards that may be of particular relevance, we have coded most entries according to the type of writing involved. See "A Note on Using This Book" for a detailed description of the codes. Attention, writers for the silver screen! In the previous edition, we acknowledged a substantial increase in the number of awards for screenwriting, and added a new category to the list. The code S alerts readers to a program that rewards a screenwriter with a prize or a production opportunity; awards for other dramatic works are coded D.

Attention, also, journalists: Scholarships intended for journalists proliferate, and we have included information on quite a few. While there are many more than those named here, we have chosen not to be exhaustive, because scholarships often give smaller (and variable) cash stipends and sometimes limit applicants to very localized groups (usually defined geographically).

The category writers' residences—indicated by the symbol R—refers to retreats, colonies, or other residences where writers may work undisturbed, and to which access is won by competitive application. Not coded as such are teacher-in-residence, playwright-in-residence, or similar positions that entail academic responsibilities or oblige the writer to lead workshops, lectures, or readings.

The symbol IN refers to those prizes or fellowships for which writers may not apply; recipients are nominated and selected by a jury or an appointed panel. As a courtesy to the sponsoring organizations, which cannot answer the numerous inquiries received, the words *By Internal Nomination Only* appear at the end of descriptions of such awards, and the usual information on restrictions, deadlines, and person to whom to apply does not appear. We stress that applications for these awards are neither accepted nor even considered. Note, furthermore, that several large and well-known foundations are not listed in *Grants and Awards* at their own request, because they do not solicit nominations and they wish to discourage pointless applications.

Many organizations have elaborate application forms and very specific guidelines, which the entries here, in the interest of brevity, summarize and condense. As a matter of course, prospective applicants should contact the sponsor of a grant or an award before sending books, manuscripts, or other material. Because deadline dates are subject to change, applicants should confirm them with the sponsoring organizations. Always include a self-addressed, stamped envelope (SASE) with any inquiry, application, or submission; this is standard practice. Some awards are not given annually, or not given at all in 2002 or 2003, but if the foundation or association is active and will administer prizes in the future, we have listed it. Wherever we have been informed that a reading fee is required for submissions, we have noted it.

This edition of *Grants and Awards* remains current until the end of 2003; the twenty-third edition will be published in mid-2004. Users should bear in mind that no directory of this nature can be definitive. Other sources to consult are the annual editions of *Study Abroad* and the Theatre Communications Group's *Dramatists Sourcebook* (one of several directories intended for playwrights and other scriptwriters). Monthly or bimonthly writers' magazines such as *Poets & Writers*, *The Writer*, and *Writer's Digest* provide updated information. Especially useful are the newsletters and occasional publications of the American Society of Journalists and Authors, the Authors League, the Dramatists Guild, the Editorial Freelancers Association, and Theatre Communications Group. *AWP Newsletter*, published by The Associated Writing Programs, is helpful in obtaining information on writers' residences, for the summer or for the academic year, and on writers' conferences. The Modern Language Association publishes its *MLA-ADE Job Information List* four times annually; some positions enumerated there may be of interest to writers.

For writers living in—or passing through—the New York metropolitan area, the library of The Foundation Center (79 Fifth Avenue, New York, NY 10003) makes available to grant-hunters extensive, reliable, up-to-date, and well-organized data on foundations offering grants, awards, and fellowships. Write to the Center for locations of its regional offices.

Every state government has a council or commission on the arts, usually located in the capital city. These agencies often sponsor grants, fellowships, or short-term residences, such as poets-in-the-schools programs, for which writers may apply. These programs usually are available only to state residents and pertain to arts and cultural matters of the region. Some of the more notable ones are listed in this book. The appendix gives the addresses of arts councils in the United States, the District of Columbia, Puerto Rico, and the U. S. Virgin Islands.

For writers interested in writing abroad or researching a subject that necessitates foreign travel, the cultural attaché of the country concerned—usually at the embassy in Washington, D. C., or in New York City—may provide information on opportunities for advanced study and research, and on international literary awards.

The revisions in this edition are based on replies to a survey conducted between January and June 2002, supplemented by material from the latest references in the field and from readers' responses. PEN American Center thanks the many foundations, universities, publishers, professional organizations, and foreign and U.S. government agencies that furnished the information for this publication. PEN assumes no responsibility for the conduct of the organizations listed, and invites readers to report on their experiences with any of them. Additional entries, suggestions for the improvement of subsequent editions, and feedback on the sponsoring organizations included are greatly appreciated. Correspondence should be addressed to: PEN American Center, 568 Broadway, New York, NY 10012-3225; fax: 212-334-2181; e-mail: jm@pen.org.

John Morrone
July 2002

# GRANTS AND AWARDS

**A Contemporary Theatre**
**The Eagles Building**
**700 Union Street**
**Seattle, WA 98101-2330**
**Web site: http://www.acttheatre.org**
**Fax: 206-292-7670**

Ⓓ The *ACT/Hedgebrook Women Playwrights Festival* selects four women playwrights for a staged readings of their unproduced work, with audience feedback. Playwrights receive one-week residences at Hedgebrook to work on revisions, based on responses to the reading. Two dramaturgs are also in residence, and there is a stipend of $1,000 for each playwright. Self-nominations are not accepted; selected literary managers, artistic directors, and established playwrights are asked to nominate playwrights. Send SASE for additional information.

Available to: Women playwrights
Deadline: Inquire
Apply to: ACT/Hedgebrook Women Playwrights Festival, above address

**Academy of American Poets**
**588 Broadway, Suite 1203**
**New York, NY 10012-3210**
**E-mail: mtyrell@poets.org**
**Web site: http://www.poets.org**

ⒾⓃ The *American Poets Fund*, established by Peter I. B. Lavan, assists poets of demonstrated ability who are in immediate and urgent financial need. Grants from this fund may not be used to promote, improve, or enhance the literary talent or reputation of the recipient, but are intended solely to reduce financial burdens. Direct applications are not accepted. Academy chancellors, fellows, and award winners may nominate poets by writing to the executive director of the Academy. *By Internal Nomination Only.*

Available to: U. S. citizens
Deadline: Ongoing
Apply to: See above

ⒾⓃ The *Fellowship of the Academy of American Poets* is awarded in recognition of "distinguished poetic achievement." One fellowship of $35,000 is awarded annually to a poet at mid-career. *By Internal Nomination Only.*

Ⓟ Ⓣ The *Harold Morton Landon Translation Award* is given for a published translation of poetry into English from any language. This may be a book-length poem, a collection of poems, or a verse drama translated into verse. One prize of $1,000 is awarded annually. Collaborations by two or more translators are accepted; anthologies of work by a number of translators are not. Self-published books are ineligible. Write, e-mail, or see the Web site for additional information.

Available to: U. S. citizens
Deadline: Manuscripts accepted January 1-December 31
Apply to: Harold Morton Landon Translation Award, above address

Ⓟ The *James Laughlin Award* is given annually for a poet's second book of poetry. The Academy awards a cash prize of $5,000 directly to the poet and purchases 10,000 copies of the winning book for distribution to its members. Only manuscripts already under contract with publishers from May 1 of the previous year to April 30 of the current year are considered. Write, e-mail, or see the Web site for guidelines and required entry form.

1

Available to: American poets who have published one volume of poetry in a standard edition (40 pages or more; print run of 500 or more)
Deadline: April 30
Apply to: James Laughlin Award, above address

(P) The *Lenore Marshall Poetry Prize* of $10,000, administered in conjunction with *The Nation*, is given annually for an outstanding book of poems published in the U. S. during the previous calendar year. Books must be in a standard edition (40 pages or more; print run of 500 or more); self-published books are not eligible. To enter, publishers should send four copies of the book to the Academy. Write, e-mail, or see the Web site for additional information.

Available to: U. S. citizens
Deadline: Submissions accepted April 1-June 1
Apply to: Lenore Marshall Poetry Prize, above address

(P) (T) The *Raiziss/de Palchi Translation Award* consists of a $5,000 book prize or a $20,000 fellowship, given in alternate years, for the translation into English of modern or contemporary Italian poetry. The book prize is awarded to a living translator for a published translation of a significant work. The fellowship is awarded to a U. S. citizen engaged in a translation; the winner also receives a residence at the American Academy in Rome. Send SASE, e-mail, or see the Web site for guidelines and application.

Available to: U. S. citizens
Deadline: November 1 in odd-numbered years for book prize; September 1-November 1 in even-numbered years for fellowship
Apply to: Raiziss/de Palchi Translation Award, above address

[IN] The *Wallace Stevens Award* carries an annual stipend of $150,000 in recognition of outstanding and proven mastery in the art of poetry. *By Internal Nomination Only.*

(P) The *Walt Whitman Award* is given annually for a manuscript of 50 to 100 pages of original poetry in English by a poet who has not published a book of poems in a standard edition (40 pages or more; print run of 500 or more). The winner receives a cash prize of $5,000, a one-month residence at the Vermont Studio Center, and publication by Louisiana State University Press. The Academy purchases 10,000 copies of the book for distribution to its members. There is a $25 entry fee. Send SASE, e-mail, or see the Web site for guidelines and required entry form.

Available to: U. S. citizens
Deadline: Manuscripts accepted September 15-November 15
Apply to: Walt Whitman Award, above address

**Academy of Motion Picture Arts and Sciences**
**Nicholl Fellowships**
**8949 Wilshire Boulevard**
**Beverly Hills, CA 90211**
**E-mail: nicholl@oscars.org**
**Web site: http://www.oscars.org/nicholl**

(S) Up to five *Don and Gee Nicholl Screenwriting Fellowships*, of $30,000 each, are available annually for original, full-length feature scripts of 100 to 130 pages, with the understanding that the recipients will complete a new feature screenplay during the fellowship year. Entries must be in English (no translations) and must display exceptional craft and engaging storytelling. Writers must not have sold or optioned a feature screenplay or teleplay, or earned more than $5,000 for writing one. There is a $30 entry fee. Contact the Academy from January through April or consult the Web site year-round for further information.

Available to: See above
Deadline: Submissions accepted January-April
Apply to: Nicholl Fellowships, above address

**Acadia National Park**
**PO Box 177**
**Bar Harbor, ME 04609**
**E-mail: acadia-information@nps.gov**

®    The *Artist-in-Residence Program* offers professional writers and other artists the opportunity to pursue their particular art form in the inspiring landscape of Acadia National park. Participants receive housing for three-week periods in spring and fall, in return for which they are asked to donate a piece of work representative of their style and their stay. They are also asked to make a public appearance during their residence. Write for additional information and guidelines.

     Available to: No restrictions
     Deadline: Applications accepted November 1-January 1
     Apply to: Coordinator, Artist-in-Residence Program, above address

**The Actors' Fund of America**
**729 Seventh Avenue, 10th floor**
**New York, NY 10019**
**Web site: http://www.actorsfund.org**

**5757 Wilshire Boulevard**
**Los Angeles, CA 90036**

**203 North Wabash, Suite 1308**
**Chicago, IL 60601**

   The Actors' Fund of America, a nonprofit organization founded in 1882, provides for the social welfare of entertainment professionals, including writers and actors. Headquarters and the Aurora Residence are located in New York City, with regional offices in Los Angeles and Chicago; nursing and retirement homes are in Englewood, New Jersey. In addition to providing emergency grants for essentials such as food, rent, and medical care, the Actors' Fund operates comprehensive programs to meet the critical needs of entertainment professionals throughout their lives: nursing and retirement homes, senior and disabled programs, mental health and chemical dependency services, services to employable professionals, a health insurance resource center, the Phyllis Newman Women's Health Initiative, an AIDS initiative, and affordable housing. Professionals who earn their living in legitimate theater, film, radio, television, music, dance, and variety are eligible.

     Available to: See above
     Deadline: Ongoing
     Apply to: Any Actors' Fund office, above addresses

**Actors' Playhouse at the Miracle Theatre**
**280 Miracle Mile**
**Coral Gables, FL 33134**
**Web site: www. actorsplayhouse.org/**
**Fax: 305-444-4181**

© Ⓓ    The *National Children's Theatre Festival* offers a first-place award of $500 and round-trip transportation within the continental U. S. and hotel accommodations during the festival, to the author of a musical for children. The target audience is age five to twelve, and scripts should reflect a running time of 45 to 60 minutes, with a flexible act-break. Musicals lending themselves to simplified and suggested settings are at a distinct advantage. Shows suitable for touring are desired. All materials submitted must be original, unpublished, and not accepted by any other publisher at the time of submission. There is a $10 reading fee. Write for guidelines and entry form, or see the Web site.

     Available to: No restrictions
     Deadline: August 1
     Apply to: Above address

Actors Theatre of Louisville
316 West Main Street
Louisville, KY 40202-4218
Phone: 502-584-1265
E-mail: mail@actorstheatre.org
Web site: http://www.actorstheatre.org

(D)   The *National Ten-Minute Play Contest* awards $1,000 to the best 10-minute play submitted. The winning play may be considered for production by Actors Theatre of Louisville during the Humana Festival. Plays submitted must not have had a previous Equity production. Playwrights may submit only one 10-minute script, no more than 10 pages, typed and fastened. The author's name and address must appear on the title page only. No scripts will be returned.

Available to: U. S. citizens and residents
Deadline: December 1
Apply to: National Ten-Minute Play Contest, above address


Agricultural History Society
Center for Agricultural History
618 Ross Hall
Iowa State University
Ames, IA 50011-1202
E-mail: rdhurt@iastate.edu
Web site: http://www.iastate.edu/%7Ehistory_info/ahahs/awards.htm
Fax: 515-294-6390

(N)   Four awards are given annually to writers: the *Theodore Saloutos Award* of $500, to the author of the best book published on U. S. agricultural history, broadly conceived; the *Gilbert C. Fite Dissertation Award* of $300, to the author of the best dissertation on agricultural history, broadly construed, completed during the calendar year; the *Vernon Carstensen Award* of $200, for the best article published by a scholar in the quarterly journal *Agricultural History*; and the *Everett Edwards Award* of $200, for the best article in agricultural history submitted by a graduate student.

Available to: No restrictions
Deadline: December 31
Apply to: R. Douglas Hurt, Editor, *Agricultural History*, above address


Alabama State Council on the Arts
201 Monroe Street, Suite 110
Montgomery, AL 36130-1800
E-mail: randy@arts.state.al.us
Web site: http://www.arts.state.al.us
Fax: 334-240-3269

(M)   Fellowships in fiction, poetry, nonfiction, and playwriting of $5,000 and $10,000 are available annually to writers who have been residents of Alabama for at least two years. Also available are the *Jonnie Dee Little Lifetime Achievement Award, Distinguished Artist Award, Governor's Arts Awards*, and *Alabama Folk Heritage Award*. See the Web site for more details.

Available to: See above
Deadline: Inquire
Apply to: Randy Shoults, Literature Program Manager, above address


Alabama Writer's Forum
Alabama State Council on the Arts
201 Monroe Street
Montgomery, AL 36130-1800
Phone: 334-242-4076

(M)   The *Harper Lee Award* is made to a living, nationally recognized Alabama writer who has made a significant lifelong contribution to Alabama letters. The award carries a $5,000 stipend and a bronze rendering of the Monroeville Courthouse clock tower, and is presented at the Writers Symposium in Monroeville, Alabama, in May. To nominate a writer, send a letter listing the writer's credentials to the above address.

Available to: See above
Deadline: December 5.
Apply to: Harper Lee Award, above address

**Alaska State Council on the Arts**
**411 West Fourth Avenue, Suite 1E**
**Anchorage, AK 99501-2343**
**Phone: 907-269-6610**
**E-mail: info@aksca.org**
**Web site: http://www.aksca.org**
**Fax: 907-269-6601**

(M) *Career Opportunity Grants* of up to $1,000 are awarded to cover travel and other expenses for writers to take advantage of opportunities that will advance their work or careers.

Available to: Alaska residents
Deadline: First of the month prior to month of activity
Apply to: Above address

**Edward F. Albee Foundation**
**14 Harrison Street**
**New York, NY 10013**
**Phone 212-226-2020**
**E-mail: albeefdtn@aol.com**
**Web site: www.pipeline.com/**

(R) The Albee Foundation offers writers, visual artists, and composers one-month residences at its center in Montauk, Long Island, from June through September. Admission is based on talent and need. Residents are given housing but must provide their own meals and transportation. Write for guidelines.

Available to: No restrictions
Deadline: Applications accepted January 1-April 1
Apply to: Above address or Web site

**Alleyway Theatre**
**1 Curtain Up Alley**
**Buffalo, NY 14202-1911**
**Phone: 716-856-2089**
**Web site: www.alleyway.com**

(C) (D) The *Maxim Mazumdar New Play Competition* annually offers a cash prize and production for unproduced plays in the categories of full-length, one-act, and children's theater. A cash prize and production at Alleyway's yearly one-act festival, Buffalo Quickies, are offered also for a one-act. Work with an unconventional setting that explores the boundaries of theatricality is preferred. There is a $5 entry fee per playwright; only one submission is allowed in each category. Visit the Web site for additional information.

Available to: No restrictions
Deadline: July 1
Apply to: Maxim Mazumdar New Play Competition, above address

**Alligator Juniper**
**Prescott College**
**301 Grove Avenue**
**Prescott, AZ 86301**

(M) The *Alligator Juniper Writing Contest* annually offers $500 each for fiction, nonfiction, and poetry. The winning entries are published in *Alligator Juniper*, the literary journal of Prescott College. Writers should submit a story or an essay, no longer than 30 pages; poets may submit up to 5 pages of poetry. There is a $10 entry fee, which covers one issue of the journal. Send SASE for guidelines.

Available to: No restrictions
Deadline: Submissions accepted May 1-October 1
Apply to: Writing Contest, above address

## American Academy of Arts and Letters
**633 West 155th Street**
**New York, NY 10032**

Awards and honors are conferred for work of distinction, with the purpose of furthering literature and the fine arts and stimulating them in the United States. Academy members are eligible for nonmonetary awards. *Applications are not accepted for any of the following. By Internal Nomination Only.*

[IN]    *Academy Awards* are given to "honor and encourage distinguished artists, composers, and writers who are not members of the Academy." Eight awards in literature, of $7,500 each, are given annually.

[IN]    The *Award of Merit Medal of the American Academy of Arts and Letters* consists of a medal and a cash prize of $10,000 given annually, in rotation, to an outstanding person in the United States representing the novel, the short story, poetry, drama, painting, or sculpture.

[IN]    The *Michael Braude Award for Light Verse* of $5,000 is given biennially for light verse written in English, regardless of the writer's country of origin.

[IN]    The *Gold Medal of the American Academy of Arts and Letters* is given each year, in rotation, for distinguished achievement in two categories of the arts: belles lettres and criticism, and painting; biography and music; fiction and sculpture; history and architecture (including landscape architecture); poetry and music; drama and graphic art.

[IN]    The *Howells Medal of the American Academy of Arts and Letters* is given once every five years in recognition of the most distinguished work of American fiction published during that period.

[IN]    The *Sue Kaufman Prize for First Fiction* of $2,500 is given annually for the best published first novel or collection of short stories of the preceding year.

[IN]    The *Addison M. Metcalf Award in Literature* of $5,000 is given every year to a young writer of great promise.

[IN]    The *Arthur Rense Poetry Prize* of $20,000 is given periodically to an exceptional poet.

[IN]    The *Rome Fellowships in Literature* are given annually to two young writers for a year's residence at the American Academy in Rome. These awards are subsidized by the American Academy in Rome and the American Academy of Arts and Letters. Recipients are selected by the Academy.

[IN]    The *Richard and Hilda Rosenthal Foundation Award* of $5,000 is granted annually for an American work of fiction published during the preceding twelve months that, though not a commercial success, is a considerable literary achievement.

[IN]    The *Mildred and Harold Strauss Livings* provide writers of English prose literature with an annual stipend to cover living expenses so that they can devote their time exclusively to writing. The most recent Livings, each amounting to $50,000 annually, were awarded in 1998 to two writers for a period of five years. Recipients must agree to resign positions of paid employment during the term of the Livings, which will be given again in 2003.

[IN]    The *Harold D. Vursell Memorial Award* of $10,000 recognizes recent writing in book form that merits recognition for the quality of its prose style. It may be given for fiction, biography, history, criticism, belles lettres, memoir, or journal, or for a translation rendered in distinguished and exceptional English prose.

IN   The *Morton Dauwen Zabel Prize* of $5,000 is given every year, in rotation, to an American poet, writer of fiction, or critic.

**American Academy in Berlin**
**14 East 60th Street, Suite 604**
**New York, NY 10022**
**E-mail: amacberline@msn.com**
**Web site: http:www.amacberlin.com**
**Fax: 212-588-1758**

®   The *Berlin Prize Fellowships* are awarded to scholars, artists, and professionals who will benefit from a residential fellowship in Berlin. Eligible are younger as well as established scholars, artists, and professionals who wish to engage in independent study in Berlin for an academic semester or, in special cases, for an entire year. Candidates may come from a range of academic disciplines or fields of practice: the arts, architecture, history, philosophy, public policy, law and society, music, journalism, film, and others. Most fellows have a concurrent association with a Berlin institution, such as a museum, library, archive, or university. Benefits include a stipend, roundtrip airfare, housing, and partial board. Appointments are open to university faculty members, artists, and practicing professionals at early, middle, or senior levels of achievement. Write, e-mail, or see the Web site for further information.

Available to: U. S. citizens or permanent residents
Deadline: February 1
Apply to: Above address

**American Academy of Religion**
**825 Houston Mill Road, Suite 300**
**Atlanta, GA 30329**
**E-mail: aar@aarweb.org**
**Web site: http://www.aarweb.org/grants/default.asp**

The *AAR Research Grants Program* provides support to AAR members for important aspects of research such as travel to archives and libraries, research assistance, and fieldwork. Grants range from $500 to $5,000 and may not be used for dissertation research or travel to the AAR annual meeting. Each proposal is judged on the basis of the project's contribution to scholarship in religious studies and the significance of that contribution for advancing the understanding of religion or discussion between religion and other humanistic and social science disciplines. Unaffiliated scholars and scholars in small institutions, departments, or programs without research support are encouraged to apply. Write or see the Web site for additional information and application procedures.

Available to: AAR members
Deadline: August 1
Apply to: AAR Research Grants Program, above address

**American Academy in Rome**
**7 East 60th Street**
**New York, NY 10022-1001**
**E-mail: info@aarome.org**
**Web site: http://www.aarome.org**
**Fax: 212-751-7220**

®   The Academy's *Rome Prize Competition* offers up to thirty fellowships with stipends of $10,000 to $20,000 for individuals of exceptional promise or achievement in architecture, landscape architecture, conservation and preservation, design, literature, musical composition, visual arts, archaeology, classical studies, history of art, modern Italian studies, and postclassical humanistic studies. Fellows receive free housing, a study or studio, and full access to library and other facilities. Applicants should be U. S. citizens with a bachelor's or master's degree, depending on the field of application. Some fellowships are open to postdoctoral candidates. There is no formal application process for the prize in literature; nominations for that award are made only by members of the American Academy of Arts and Letters (see listing above). Applications for all other fields may be downloaded from the Web site.

Available to: See above
Deadline: November 1
Apply to: Programs Department, above address

**American Alliance for Theatre and Education (AATE)**
**Arizona State University Theatre Department**
**PO Box 872002**
**Tempe, AZ 85287**
**Web site: www.aate.com**

The *Unpublished Play Reading Project* for plays for young audiences provides an opportunity for playwrights to receive constructive critiques of their work from noted and professional playwrights, producers, directors, actors, and others in the field of youth theater. An annotated list of plays deemed worthy of production is distributed by the AATE Playwrights Network to theater companies and publishers, and rehearsed readings from selected plays are featured at the annual AATE conference. For guidelines, send SASE to Jeremy Kisling, AATE/UPRP, Lexington Children's Theatre, 418 West Short Street, Lexington, KY 40507; phone 859-254-4546 ext. 226, or see the Web site.

Available to: No restrictions
Deadline: December 1
Apply to: See above

**American Antiquarian Society**
**185 Salisbury Street**
**Worcester, MA 01609-1634**
**E-mail: jdm@mwa.org**
**Fax: 508-754-9069**

® *Long-Term Postdoctoral Fellowships* provide support for four-to-twelve-month residences in the Society's library and carry stipends of up to $35,000. These include the *AAS-National Endowment for the Humanities Fellowships*, with a maximum stipend of $30,000, and the *Mellon Postdoctoral Research Fellowships*, with a maximum stipend of $35,000. The latter are awarded for an academic year (nine or ten months).

Available to: See above
Deadline: January 15
Apply to: Above address

® *Short-Term Fellowships* provide support for one to three months' residence in the Society's library and carry stipends of $950 per month. These include the *Kate B. and Hall J. Peterson Fellowship* and the *Legacy Fellowship*, for research on any topic supported by the collections; the *Stephen Botein Fellowships*, for research in the history of the book in American culture; the *AAS-American Society for Eighteenth-Century Studies Fellowships*, for research on projects related to the American eighteenth century; the *American Historical Print Collectors Society Fellowship*, for research on American prints of the eighteenth and nineteenth centuries or for projects using prints as primary documentation; the *Joyce A. Tracy Fellowship*, for research on newspapers and magazines or for projects using these as primary documentation; the *Reese Fellowship* for bibliographical research and projects in the history of the book in American culture; the *AAS-Northeast Modern Language Association Fellowship* for research in American literary studies through 1876; and the *Richard F. and Virginia P. Morgan Fellowship* for research on Ohio history or using Ohio-printed materials in bibliography, the history of the book, or both. Application packets, with full details about the fellowships, must be requested before an application is made. Write, e-mail, or fax for materials.

Available to: See above
Deadline: January 15
Apply to: Above address

® At least three *Visiting Fellowships for Historical Research by Creative and Performing Artists and*

*Writers* will be awarded, for four-to-eight-week residences at the Society. The stipend is $1,200 per four-week period, plus an allowance for travel expenses. (There are no funds available for housing, which is, however, available in the Society's Goddard-Daniels House. Room rents range from $295 to $495 per week.) The Society seeks fellows whose goals are to produce works on pre-twentieth-century American history intended for the general public rather than for academic or educational communities. Research and study carried out under these fellowships may focus on virtually any subject within the general area of American history and culture before 1877. The end products of research developed under these fellowships may include but are not limited to historical novels, historical nonfiction for general audiences of adults or children, plays or screenplays, and magazine or newspaper articles. Write for additional information and guidelines.

Available to: No restrictions
Deadline: October (inquire for exact date)
Apply to: James David Moran, above address


**American Association for the Advancement of Science**
**1200 New York Avenue, NW**
**Washington, DC 20005**
**E-mail: media@aaas.org**

Ⓙ The *AAAS Science Journalism Awards* are given for outstanding coverage of science, engineering, and mathematics. Entries are judged on the basis of initiative, originality, scientific accuracy, clarity of interpretation, and value in promoting the understanding of science by the public. There are six awards, of $2,500 each: for writing in newspapers with a circulation of more than 100,000; for writing in newspapers with a daily circulation of less than 100,000; for writing in general-circulation magazines; for on-line reporting; for radio reporting; and for television reporting. Entries must have been published in a publication or broadcast in the U. S. during the contest year, which runs from July 1 through June 30 of the following year.

Available to: See above
Deadline: August 1
Apply to: Office of News and Information, Science Journalism Awards, above address


**American Association of University Women**
**2201 North Dodge Street**
**Iowa City, IA 52243-4030**
**Web site: www.aauw.org**

The AAUW Educational Foundation offers a variety of fellowships and grants to help women reach their personal and professional goals, including: *American Fellowships,* which support women doctoral candidates writing dissertations and scholars seeking postdoctoral/research leave funds; *Career Development Grants,* for women with a bachelor's degree and who are seeking support for graduate studies in order to reenter the work force, change careers, or advance their current career; and *International Fellowships,* for full-time graduate or postgraduate study or research for women who are not U. S. citizens to study in the U. S. Stipends vary. Write for additional information and application procedures.

Available to: Women; see above
Deadline: Varies according to program (inquire)
Apply to: Educational Foundation, above address


**American Booksellers Association**
**828 South Broadway**
**Tarrytown, NY 10591**
**E-mail: jill@bookweb.org**
**Web site: http://www.bookweb.org**

IN The *Book Sense Book of the Year Award*, formerly known as the American Booksellers Book of the Year, is chosen by Book Sense independent booksellers from across the country, who nominate the books they most enjoyed hand-selling to their customers throughout the year. Awards are given for adult fiction, adult nonfiction, children's illustrated, and children's literature. Winners each receive a plaque, and $2,500 will be donated to the charity of their choice; all finalists receive a special gift. There is no application process. *By Internal Nomination Only.*

**American Chemical Society**
**1155 16th Street, NW**
**Washington, DC 20036**
**Phone: 202-452-2109**
**Web site: www.chemistry.org/awards**
**Fax: 202-776-8211**

ⓙ The *James T. Grady-James H. Stack Award for Interpreting Chemistry for the Public* is given to recognize, encourage, and stimulate outstanding reporting that materially increases the public's knowledge and understanding of chemistry, chemical engineering, and related fields. This information must have been disseminated through press, radio, television, film, lecture, or book or pamphlet for the lay public. The award, which consists of $3,000 and a gold medal, is given annually. Recipients must be nominated by a colleague for a career accomplishment.

Available to: No restrictions
Deadline: February 1
Apply to: Office of the Awards Program, above address

**American Council of Learned Societies**
**228 East 45th Street**
**New York, NY 10017**
**E-mail: Grants@acls.org**
**Web site: http://www.acls.org**
**Fax: 212-949-8058**

The Council offers various types of grants for which scholars doing research in the humanities and humanities-related social sciences may qualify. Fellowships are given for holders of a doctorate or its equivalent tenable in the U. S. or abroad, with specialized fellowships for dissertation or postdoctoral work in American art, Eastern European studies, Chinese studies, and contemplative practice. Stipends and fellowship tenure periods vary by program.

Available to: U. S. citizens and permanent residents
Deadline: September (inquire for exact dates)
Apply to: Office of Fellowships, above address

**American Film Institute**
**2021 North Western Avenue**
**Los Angeles, CA 90027-1657**
**Web site: www.AFIonline.org**

Ⓢ The *AFI Directing Workshop for Women* selects up to eight women annually to attend a hands-on training program. They are provided with $5,000 for their production and a production equipment package. Women directors may apply with a script they have written or with another screenwriter's work for which all necessary rights have been obtained. There is a $60 application fee. See the Web site for more details.

Available to: Women who are U. S. citizens or permanent residents
Deadline: January 14
Apply to: Above address

**American Historical Association**
**400 A Street, SE**
**Washington, DC 20003**
**E-mail: aha@theaha.org**
**Web site: http://www.theaha.org**
**Fax: 202-544-8307**

*Albert J. Beveridge Grants* of up to $1,000 are offered annually to AHA members to support research in the history of the Western Hemisphere.

Available to: AHA members
Deadline: February 1
Apply to: Above address

The *J. Franklin Jameson Fellowship*, co-sponsored by the Library of Congress and the AHA, awards a stipend of $10,000 to a young historian for significant scholarly research in the collections of the Library.

Available to: No restrictions
Deadline: January 15
Apply to: Above address

*Michael Kraus Research Grants* of up to $800 are offered to AHA members for research in American colonial history, with particular reference to the intercultural aspects of American and European relations.

Available to: AHA members
Deadline: February 1
Apply to: Above address

*Littleton-Griswold Research Grants* of up to $1,000 are offered to AHA members to support research in American legal history and the field of law and society.

Available to: AHA members
Deadline: February 1
Apply to: Above address

The *NASA Fellowship* annually provides applicants of unusual ability the opportunity to engage in significant and sustained advanced research in NASA aerospace science, technology, management, or policy. The fellowship awards a stipend of $25,000 to postdoctoral candidates and $16,000 to predoctoral.

Available to: U. S. citizens
Deadline: February 15
Apply to: Above address

*Bernadette E. Schmitt Research Grants* of up to $1,000 are offered annually to AHA members to support research in the history of Europe, Africa, and Asia.

Available to: AHA members
Deadline: September 1
Apply to: Above address

For the following book prizes, updated applications/guidelines are available on the AHA Web site approximately two months before the submission deadline; obtain current guidelines before submission. Do not send books directly to the AHA for consideration. Current guidelines will provide addresses of judging committee members.

Ⓝ The *AHA Prize in Atlantic History* is awarded annually for an outstanding book exploring aspects of the integration of the Atlantic worlds before the 20th century.

Available: No Restrictions
Deadline: May 15
Apply to: Above address

Ⓝ The *Herbert Baxter Adams Prize* is awarded for an author's first book on ancient, medieval, or early modern European history.

Available to: U. S. and Canadian residents
Deadline: May 15
Apply to: Above address

Ⓝ The *George Louis Beer Prize* is awarded annually in recognition of outstanding historical writing by a U. S. citizen on European international history since 1895.

Available to: U. S. citizens
Deadline: May 15
Apply to: Above address

(N) The *Albert J. Beveridge Award* is given annually for the best book on the history of the Americas (U. S., Canada, or Latin America) from 1492 to the present.

Available to: No restrictions
Deadline: May 15
Apply to: Above address

(N) The *Paul Birdsall Prize* is awarded in even-numbered years for a major work on European military and strategic history.

Available to: U. S. or Canadian citizens
Deadline: May 15
Apply to: Above address

(N) The *James Henry Breasted Prize* is offered annually for the best book in any field of history before the year 1000.

Available to: No restrictions
Deadline: May 15
Apply to: Above address

(N) The *Albert B. Corey Prize in Canadian-American Relations* is awarded biennially for the best book on the history of Canadian-American relations or the history of both countries. The prize is awarded jointly by the Canadian Historical Association and the AHA.

Available to: No restrictions
Deadline: May 15
Apply to: Above address

(N) The *John H. Dunning Prize* is awarded in odd-numbered years for an author's first or second book on any subject relating to U. S. history.

Available to: No restrictions
Deadline: May 15
Apply to: Above address

(N) The *John E. Fagg Prize* was established in 2001 to recognize the best publication in the history of Spain, Portugal, or Latin America. The prize will be awarded annually through 2011.

Available to: No restrictions
Deadline: May 15
Apply to: Above address

(N) The *John K. Fairbank Prize in East Asian History* is awarded annually for an outstanding book on the history of China proper, Chinese Central Asia, Japan, Korea, Mongolia, or Vietnam since 1800.

Available to: No restrictions
Deadline: May 15
Apply to: Above address

(N) The *Herbert Feis Award*, funded by a grant from the Rockefeller Foundation, is given annually for the best book, article, or policy paper by an independent scholar or public historian.

Available to: No restrictions
Deadline: May 15
Apply to: Above address

(N) The *Morris O. Forkosch Prize* is given annually for the best work published on modern British, British imperial, and British Commonwealth history by a U. S. citizen.

Available to: U. S. citizens
Deadline: May 15
Apply to: Above address

Ⓝ    The *Leo Gershoy Award* is given annually to the author of the most outstanding work in English on any aspect of seventeenth- and/or eighteenth-century European history.

Available to: No restrictions
Deadline: May 15
Apply to: Above address

Ⓝ    The *Clarence H. Haring Prize* is awarded every five years to the Latin American who has published the most outstanding book of Latin American history during the preceding five years. The next award will be given in 2006.

Available to: Latin American historians
Deadline: May 15
Apply to: Above address

Ⓝ    The *J. Franklin Jameson Prize* is a quinquennial award for outstanding achievement in the editing of historical sources; it will be granted next in 2005.

Available to: No restrictions
Deadline: May 15
Apply to: Above address

Ⓝ    The *Joan Kelly Memorial Prize in Women's History* is offered annually for the best work in women's history and/or feminist theory.

Available to: No restrictions
Deadline: May 15
Apply to: Above address

Ⓝ    The *Waldo G. Leland Prize,* offered for an outstanding reference tool in the field of history, is given every five years. The next award will be given in 2006.

Available to: No restrictions
Deadline: May 15
Apply to: Above address

Ⓝ    The *Littleton-Griswold Prize* is offered annually for the best book on any subject in the history of American law and society.

Available to: No restrictions
Deadline: May 15
Apply to: Above address

Ⓝ    The *J. Russell Major Prize* is awarded annually to the best work in English on any aspect of French history.

Available to: No restrictions
Deadline: May 15
Apply to: Above address

Ⓝ    The *Helen and Howard R. Marraro Prize* is given for the best work on any epoch of Italian history or cultural history or on Italian-American relations.

Available to: U. S. and Canadian residents
Deadline: May 15
Apply to: Above address

Ⓝ    The *G. L. Moss Prize* will be awarded annually for a major work in European intellectual and cultural history since the Renaissance.

Available to: No restrictions
Deadline: May 15
Apply to: Above address

Ⓝ    The *Premio del Rey* is awarded in even-numbered years for the best book in English on Hispanic history and culture in Spain and/or other Hispanic countries before 1516.

Available to: No restrictions

Deadline: May 15
Apply to: Above address

Ⓝ The *James Harvey Robinson Prize* is awarded in even-numbered years for the teaching aid that has made the greatest contribution to the teaching of history.

Available to: No restrictions
Deadline: May 15
Apply to: Above address

Ⓝ The *Wesley-Logan Prize* is given annually for an outstanding book on any aspect of the dispersion, settlement, and adjustment of peoples originally from Africa, or their return.

Available to: No restrictions
Deadline: May 15
Apply to: Above address

**American Institute of Indian Studies**
**University of Chicago**
**1130 East 59th Street**
**Chicago, IL 60637**
**E-mail: aiis@uchicago.edu**
**Web site: http://indiastudies.org**

The American Institute of Indian Studies annually offers *Senior Research Fellowships* (postdoctoral), *Senior Scholarly Development Fellowships, Junior Research Fellowships* (doctoral), and *Senior Performing and Creative Arts Fellowships* for study and research in India. Award funds are made available in foreign currency only. Requirements vary; query the Institute before applying. (Also available is a limited intensive-language program in India; contact the Institute for further information and deadline.)

Available to: U. S. citizens at the doctoral or postdoctoral level and foreign nationals enrolled at the doctoral level or teaching full-time (postdoctoral) at American colleges or universities. U. S. and Indian government employees are ineligible.
Deadline: July 1
Apply to: Above address

**American Institute of Physics**
**Media & Government Relations**
**One Physics Ellipse**
**College Park, MD 20740-3843**
**Phone: 301-209-3090**
**E-mail: fgonzale@aip.org**
**Web site: www.aip.org/aip/writing**

Ⓝ The AIP *Science Writing Awards in Physics and Astronomy* recognize distinguished writing that improves the public's understanding and appreciation of physics and astronomy in four categories: children's writing; professional journalism; science; and broadcast media. Winners receive a $3,000 prize, an engraved Windsor chair, and a certificate. International entries are accepted, but must be translated into English. Call or see the Web site for more information.

Available to: U. S., Canadian, and Mexican residents
Deadlines: March 1
Apply to: Above address

**American Jewish Archives**
**3101 Clifton Avenue**
**Cincinnati, OH 45220**
**E-mail: aja@huc.edu**
**Web site: http://www.huc.edu/aja**

Fellowships for active research or writing at the American Jewish Archives are offered to doctoral and postdoctoral candidates in American Jewish studies and to unaffiliated, independent, and senior scholars. Stipends cover living expenses while in residence in Cincinnati. Write, e-mail, or consult the Web site for further information and application guidelines.

Available to: No restrictions
Deadline: March 1
Apply to: Administrative Director, above address

**The American Legion**
**Public Relations Division**
**700 North Pennsylvania Street**
**Indianapolis, IN 46204**
**E-mail: pr@legion.org**
**Web site: http://www.legion.org**

Ⓙ Ⓝ  The *American Legion Fourth Estate Award* is given for the best work published or broadcast during the calendar year that "covers an issue of national interest and contributes to the American way of life." A stipend of $2,000 is intended to defray the recipient's expenses in accepting the award at the Legion National Convention in September. Each entry must include a cover letter explaining the entry, and documentation or evidence of its impact on the community, state, or nation. Write or see the Web site for additional information.

Available to: No restrictions
Deadline: January 31
Apply to: Fourth Estate Award, above address

**American Library Association**
**50 East Huron Street**
**Chicago, IL 60611**
**E-mail: awards@ala.org**
**Web site: http://www.ala.org**

Ⓕ  The *Bill Boyd Library Literature Award* of $5,000 is given for the best book-length work of fiction set in a period when the U. S. was at war. The award recognizes the service of American veterans and military personnel and encourages outstanding war-related fiction. Publishers or authors should submit six copies of the work; the book must have been published during the year prior to the submission deadline. Write for additional information.

Available to: No restrictions
Deadline: December 1
Apply to: ALA Awards Program, Member Programs and Services, above address

Ⓜ  The *Gay, Lesbian, Bisexual, and Transgendered (GLBT) Book Award* is given annually to English-language books of exceptional merit relating to gay, lesbian, bisexual, and transgendered experience. Awards are made in literature, which includes novels, short stories, poetry, and drama, and in nonfiction, which includes biography, history, criticism, reference, fine arts, and other traditional nonfiction genres. Each winner receives a commemorative plaque and a cash stipend to be determined by the GLBT Round Table of the ALA. Nominations for books published between December 1 of the previous year and November 30 of the current year may be made by the general public, librarians, or members of the GLBT Round Table. Write, e-mail, or see the Web site for additional information.

Available to: No restrictions
Deadline: November 30
Apply to: GLBT Book Award, GLBT Round Table, above address

Ⓒ  The *Coretta Scott King Award* is given annually by the Social Responsibilities Round Table (SRRT) of the ALA to honor African-American authors and illustrators for "outstanding contributions to children's and young adult literature that promote understanding and appreciation of the culture and contribution of all people to the realization of the American Dream." Winners receive a framed citation, an honorarium, and a set of the *Encyclopaedia Britannica* or *World Book Encyclopedia*. The SRRT also offers the *Coretta Scott King/John Steptoe Award for New Talent* to a black author and a black illustrator at the beginning of their careers. Candidates for this award cannot have published more than three books. Write, e-mail, or see the Web site for additional information.

Available to: African-Americans
Deadline: Inquire
Apply to: Coretta Scott King Award or Coretta Scott King/John Steptoe Award, SRRT, above address

Ⓝ  The *Eli M. Oboler Memorial Award* biennially offers $1,500 for a published work in English or in English translation dealing with issues, events, or questions in the area of intellectual freedom. Nominated books must be published in the two-year period prior to the year in which the award is granted.

Available to: No restrictions
Deadline: December 1
Apply to: Eli M. Oboler Memorial Award, Office for Intellectual Freedom, IRFT Staff Liaison, above address

**American Literary Review**
**University of North Texas**
**English Department**
**PO Box 311307**
**Denton, TX 76203-1307**
**Phone: 940-565-2755**
**E-mail: americanliteraryreview@yahoo.com**
**Web site: http://www.engl.unt.edu/alr**

Ⓕ Ⓟ  The *American Literary Review Short Fiction Contest* awards, in odd-numbered years, $500 and publication for a short story of up to 10,000 words. In even-numbered years, the review sponsors its *Poetry Contest*. There is a $10 reading fee, for which each entrant will receive a copy of the spring issue of the *Review,* where the winning story or poem appears. Send SASE or see the Web site for guidelines.

Available to: No restrictions
Deadline: October 1
Apply to: Short Fiction or Poetry Contest, above address

**American Literary Translators Association**
**University of Texas at Dallas**
**Box 830688 (MC 35)**
**Richardson, TX 75083-0688**
**Fax: 972-883-6303**

Ⓣ  The *National Translation Award*, funded by the Larry McMurtry Center for the Arts and Humanities, offers a cash prize of at least $2,000 for an English translation of a book-length work of fiction, poetry, drama, or creative nonfiction published during the calendar year. Literary criticism and philosophy are not eligible. Publishers must provide an original-language version of all books selected as finalists by August 1; finalists will be excluded from further consideration if no original-language version is provided. Translations of contemporary works receive preference, although important retranslations or first-time translations of older works are considered if they make significant contributions to literature. Publishers should submit a letter of nomination and three copies of each nominated book. Write for additional information.

Available to: No restrictions
Deadline: March 31
Apply to: National Translation Award, above address

**American Musicological Society**
**201 South 34th Street**
**Philadelphia, PA 19104-6313**
**Phone: 215-898-8698**
**E-mail: ams@sas.upenn.edu**
**Web site: http://www.sas.upenn.edu/music/ams**
**Fax: 215-573-3673**

Ⓝ The *Philip Brett Award*, consisting of monetary prize and a certificate, is given each year to honor an exceptional musicological work in the field of gay, lesbian, bisexual, or transgender/transsexual studies completed during two academic years in any country and in any language. This may be a published article, book, edition, annotated translation, conference paper, teaching material, or other scholarly work. See the Web site for additional information.

> Available to: No restrictions
> Deadline: July 1
> Apply to: Consult AMS directory for name and address of committee chairperson

Ⓝ The *Alfred Einstein Award* is given annually for a musicological article of exceptional merit by a scholar in the early stages of his or her career. The article must have been published during the preceding calendar year, in any country and in any language. The award consists of a monetary prize and a certificate signed by the president of the Society.

> Available to: U. S. and Canadian citizens or permanent residents
> Deadline: June 1
> Apply to: Consult AMS directory for name and address of committee chairperson

Ⓝ The *Otto Kinkeldey Award* of $400 is given each year for the work of musicological scholarship deemed by a committee of scholars to be the most distinguished published during the previous year in any language and in any country.

> Available to: U. S. and Canadian citizens and permanent residents
> Deadline: None
> Apply to: Consult AMS directory for name and address of committee chairperson

Ⓝ The *Paul A. Pisk Prize* is awarded annually to a music graduate student for a scholarly paper, which will be read at the Society's annual meeting. The prize, entailing a stipend determined by the Pisk Prize committee, is presented at the meeting. See the Web site for guidelines.

> Available to: No restrictions
> Deadline: October 1
> Apply to: Consult AMS directory for name and address of committee chairperson

**American Poetry Review**
**1721 Walnut Street**
**Philadelphia, PA 19103**
**Web site: www.aprweb.org**

Ⓟ The *American Poetry Review/Honickman First Book Prize* awards $3,000 and publication of a book-length volume of poems to a poet who has never published a book of poems. The winning volume will be distributed by Copper Canyon Press through Consortium. There is a $20 entry fee. Send SASE for guidelines.

> Available to: U. S. citizens
> Deadline: October 31
> Apply to: APR/Honickman First Book Prize, above address

Ⓟ The *S. J. Marks Memorial Poetry Prize* of $500 is awarded annually for a writer's first appearance in *American Poetry Review* during the preceding calendar year.

> Available to: See above
> Deadline: Ongoing
> Apply to: Submit manuscripts to above address with SASE

(P)    The *Jerome J. Shestack Poetry Prizes* of $1,000 are awarded annually to each of two poets whose work has appeared in the *Review* during the preceding calendar year.

Available to: See above
Deadline: Ongoing
Apply to: Submit manuscripts to above address with SASE


**American Political Science Association**
**1527 New Hampshire Avenue, NW**
**Washington, DC 20036-1206**
**E-mail: apsa@apsanet.org**
**Web site: http://www.apsanet.org**
**Fax: 202-483-2657**

(J)    The *APSA Congressional Fellowship Program* is designed to bring academics, political reporters, and scholars, among other professionals, to Washington to work as legislative aides on Capitol Hill. The fellowship period is divided into two or three general parts: a month long orientation (early November to early December); a congressional office assignment (early December to mid-April); and for many, a second assignment (mid-April to mid-August). Fellows receive a stipend of $35,000 plus travel allowance. Interested journalists must have a bachelor's degree and two to ten years' full-time professional experience in newspaper, magazine, radio, or television reporting; scholars must have completed a Ph.D. in the last fifteen years or be near completion. Preference is given to applicants without extensive experience in Washington. Write, e-mail, or consult the Web site for additional information.

Available to: See above
Deadline: December 1
Apply to: Director, Congressional Fellowship Program, above address


**American Psychiatric Association**
**Division of Public Affairs/Media Awards**
**1400 K Street, NW**
**Washington, DC 20005**

(J)    The *Robert T. Morse Writers Award* of $1,000 is given annually to popular newswriters or groups of writers who have covered the mental health/illness field over an extended period or who have written an exemplary article or series for the general public on mental health/illness topics and the role of psychiatry. Articles must have been published between August 1 and July 31 of the twelve-month period under consideration. Write for additional information and entry form.

Available to: No restrictions
Deadline: August 31
Apply to: Robert T. Morse Writers Award, above address


**American Research Center in Egypt**
**30 East 20th Street, Suite 401**
**New York, NY 10003-1310**

The *American Research Center in Egypt Fellowship Program* is designed to "promote a fresh and more profound knowledge of Egypt and the Near East through scholarly research" and to "aid in the training of American specialists in Middle Eastern studies in academic disciplines that require familiarity with Egypt." Fellowships are for three-to-twelve-month periods and include the *Islamicist-in-Residence Program*, for a postdoctoral scholar wishing to spend up to a year in Cairo carrying out a specific research project, and the *Kress Fellowship in Egyptian Art and Architecture* of $15,000 for a predoctoral student. Write for additional information and application form.

Available to: Pre- and postdoctoral scholars (predoctoral must be U. S. citizens; postdoctoral may be U. S. citizens, or foreign citizens who have held a teaching position at a U. S. university for a minimum of three years)
Deadline: October 1
Apply to: Above address

**American-Scandinavian Foundation**
58 Park Avenue
New York, NY 10016
Phone: 212-879-9779
E-mail: info@amscan.org
Web site: www.amscan.org

To encourage research and increase understanding between the U. S. and Denmark, Finland, Iceland, Norway, and Sweden, the Foundation administers fellowships and grants for qualified university graduates to undertake study projects that make a stay in Scandinavia (Denmark, Finland, Iceland, Norway, Sweden) essential. Approximately twenty-five awards, ranging from $3,000 to $18,000, are given annually. (Awards are also given to citizens of the Scandinavian countries for advanced study in the U. S.) See the Web site for more details.

Available to: U. S. citizens and permanent residents
Deadline: November 1 (for the following academic year)
Apply to: Exchange Division, above address

(T)    The *ASF Translation Prize* is offered annually by the Foundation for the best translation into English of poetry, fiction, drama, or literary prose by a Scandinavian author born after 1800. The award includes $2,000, publication in an issue of *Scandinavian Review*, and a bronze medallion. The *Inger Sjöberg Award* of $500 is given to the runner-up. For rules and instructions, write to the Foundation.

Available to: No restrictions
Deadline: June 1
Apply to: Translation Prize, above address

**American Society of Church History**
PO Box 8517
Red Bank, NJ 07701

(N)    The *Frank S. and Elizabeth D. Brewer Prize* offers $1,000 to assist an author in publishing a first book-length manuscript on church history. The winning manuscript will be published in a manner acceptable to the Society. If competing essays are of equal quality, preference is given to topics relating to the history of Congregationalism.

Available to: First-book authors
Deadline: November 1
Apply to: Henry W. Bowden, Secretary, Frank S. and Elizabeth D. Brewer Prize, above address

**American Society of Composers, Authors, and Publishers (ASCAP)**
One Lincoln Plaza
New York, NY 10023
Phone: 212-621-6323

(J) (N)    The *ASCAP-Deems Taylor Awards* are given in two categories: best nonfiction book and best nonfiction newspaper or magazine article about music and/or its creators. Works may be biographical or critical, reportorial or historical, but not textbooks, how-to guides, or fiction. They must have been published in the U. S. in English during the calendar year under review. The book award is $500 and a plaque; the article award, $250 and a plaque. Call Esther SanSaurus at the above phone number for more information.

Available to: No restrictions
Deadline: April 30
Apply to: ASCAP-Deems Taylor Awards, above address

American Society for Eighteenth-Century Studies
Wake Forest University
PO Box 7867
Winston-Salem, NC 27109
E-mail: asecs@wfu.edu
Web site: http://asecs.press.jhu.edu/awards.html
Fax: 336-727-4697

Ⓝ The *James L. Clifford Prize* of $500 is awarded annually for an outstanding article appearing in a festschrift, or a journal or other serial publication. The article must be a study of some aspect of eighteenth-century culture of interest to any eighteenth-century specialist, regardless of discipline. The article may be nominated by a member of the Society, its author, or the editor of the publishing journal. Nominations must be accompanied by eight copies of the article.

Available to: Society members
Deadline: January 1
Apply to: Byron Wells, Executive Director, above address

Ⓝ The *Émilie Du Châtelet Award for Independent Scholarship* of $500 is made annually by the Women's Caucus of ASECS to support research in progress by an independent or adjunct scholar on a feminist or women's studies subject. The award is open to the ASECS members who have received their Ph. D. and do not hold a tenured, tenure-track, or job-secure position in a college or university, or any permanent position that requires or supports the pursuit of research. Faculty emeritae are not eligible. The award is meant to fund works in progress, commensurate in scope with a scholarly article, book chapter, or edition, for which research is under way. Projects must advance understanding of women's experiences and/or contributions to eighteenth-century culture, or offer a feminist analysis of any aspect of eighteenth-century culture and/or society. Applications must include a five copies of each of the following: a curriculum vitae; a three-to-five-page research proposal outlining the project and the candidate's plans for using the funds; and evidence of progress on this project in the form of a conference paper, a related published essay, an essay submitted for publication, etc. (The Women's Caucus also administers the *Catherine Macaulay Prize* of $200, for the best graduate student paper on a feminist or women's studies subject. Consult the Web site for more information.)

Available to: See above
Deadline: March 1
Apply to: Émilie Du Châtelet Prize, above address

Ⓝ The *Louis Gottschalk Prize* of $1,000 is awarded annually for an outstanding historical or critical study on a subject of eighteenth-century interest. Eligible books are commentaries, critical studies, biographies, and critical editions, which may be written in any modern language; books that are primarily translations are not eligible. Books must have been published between the November 1 preceding the award year and October 31 of the award year. Five copies of each book must be submitted by the author's publisher.

Available to: Society members
Deadline: November 15
Apply to: Byron Wells, Executive Director, above address

Ⓝ The *Annibel Jenkins Prize* of $1,000 is given biennially to the author of the best book-length biography of a late seventeenth-century or eighteenth-century subject. Eligible books must be copyrighted between November 1, 2001, and October 31, 2003. Five copies of each book must be submitted by the publisher.

Available to: Society members
Deadline: November 15
Apply to: Byron Wells, above address

**American Society of Journalists and Authors Charitable Trust**
**1501 Broadway, Suite 302**
**New York, NY 10036**
**Web site: http://www.asja.org/miller.php**

The *Llewellyn Miller Fund* is open to professional freelance writers of nonfiction books and magazine articles who are sixty or older, disabled, or in an extraordinary professional crisis, and in financial need. The Fund provides grants of up to $3,500. Proof of professional freelance work must be supplied.

Available to: See above
Deadline: None
Apply to: Murray Teigh Bloom, Chairman, above address

**American Society of Magazine Editors**
**919 Third Avenue**
**New York, NY 10022**
**E-mail: asme@magazine.org**
**Web site: asme.magazine.org/asme_internships**

Ⓙ The ASME *Magazine Internship Program*, a ten-week summer session during which students learn about magazines by working in the editorial offices of consumer magazines and business publications, is available to college students between their junior and senior years. Applicants must be journalism majors or liberal arts majors who are deeply involved in campus journalism. Interns will be temporary employees of the magazines to which they are assigned and will be paid a minimum weekly stipend. The emphasis of the program is on editing; at some magazines there may be some reporting and writing. Interns are responsible for their own travel, housing, food, and personal expenses; ASME will assist in making dormitory arrangements in New York and Washington, D.C. Applications are available through college deans, department heads, or professors. Consult the Web site for more information.

Available to: See above
Deadline: November 16
Apply to: Magazine Internship Program, above address

**American Translators Association**
**Honors and Awards Committee**
**225 Reinekers Lane #590**
**Alexandria, VA 22314**
**E-mail: ata@atanet.org**
**Web site: http://www.atanet.org**
**Fax: 703-683-6122**

Ⓣ The *German Literary Translation Prize* of $1,000 is awarded in odd-numbered years for translations from the German into English that have been published, as a single volume or as part of a collection, by an American publisher in the U. S. within the two years preceding the prize year. Submit two copies of the book and 10 pages of the German original.

Available to: No restrictions
Deadline: Inquire
Apply to: German Literary Translation Prize, above address

Ⓣ The *Lewis Galantiere Prize* of $1,000 is awarded in even-numbered years for distinguished published literary works translated from any language other than German into English. Submit two copies of the book and 10 pages of the original.

Available to: No restrictions
Deadline: Inquire
Apply to: Lewis Galantiere Prize, above address

**Amy Foundation**
PO Box 16091
Lansing, MI 48901
E-mail: Amyfoundtn@aol.com
Web site: http://www.amyfound.org
Fax: 517-323-7293

Ⓝ    The *Amy Foundation Writing Awards* offer a $10,000 first prize, a $5,000 second prize, a $4,000 third prize, a $3,000 fourth prize, a $2,000 fifth prize, plus ten prizes of $1,000 each, for "creative, skillful writing that presents in a sensitive, thought-provoking manner the biblical position on issues affecting the world today." Submitted articles must have been published in a secular, nonreligious publication during the preceding calendar year.

Available to: No restrictions; U. S. citizens preferred
Deadline: January 31
Apply to: Writing Awards, above address


**Anamnesis Press**
PO Box 51115
Palo Alto, CA 94303
Web site: http://www.anamnesispress.com
Fax: 510-481-7193

Ⓟ    The annual *Anamnesis Poetry Chapbook Award Competition* offers a prize of $1,000, chapbook publication, and 20 author's copies. Poets should submit a manuscript of 20 to 30 pages, with an entry fee of $15. E-mail submissions are not accepted. Send SASE or see the Web site for guidelines.

Available to: No restrictions
Deadline: Submissions must be postmarked by March 15
Apply to: Poetry Chapbook Award, above address


**Mary Anderson Center for the Arts**
101 St. Francis Drive
Mount St. Francis, IN 47146
Phone: 812-923-8602
E-mail: maca@iglou.com
Fax: 812-923-3200

Ⓡ    Residences at the Center, located north of Louisville, Kentucky, are available from one week to three months for seven writers and visual artists concurrently. Residents pay $30 per day (which covers a private room, a studio if applicable, and meals). The Center has a communal kitchen, living room, and restrooms. Residence fellowships are sometimes available. Write or call for further information and guidelines.

Available to: No restrictions
Deadline: Ongoing
Apply to: Debra Carmody, Executive Director, above address


**Anhinga Press**
Drawer W
PO Box 10595
Tallahassee, FL 32302
Web site: http://www.anhinga.org
Fax: 850-442-6323

Ⓟ    The *Anhinga Prize for Poetry* is awarded annually for a book-length manuscript of original poetry in English. The winner receives $2,000 and publication by Anhinga within six months after selection. There is a $20 reading fee. Send SASE for application instructions.

Available to: Poets seeking to publish their first or second book of poetry
Deadline: Submissions accepted February 15-May 1
Apply to: Above address

**Another Chicago Magazine**
3709 North Kenmore
Chicago, IL 60613

Ⓕ Ⓟ The *Chicago Literary Awards* offer $1,000 each for an unpublished short story and a poem, plus publication in *Another Chicago Magazine*, a biannual journal of fiction, poetry, essays, and art. Writers may submit a story of no more than 6,500 words or up to three poems of no more than 300 lines total. The entry fee is $10. Send SASE for guidelines.

> Available to: No restrictions
> Deadline: Submissions must be postmarked by December 15
> Apply to: Chicago Literary Awards, above address

**Anthology of New England Writers**
PO Box 483
Windsor, VT 05089
Phone: 802-674-2315
E-mail: newvtpoet@aol.com

Ⓕ Ⓟ The New England Writers Free Verse Contest offers the *Robert Penn Warren Awards* of $500, $200, and $100. The Short Fiction Contest offers the *Marjory Bartlett Sanger Award* of $300. Free-verse submissions should be no longer than 30 lines; short fiction entries no more than 1,000 words. There is a $6 entry fee for three poems or one piece of short fiction; $5 each for two or more entries.

> Available to: No restrictions
> Deadline: June 15
> Apply to: Frank Anthony, above address

**Archaeological Institute of America**
656 Beacon Street, 4th floor
Boston, MA 02215-2010
E-mail: aia@aia.bu.edu
Fax: 617-353-6550

The *Anna C. and Oliver C. Colburn Fellowship* of $14,000 is awarded biennially to an incoming or student associate member of the American School of Classical Studies in Athens. Candidates must apply concurrently to the American School for associate membership.

> Available to: U. S. or Canadian citizens or permanent residents
> Deadline: Inquire for 2004
> Apply to: Colburn Fellowship, above address

The *Kenan T. Erim Award*, established by the American Friends of Aphrodisias, awards $4,000 annually to an American or international research and/or excavating scholar working on Aphrodisias material.

> Available to: No restrictions
> Deadline: November 1
> Apply to: Erim Award, above address

The *Olivia James Traveling Fellowships* of $22,000 are awarded for an academic year to students desiring to travel and study in Greece, the Aegean Islands, Sicily, southern Italy, Asia Minor, or Mesopotamia. The classics, sculpture, architecture, archaeology, and history are the most suitable areas of study. The word "student" does not mean only individuals registered in academic institutions.

> Available to: U. S. citizens or permanent residents
> Deadline: November 1
> Apply to: James Fellowship, above address

The *Harriet and Leon Pomerance Fellowship* is awarded for work on an individual project of a scholarly nature relating to Aegean Bronze Age archaeology. Preference is given to candidates whose project requires travel to the Mediterranean. One fellowship carrying a stipend of $4,000 is available annually.

Available to: U. S. and Canadian residents
Deadline: November 1
Apply to: Pomerance Fellowship, above address

**Arizona Commission on the Arts**
**417 West Roosevelt**
**Phoenix, AZ 85003-1326**
**E-mail: general@ArizonaArts.org**
**Web site: http://www.arizonaarts.org**
**Fax: 602-256-0282**

Ⓜ Poetry, playwriting, and fiction fellowships, between $5,000 and $7,500, are available in rotating years to Arizona residents at least eighteen years of age who are not students.

Available to: See above
Deadline: Inquire
Apply to: Paul Morris, Literature Director, pmorris@arizonaarts.org

**Arizona Film Commission**
**3800 North Central Avenue, Suite 1500**
**Phoenix, AZ 85012**
**Phone: 602-280-1386**
**Web site: www.azcommerce.com/azfilmcommission.htm**

Ⓢ The *Film in Arizona Screenwriting Competition* offers a grand prize of $1,000, round trip transportation to Los Angeles, hotel accommodations, and meetings with film industry professionals, to the author of screenplay which is largely set in Arizona and utilizes the state's diverse geography. There is an entry fee of $30 for submissions received by April 15; $40 for those received by May 15. See the Web for additional information and applications.

Available to: No restrictions
Deadline: See above
Apply to: Above address

**Arizona Theatre Company**
**40 East 14th Street**
**Tucson, AZ 85701**
**E-mail: info@arizonatheatre.org**
**Web site: http://www.aztheatreco.org**

**502 West Roosevelt Street**
**Phoenix, AZ 85003**

Ⓓ The *National Latino Playwriting Award* offers $1,000 for an original play or adaptation (minimum 50 pages) by a playwright of Hispanic heritage residing in the U. S., its territories, or Mexico. Plays may be in English or in Spanish with an English translation. The contest is sponsored in association with the Centro Cultural Mexicano de Phoenix. Write for guidelines.

Available to: See above
Deadline: Inquire
Apply to: National Latino Playwriting Award, above address

**Arrowhead Regional Arts Council**
**101 West Second Street, Suite 204**
**Duluth, MN 55802-2086**
**E-mail: ARACouncil@aol.com**
**Web site: http://members.aol.com/ARACouncil**
**Fax: 218-722-4459**

Ⓜ The Council annually offers *Individual_Artists Fellowships* of $4,500 to writers residing in the seven-county Arrowhead region of Minnesota. Write for further information.

Available to: See above
Deadline: Inquire
Apply to: Individual Artists Fellowships, above address

Ⓜ *Career Development Grants* of up to $1,000 are available to writers residing in the seven-county Arrowhead region of Minnesota as financial support to those who wish to take advantage of impending, concrete opportunities to advance their work or careers.

Available to: See above
Deadline: July, November, and April (inquire for exact dates)
Apply to: Career Development Grants, above address

**Artist Trust**
**1835 12th Avenue**
**Seattle, WA 98122**
**E-mail: info@artisttrust.org**
**Web site: http://www.artisttrust.org**
**Fax: 206-467-9633**

Ⓜ *Artist Trust/Washington State Arts Commission Fellowships* of $6,000 are available to practicing professional artists of exceptional talent and demonstrated ability. The stipend is unrestricted and any work created with the support of the Fellowship remains in the artist's possession. Fellows must participate in a "Meet the Artist" presentation to a community or group that has little or no access to artists and their work. The fellowships are awarded in two-year cycles: playwriting in even-numbered years; literature in odd-numbered years.

Available to: See above
Deadline: June 14
Apply to: above address

Ⓜ The *GAP (Grants for Artist Projects) Program* provides support of up to $1,400 for artist-generated projects, which can include the development, completion, or presentation of new work. All disciplines and interdisciplinary projects are eligible. Send SASE or see the Web site for guidelines and application.

Available to: See guidelines
Deadline: February 22
Apply to: GAP, above address

**Arts & Letters Journal of Contemporary Culture**
**Campus Box 89**
**Georgia College & State University**
**Milledgeville, GA 31061**
**E-mail: al@gcsu.edu**
**Web site: http://al.gcsu.edu**

Ⓜ The *Arts & Letters Prizes Competition* offers $1,000 and publication in *Arts & Letters*, in three categories: poetry, fiction (short stories), and drama (one-act plays). All submissions will be considered for publication. There is a $15 submission fee, which covers a two-issue subscription to the journal. Send SASE, e-mail, or see the Web site for guidelines.

Available to: No restrictions
Deadline: Submissions accepted January 1-April 30
Apply to: Arts & Letters Prizes, above address

**ArtServe Michigan**
**17515 West Nine Mile Road, Suite 1025**
**Southfield, MI 48075**
**Phone: 248-557-8288 ext. 14**
**E-mail: artists@ArtServeMichigan.com**
**Web site: http://www.artservemichigan.org**
**Fax: 248-557-8581**

Ⓜ ArtServe Michigan (formerly known as the Arts Foundation of Michigan), in partnership with the Michigan Council for Arts and Cultural Affairs, offers *Creative Artists Grants* of up to $8,000 in fiction, nonfiction, poetry, playwriting, and screenwriting. Funding is not available to those enrolled in degree or certificate programs.

Available to: Michigan residents
Deadline: Inquire
Apply to: Christine Schefmar, Program Director, above address


**Ashland Poetry Press**
**Ashland University**
**Ashland, OH 44805**
**Web site:**
    **http://www.ashland.edu/colleges/arts_sci/english/aupoetry/app-about.htm#rsprize**

(P)   The *Richard Snyder Poetry Award* annually offers $500 and publication in a paperback edition of 1,000 copies for a book-length collection of original poems. Poets should submit a manuscript of 50 to 80 pages, with no more than one poem per page, and a $20 reading fee. Send SASE for guidelines or consult the Web site.

Available to: No restrictions
Deadline: June 30
Apply to: Richard Snyder Poetry Award, above address


**Asian American Writers Workshop**
**16 West 32nd Street, Suite 10A**
**New York, NY 10001-3808**
**Phone: 212-494-0061**
**E-mail: desk@aaww.org**
**Web site: http://www.aaww.org**

(F)   Three *Van Lier Fellowships*, of $7,000 each, are offered to unpublished Asian-American novelists under age thirty who live in New York City and demonstrate strong commitment to the arts community. Send SASE, e-mail, or consult the Web site for further information and guidelines.

Available to: See above
Deadline: September (inquire for exact date)
Apply to: Van Lier Fellowships, above address


**Asian Cultural Council**
**437 Madison Avenue**
**New York, NY 10104**
**E-mail: acc@accny.org**
**Web site: http://www.asianculturalcouncil.org**

(R)   The Asian Cultural Council helps support residences in Japan for American artists interested in pursuing creative projects or creative collaboration with Asian artists. Preference is given to performing and visual artists, though playwrights and writers will be considered. Duration of residence is usually one to six months.

Available to: U. S. citizens
Deadline: Inquire
Apply to: Above address


**Isaac Asimov Award**
**University of South Florida**
**School of Mass Communications**
**4202 East Fowler, CIS 1040**
**Tampa, FL 33620-7800**
**Web site: http://www.sfsite.com/asimovs/**

(F)   The *Isaac Asimov Award for Undergraduate Excellence in Science Fiction and Fantasy Writing* annually offers $500 and consideration for publication in *Asimov's Science Fiction* magazine for a science fiction or fantasy short story by a full-time college undergraduate. The winner receives an expenses-paid trip to the annual Conference on the Fantastic in Fort Lauderdale, in mid-March. There is a $10 entry fee for up to three submissions, payable to the Asimov Award. Send SASE for guidelines.

Available to: See above
Deadline: December 15
Apply to: Asimov Award, above address


**A.S.K. Theatre Projects**
**11845 West Olympic Boulevard, Suite 1250 West**
**Los Angeles, CA 90064-5026**
**Phone: 310-478-3200**
**E-mail: info@askplay.org**
**Web site: www.askplay.org**
**Fax: 310-478-5300**

Ⓓ The *Unsettled Scores Program* offers free theater labs to playwrights, composers and other theater artists. The program provides playwright and composer with professional resources (such as director, musical director, performers) and a public presentation of their work. Works are developed in an environment free from the pressures of production values and ticket revenues. To be considered, artists should submit a project description / synopsis, 5-10 pages of sample dialogue / musical scores, a demo tape or CD, and a résumé. Include SASE.

Available to: no restrictions
Deadline: January 1
Apply to: Unsettled Scores, c/o A.S.K. Theatre Projects, above address


**Associated Press**
**50 Rockefeller Plaza**
**New York, NY 10020**
**Web site: http://www.ap.org**

Ⓙ The *Associated Press Summer Internship Program* is a twelve-week training period for up to twenty-two American college / university students. At time of application, candidates must be enrolled full-time as juniors, seniors, or graduate students. Interns will work in an AP bureau under the supervision of a designated trainer and will be paid a weekly wage based on classifiable experience. The application procedure involves an application package, a timed newswriting test, a 300-word autobiographical essay, a résumé with clippings, and an interview with AP bureau chief. Minority students are encouraged to apply. See the Web site or write to the nearest AP office for more details.

Available to: See above
Deadline: December
Apply to: Director of Recruiting, above address


**Associated Writing Programs**
**MS-1E3**
**George Mason University**
**Fairfax, VA 22030**
**E-mail: awp@gmu.edu**
**Web site: http://www.awpwriter.org**
**Fax: 703-993-4302**

Ⓜ The AWP, together with university and independent presses that have combined efforts to publish a number of book-length manuscripts every year, offer the *AWP Award Series*, for poetry, short fiction, the novel, and creative nonfiction. The competitions are open to authors, published as well as unpublished, writing in English. Mixed-genre manuscripts are not accepted. Winning works will be published through prearranged agreements with four university presses; the AWP acts as a literary agent to try to place finalists' manuscripts. Authors receive a standard royalty from books sold. A $2,000 honorarium is given in each category; winners in the novel category receive $10,000 and a standard royalty contract. Work being considered by other publishers is eligible if the author states to whom the manuscript has been submitted and agrees to inform the AWP if the work is accepted by another publisher. The reading and handling fee is $10 for AWP members, $20 for nonmembers. Send SASE or see the Web site for guidelines.

Available to: No restrictions
Deadline: Submissions accepted January 1-February 28
Apply to: Award Series (specify genre), above address

Three *AWP/Prague Summer Seminars Fellowships* are awarded each year, to a fiction writer, a nonfiction writer, and a poet who have not published a full-length book. Fellows receive full support and tuition to attend the Prague Summer Seminars, held in July. Travel and food expenses are their own responsibility. There is a $5 handling fee. Write, e-mail wlavende@uno.edu, or visit http://www.uno.edu/prague for guidelines.

Available to: No restrictions
Deadline: December (inquire for exact date)
Apply to: AWP/Prague Summer Seminars Fellowship (specify genre), above address

**Association of American Colleges and Universities**
**1818 R Street, NW**
**Washington, DC 20009**
**Web site: http://www.aacu-edu.org**

The *Frederic W. Ness Book Award* of $2,000 is given for a book published during the preceding calendar year that contributes to the understanding and improvement of liberal education. Histories of colleges are not eligible.

Available to: No restrictions
Deadline: May 1
Apply to: Frederic W. Ness Book Award, above address

**Association for Asian Studies**
**1021 East Huron Street**
**Ann Arbor, MI 48104-1628**
**E-mail: postmaster@aasianst.org**
**Web site: http:www.aasianst.org**
**Fax: 734-665-3801**

The *John Whitney Hall Book Prize* of $1,000 is given for an outstanding book in English on Japan or Korea published during the year preceding the prize deadline. Nominated books may address either contemporary or historical topics in any field of the humanities or the social sciences. Translations from Japanese or Korean into English are eligible only if they include a substantial introduction, annotation, and critical apparatus. Books must be nominated by publishers (trade or university presses); nominations by authors are not accepted. Write for additional information and addresses of prize committee members.

Available to: No restrictions
Deadline: June 30
Apply to: Above address for list of prize committee members

The *Joseph Levenson Book Prizes,* of $1,500 each, are awarded annually to two outstanding scholarly works that further broad understanding of China. One award is given for books on China before 1900, and the other for books on twentieth-century China. A copy of each entry must be sent to each member of the appropriate committee. Write for additional information and addresses of prize committee members.

Available to: No restrictions
Deadline: June 30
Apply to: Above address for list of prize committee members

The *A. K. Ramanujan Book Prize for Translation* of $1,000 is given in odd-numbered years to recognize and encourage translations from South Asian languages into English. Special consideration is given to innovative work that reaches a wide audience. Books must have been published during the two-year period preceding the prize deadline. A copy of each entry must be sent to each member of the committee. Write for additional information and addresses of prize committee members.

Available to: No restrictions
Deadline: Inquire
Apply to: Above address for list of prize committee members

In addition to the above book prizes, the Association offers numerous grants, scholarships, and fellowships in support of a wide range of Asian studies projects, for which writers may apply. See the Web site for detailed information.

**Association of College English Teachers**
**Samford University**
**Department of English**
**800 Lakeshore Drive**
**Birmingham, AL 35229**
**Phone: 205-726-2926**
**E-mail: M.lasseter@samford.edu**

Ⓝ The *Eugene Current-Garcia Award for Distinction in Literary Scholarship* is given to an outstanding literary scholar who is from Alabama, has worked primarily in Alabama, or has focused primarily on Alabama writers. The award carries a $5,000 stipend and a bronze rendering of the Monroeville courthouse clock tower. The award, which reflects the respect of the scholar's peers in the academic community and signals the importance of literature and the pursuit of knowledge, is presented in May at a writers' symposium in Monroeville. To nominate, send a letter stating briefly why the nominee should be considered.

Available to: See above
Deadline: January 15
Apply to: Janice Lasseter, President, above address

**Association of Jesuit Colleges and Universities**
**One Dupont Circle, Suite 405**
**Washington, DC 20036**
**E-mail: blkrobe@aol.com**
**Web site: http://www.mu.edu/dept/ASN**
**Fax: 202-862-8523**

Ⓝ The *National Jesuit Book Award Competition*, sponsored by Alpha Sigma Nu, the national Jesuit Honor Society, offers four cash prizes, of $1,000 each, to the best nonfiction books in categories that alternate in a three-year cycle. The 2002 award will be in the humanities, the 2003 in the sciences, the 2004 in the professional fields. Application forms are available at local ASN chapters or from the above-listed Web site.

Available to: Full-time or part-time faculty or administrators or anyone with emeritus status at a U. S. Jesuit college or university
Deadline: March 1
Apply to: National Jesuit Book Award, above address

**Association of Jewish Libraries**
**15 East 26th Street, Room 1034**
**New York, NY 10001-1579**

© The *AJL Sydney Taylor Book Awards* honor outstanding children's books of positive Jewish content published during the current calendar year. Cash prizes are offered in two categories: books for younger readers (usually preschool through grade 3) and books for older readers (usually grade 4 and up). If an award involves separate authors, illustrators, or translators, the prize money is divided. Books must be submitted by the publisher in the year in which they are published.

Available to: No restrictions
Deadline: December 31 of each year
Apply to: AJL Sydney Taylor Book Awards, c/o Libby K. White, Beth Israel Congregation, 3706 Crondall Lane, Mills, MD 21117, or e-mail white_libby@juno.com

© The *AJL Sydney Taylor Manuscript Award* of $1,000 is given to the author of a new children's book with universal appeal of Jewish content for readers ages eight to eleven. Manuscripts should be between 64 and 200 pages long. Writers must have not previously published books. Send SASE to the address below for additional information and application form, or fax 770-671-8380.

Available to: No restrictions
Deadline: January 15
Apply to: AJL Sydney Taylor Manuscript Award, c/o Paula Sandfelder, 1327 Wintercreek Lane, Dunwoody, GA 30338

**Association for Library Services to Children**
**American Library Association**
**50 East Huron Street**
**Chicago, IL 60611**
**E-mail: alsc@ala.org**
**Web site: http://www.ala.org/alsc**

© The *John Newbery Medal* is awarded annually to the author of the most distinguished contribution to American literature for children published in the U. S. during the preceding year. Authors and publishers are invited to submit books to the medal committee for review during the ALA midwinter meeting. No cash award is given; winners receive a medal. The prestige of the Newbery Medal in the field of children's literature warrants its inclusion here.

Available to: U. S. citizens or residents
Deadline: January (inquire for exact date)
Apply to: John Newbery Medal, above address

**Astraea Lesbian Action Foundation**
**116 East 16th Street, 7th floor**
**New York, NY 10003**
**E-mail: info@astraea.org**
**Web site: http://www.astraea.org**
**Fax: 212-982-3321**

Ⓕ Ⓟ The *Lesbian Writers' Fund Awards* offer grants of $10,000 each to emerging lesbian writers in fiction and poetry who have published at least once in a magazine, literary journal, or anthology. Write or see the Web site for guidelines and application.

Available to: U. S. resident lesbian writers
Deadline: March 8
Apply to: Lesbian Writers' Fund Awards, above address

**Atlanta Review**
**PO Box 8248**
**Atlanta, GA 31106**
**E-mail: contest@atlantareview.com**
**Web site: http:www.atlantareview.com**

Ⓟ The *Atlanta Review International Poetry Competition* awards a $2,000 first prize, a $500 second prize, and a $250 third prize for unpublished poems of any length or style. Many entrants are published in *Atlanta Review*. An entry fee of $5 is required for the first poem, and $2 for each additional poem. Enclose SASE for notification of winners.

Available to: No restrictions
Deadline: May 1
Apply to: International Poetry Competition, above address

**Atlantic Center for the Arts**
**1414 Art Center Avenue**
**New Smyrna Beach, FL 32168**
**Phone: 386-427-6975**
**Web site: http://www.atlantic-centerarts.org**
**Fax: 904-427-5669**

®  The *Master Artists-in-Residence Program* provides a three-week residence for writers and artists
   at a sixty-nine-acre ecological preserve in eastern Florida. Associates spend half their
   time working with master artists in meetings, workshops, casual conversations, and
   recreational activities, and are free to spend other time on their own projects. Free tuition,
   and free room and board are available to writers accepted into the Program. Write or see
   the Web site for more information and guidelines.

   Available to: No restrictions
   Deadline: Inquire
   Apply to: Above address


**Austin Film Festival**
**1604 Nueces**
**Austin, TX 78701-1106**
**E-mail: austinfilm@aol.com**
**Web site: http://www.austinfilmfestival.org**

Ⓢ  The *Austin Film Festival Screenwriters Competition* offers two first prizes of $500, one for an
   adult film screenplay and one for a comedy film screenplay. Winners are reimbursed for
   roundtrip airfare to/from Austin and hotel accommodation, up to $500 each. They also
   receive an all-access pass to the Festival and a screenwriters' conference. There is a $40
   submission fee. Send SASE, e-mail, or see the Web site for guidelines and entry form.

   Available to: No restrictions
   Deadline: May 15
   Apply to: Screenwriters Competition, above address


**AUSTRALIA**
**Arts Management Pty, Ltd.**
**Station House, Rawson House**
**L4, 790 George Street**
**Sydney NSW 2000**
**Australia**
**E-mail: claudia@artsmanagement.com.au**
**Fax: 61-2-9211-7762**

Ⓓ Ⓕ  The *Miles Franklin Award,* of $28,000 Australian, is offered annually for a novel of the highest
   literary merit, published in the year previous to the award, that reflects an aspect of Australian
   life. If no novel is considered worthy of the prize, the award may be given for a play.

   Available to: No restrictions
   Deadline: Second Friday in December of the year preceding the award
   Apply to: Above address


**Authors League Fund**
**31 East 28th Street, 10th floor**
**New York, NY 10016**
**E-mail: authlgfund@aol.com**
**Fax: 212-564-8363**

The Fund makes interest-free loans to professional published authors and produced
   playwrights in need because of illness, misfortune, or other temporary emergency. The
   Fund does not make grants. Write for application.

   Available to: See above
   Deadline: None
   Apply to: Administrator, above address

**Authors in the Park**
**PO Box 85**
**Winter Park, FL 32790-0085**
**E-mail: foley@magicnet.net**
**Fax: 407-275-8688**

(F)   The *Authors in the Park Short Story Contest* offers a $1,000 first prize, a $500 second prize, and a $250 third prize for short stories written in English, with a 5,000-word maximum. Winners are published in *Fine Print*, which is mailed to each contestants and to small presses throughout the U. S. Send SASE or e-mail for guidelines before submitting.

   Available to: No restrictions
   Deadline: April 30
   Apply to: Short Story Contest, above address

**BACHE**
**401-A Ulman Building**
**Birmington, AL 35294**

The BACHE Visiting Writer Series is designed to bring writers of national and regional significance to north central Alabama for readings and workshops open to the community. The series is sponsored by five BACHE institutions (Birmingham-Southern College, Miles College, Samford University, the University of Montevallo and the University of Alabama at Birmingham), and provides stipends for the visiting writers. Write for more information.

   Available to: Inquire
   Deadline: Inquire
   Apply to: Above address

**The Backwaters Press**
**3502 North 52nd Street**
**Omaha, NE 68104-3506**
**Web site: http://www.thebackwaterspress.homestead.com/**

(P)   The *Backwaters Prize* of $1,000 and publication by the Press is awarded for a previously unpublished manuscript of poetry, up to 80 pages. There is a $20 entry fee. Send SASE for guidelines. The *Reader's Choice Awards*, offering publication only, are given to two among twenty finalists for the Backwater Prize.

   Available to: No restrictions
   Deadline: June 4
   Apply to: Backwaters Prize, above address

(F)   The *Omaha Prize* of $1,000 and publication by the Press is awarded for a previously unpublished novel, of 250 to 500 manuscript pages. Translations and collections of short stories are not eligible. There is a $20 entry fee. Send SASE for guidelines.

   Available to: No restrictions
   Deadline: December 24
   Apply to: Omaha Prize, above address

**Baker's Plays**
**PO Box 699222**
**Quincy, MA 02269-9222**
**Web site: http://bakersplays.com/submiss.htm**

(D)   The *High School Playwriting Contest* offers a first prize of $500 and publication in Baker's Plays *Best Plays from High School* series for a full-length or one-act play by a high school student. Plays should be suitable for production on high school stages and preferably about "the high school experience." Student playwrights must be sponsored by a high school drama or English teacher. A second prize of $250 and a third prize of $100 are also awarded. Write for further information and guidelines.

   Available to: High school students
   Deadline: January 31
   Apply to: High School Playwriting Contest, above address

**Bank Street College of Education**
**Children's Book Committee**
**610 West 112th Street**
**New York, NY 10025**
**Phone: 212-875-4540**
**Fax: 212-875-4759**
**E-mail: bookcom@bnkst.edu**
**Web site: http://www.bnkst.edu/bookcom**

IN  The Children's Book Committee annually confers three awards, carrying a stipend of $500 each. The *Josette Frank Award* honors an outstanding book of children's fiction in which children or young people deal in a positive and realistic way with difficulties in their world and grow emotionally and morally. The *Flora Stieglitz Straus Award* is given for a distinguished work of children's nonfiction that fulfills the ideals of the award's namesake, who led the Committee for more than seventy-five years, and that serves as an inspiration to young people. The *Claudia Lewis Award* is given for the best children's poetry book of the year. *By Internal Nomination Only.*

**Bantam Doubleday Dell Books for Young Readers**
**1540 Broadway**
**New York, NY 10036**

©  The *Marguerite de Angeli Prize* is awarded annually to encourage the writing of fiction, either contemporary or historical, for children, in the spirit of the works of Marguerite de Angeli. Manuscripts must be between 40 and 144 pages, and suitable for readers seven to ten years of age. The award consists of a $1,500 cash prize and a $3,500 advance against royalties when the winning manuscript is published. Send SASE for guidelines.

Available to: U. S. or Canadian writers who have not previously published a novel for middle-grade readers
Deadline: Submissions must be postmarked April 1-June 30
Apply to: Marguerite de Angeli Prize, above address

©  The *Delacorte Press Prize for a First Young Adult Novel* offers a book contract for hardcover and paperback editions, a $1,500 cash prize, and a $6,000 advance against royalties. Manuscripts should be book length, 100 to 224 typed pages; they should have a contemporary setting and be suitable for ages twelve to eighteen. Write for submission guidelines.

Available to: U. S. and Canadian writers who have not previously published a young adult novel
Deadline: Submissions must be postmarked October 1-December 31
Apply to: Delacorte Press Prize, above address

**Bard College**
**PO Box 5000**
**Annandale-on-Hudson**
**New York 12504-5000**
**Phone: 845-758-7087**
**E-mail: bfp@bard.edu**
**Web site: www.bard.edu/bfp**
**Fax: 845-758-7411**

Ⓕ  The *Bard Fiction Prize* annually recognizes a promising young fiction writer; it consists of a $30,000 award and appointment as writer-in-residence at Bard College for one semester. Call, e-mail or see the Web site for more details.

Available to: Inquire
Deadline: Inquire
Apply to: Above address

**Barnard College**
**Department of English**
**3009 Broadway**
**New York, NY 10027-6598**

Ⓟ  The *Barnard New Women Poets Prize* offers an honorarium of $1,000 and publication by W. W. Norton for a woman writer's second book-length manuscript of poems. Poets who have published chapbooks or similar works with fewer than 500 copies are eligible. Write for guidelines before submission. *(PEN was unable to confirm the information for this edition but believes it is current. Inquire before applying.)*

Available to: Women poets
Deadline: October 15
Apply to: Barnard New Women Poets Prize, above address

**Barnes & Noble**
**122 Fifth Avenue**
**New York, NY 10011**
**E-mail: kruden@bn.com**

Ⓕ Ⓝ  The *Discover Great New Writers Awards*, of $10,000 each, are offered annually to the authors of the best first works of fiction and nonfiction written in English and published during the previous calendar year. To submit a book for consideration, publishers *only* should send a minimum of three galley copies (or one manuscript if galleys are not available) by an author making a strong literary debut. Books must be submitted prior to publication date according to a seasonal schedule, which has four quarterly deadlines. Self-published books and books by more than one author are not eligible. Write or e-mail for additional information and schedule of deadlines.

Available to: Authors whose work has been selected for the Discover Great New Writers Program
Deadline: Inquire
Apply to: Jill Lamar, Manager & Editor, Discover Great New Writers, above address

**Bear Star Press**
**185 Hollow Oak Drive**
**Cohasset, CA 95973**
**Web site: www.bearstarpress.com**

Ⓟ  The *Dorothy Brunsman Poetry Prize* awards $1,000 for a poetry manuscript, 50 to 65 pages, by a writer living in the western/Pacific states (including Alaska and Hawaii). Send SASE for guidelines or consult the Web site.

Available to: See above
Deadline: November 30
Apply to: Above address

**Bellagio Study and Conference Center.** *See* **Rockefeller Foundation**

**Bellingham Review**
**Mail Stop 9053**
**Western Washington University**
**Bellingham, WA 98225**
**Web site: http://www.wwu.edu/~bhreview/**

Ⓝ  The *Annie Dillard Award for Nonfiction* offers $1,000 and publication for an essay in any style and on any subject, maximum 10,000 words. The entry fee is $15 for each essay. Send SASE or see the Web site for guidelines.

Available to: No restrictions
Deadline: Submissions accepted December 1 through March 15
Apply to: Annie Dillard Award, above address

(P)     The *49th Parallel Poetry Award* offers $1,000 and publication for an original poem of any length. There is a $15 entry fee, which covers a one-year subscription to *Bellingham Review*. Send SASE for guidelines or see the Web site.

Available to: No restrictions
Deadline: Submissions accepted December 1 through March 15
Apply to: 49th Parallel Poetry Award, above address

(F)     The *Tobias Wolff Award for Fiction* offers $1,000 and publication for a short story or a novel excerpt no longer than 10,000 words. A $250 second prize and a $100 third prize are also awarded. The fee is $15 for the first entry, $5 per entry thereafter. All entrants will receive a two-issue subscription to *Bellingham Review*. Send SASE for guidelines or see the Web site.

Available to: No restrictions
Deadline: Submissions accepted December 1 through March 15
Apply to: Tobias Wolff Award, above address

**The Beloit Poetry Journal**
**24 Berry Cove Road**
**Lamoine, ME 04605**
**Web site: http://www.bpj.org**

(P)     The *Chad Walsh Poetry Award* annually offers a cash prize ($3,000 in 2001) for a poem or group of poems published in the *Journal* in the preceding year.

Available to: Poets published in *The Beloit Poetry Journal*
Deadline: Ongoing
Apply to: Above address

**Berea College**
**The Appalachian Center**
**CPO 2166**
**Berea, KY 40404**
**Web site: http://www.berea.edu/ApCenter/WeatherfordAward.html**

(M)     The *Weatherford Award* of $500 is given annually to the writer whose published work "best describes and analyzes the challenges, personalities, and qualities of the Appalachian South." Eligible are book-length or shorter works of fiction, nonfiction, or poetry first published during the year for which the award is given. Send SASE for guidelines.

Available to: No restrictions
Deadline: December 31
Apply to: Chair, Weatherford Award Committee, above address

**Berkshire Conference of Women Historians**
**c/o Barbara Winslow, Secretary-Treasurer**
**124 Park Place**
**Brooklyn, NY 11217**
**Web site: http://www-berks.aas.duke.edu**

(N)     The *Publication Awards* offer a $1,000 prize for the best first-published book on any subject, and a $500 prize for the best published article in any field of historical scholarship by a U. S. or Canadian woman. The following are not eligible: textbooks; juveniles; documentary collections; collections of essays. Publishers are notified of the competition and asked to submit eligible works, but submissions by authors are also welcome.

Available to: U. S. or Canadian women historians
Deadline: January 15
Apply to: Above address for list of award committee members

**Bertelsmann USA**
**1540 Broadway, 33rd floor**
**New York, NY 10036-4098**
**E-mail: bwoesp@bmge.com**
**Fax: 212-930-4783**

(M)     The *World of Expression Scholarship Program* offers scholarships for exemplary displays of self-expression in music, literature and new media to New York City high school seniors as follows: three $10,000 first prizes, three $5,000 second prizes, and three $2,000 third prizes, in each of three categories: poetry, fiction and drama, and personal essay. Fifteen "Best of Borough" scholarships of $1,000 and fifteen $500 "Artist Recognition" scholarships are also given. Submissions must be no longer than 10 pages or 2,500 words. All monetary awards will be paid by the World of Expression Foundation to the winner's choice of institution of postsecondary education. Write or e-mail for guidelines and application.

    Available to: New York City high school seniors
    Deadline: February 1
    Apply to: Bertelsmann's World of Expression Scholarship Program, c/o Citizen's Scholarship Foundation of America, 1505 River View Road, P.O. Box 297, St. Peter, MN 56082

**Beverly Hills Theatre Guild**
**2815 North Beachwood Drive**
**Los Angeles, CA 90068**
**Phone: 323-465-2703**
**Fax: 323-666-3478**

(D)     The *Julie Harris Playwright Competition* awards an annual cash prize of $5,000 for the best play submitted by a U. S. playwright. An additional $2,000 is available to help finance a showcase production if the award-winning play is presented in the Los Angeles area within one year of receiving the award. The second-place *Janet and Maxwell Salter Award* offers a prize of $2,000, and the third-place *Dr. Henry and Lilian Nesburn Award* offers $1,000. Entries must be original full-length plays (minimum of 90 minutes) that have not been published, have never had an Equity or non-Equity production for which actors or authors were paid or admission was charged, and are not under option. Musicals, one-act plays (shorter than 90 minutes), adaptations, translations, plays that have won any other competition, and plays that have entered previous Beverly Hills Theatre Guild competitions are ineligible. Send SASE for rules and applications.

    Available to: U. S. citizens
    Deadline: Submissions accepted August 1-November 1; winners announced in June
    Apply to: Above address

(C) (D)     The *Beverly Hills Theatre Guild Plays for Children's Theatre Competition* annually awards three prizes in the amounts of $500, $300 and $200 for plays suitable for grades 6 through 8 or grades 9 through 12, 45 to 75 minutes in length. Send SASE for guidelines and entry form.

    Available to: U. S. citizens
    Deadline: Submissions accepted January 15 through February 28
    Apply to: Above address

**Beyond Baroque Literary/Arts Center**
**681 Venice Boulevard**
**Venice, CA 90291**
**Web site: http://www.beyondbaroque.org**
**Fax: 310-827-7432**

(P)     Beyond Baroque periodically sponsors chapbook contests. In 1998, the *Beyond Baroque Poetry Chapbook Contest* awarded $500 and publication by Beyond Baroque Books in a 500-copy run for a poetry manuscript no longer than 20 pages. The winner was invited to read at the Center. Criteria and guidelines may change; contact the Center directly for updated information. The Center offers free weekly workshops in poetry and fiction year-round, including Los Angeles's longest-running poetry session, the Wednesday Night Workshop, and a regular program of readings by some 500 poets and fiction writers a year. Write or consult the Web site for additional information.

Available to: No restrictions
Deadline: Inquire
Apply to: Poetry Chapbook Contest, above address

**Binghamton University**
**Department of English, General Literature, and Rhetoric**
**PO Box 6000**
**Binghamton, NY 13902-6000**

(F) The *John Gardner Fiction Book Award* is given for the strongest collection of fiction published in the year preceding the award by a small or university press. The award consists of a $1,000 cash prize, and is given at the award ceremony. The winner is asked to give a reading at the University. Write for an application form.

Available to: See above
Deadline: April 1
Apply to: Maris Mazziotti Gillan, Director, Creative Writing Program, above address

(P) The *Milt Kessler Poetry Book Award* of $1,000 is given for the strongest collection of poems, 48 pages or longer, by a poet over forty years old, published in the year previous to the award. The winning author is asked to give a reading at the University. Write for an application form.

Available to: See above
Deadline: April 1
Apply to: Maris Mazziotti Gillan, Director, Creative Writing Program, above address

**Birmingham-Southern College**
**Box 549003**
**Birmingham, AL 35254**
**E-mail: dcwilson@bsc.edu**
**Web site: www.bsc.edu**
**Fax: 205-226-3072**

(F) (P) The *Hackney Literary Awards* offer $5,000 in prizes for poetry and short stories and a $5,000 award for the novel. There is a $10 reading fee per poetry or short story entry, and a $25 reading fee for novel entries. All work submitted must be original and unpublished. Send SASE for guidelines.

Available to: No restrictions
Deadlines: Submissions accepted October 1-December 31 for poetry and short stories; June 1-September 30 for novels
Apply to: Hackney Literary Awards, above address

**The Bitter Oleander**
**4983 Tall Oaks Drive**
**Fayetteville, NY 13066-9776**
**E-mail: bones44@ix.netcom.com**
**Web site: www.bitteroleander.com**

(P) The *Frances Locke Memorial Poetry Award* offers $1,000 and publication in *The Bitter Oleander*, a twice-yearly magazine of essays, fiction, poetry, and reviews, for an unpublished poem. Poets may submit up to five poems with a $10 entry fee; $2 for each additional poem. Send SASE for guidelines.

Available to: No restrictions
Deadline: Submissions accepted March 1-June 15
Apply to: Frances Locke Memorial Poetry Award, above address

**BkMk Press Literary Contests**
**University of Missouri at Kansas City**
**5101 Rockhill Road**
**Kansas City, MO 64110**
**Phone: 816-235-2558**
**E-mail: bkmk@umkc.edu**
**Web site: www.umkc.edu/bkmk/**
**Fax: 816-235-2611**

Ⓟ    The *John Ciardi Prize for Poetry* and the *G.S. Chandra Prize for Short Fiction* annually offer $1,000
       each and publication by BkMk Press. Manuscripts must be written in English (translations
       are not eligible) by a living author. Works should be book-length collections: poetry
       submissions are preferably between 50 and 110 single-spaced pages; short fiction
       submissions between 50,000 and 100,000 words, double-spaced. There is a $25 reading
       fee. E-mail or send SASE for guidelines.

       Available to: U. S. citizens
       Deadline: December 1
       Apply to: Above address

**Black Caucus of the American Library Association**
**c/o New York Public Library**
**Office of Adult Services**
**455 Fifth Avenue**
**New York, NY 10016**
**E-mail: jpage@wrlc.org**
**Web site: http://www.bcala.org**

Ⓕ Ⓝ   Three *Black Caucus of the American Library Association Literary Awards,* of $500 each, are given
       in the categories of adult fiction, nonfiction, and first novel by African-American authors.
       Publishers may submit books published during the calendar year. The Caucus also
       annually presents an *Honor Book Citation* and an *Outstanding Contributions to Publishing
       Citation.* Consult the Web site for guidelines.

       Available to: African-American writers
       Deadline: December 31
       Apply to: Literary Awards, above address

**Black Warrior Review**
**University of Alabama**
**PO Box 862936**
**Tuscaloosa, AL 35486-0027**
**Web site: http://www.sa.ua.edu/osm/bwr**

Ⓕ Ⓟ   *Black Warrior Review* awards $500 each to a poet and a fiction writer whose work has been
       published in either the fall or the spring issue of the *Review*. Winners are selected by a
       prominent writer or critic; names of the recipients and the award judge are announced in
       the fall issue of the *Review*.

       Available to: See above
       Deadlines: July 15 for fall issue; January 15 for spring
       Apply to: Editor, above address

**Susan Smith Blackburn Prize**
**3239 Avalon Place**
**Houston, TX 77019**
**Fax: 713-654-8184**

Ⓓ    The *Susan Smith Blackburn Prize* is given annually to women playwrights for full-length plays,
       unproduced or produced within one year of the deadline. The first prize is $10,000 and a
       signed and numbered Willem de Kooning print; an honorable mention of $1,000 may be
       given, at the discretion of the judges. Other finalists each receive $500. Plays will be received
       only from recognized sources, which include professional regional and off-Broadway theaters
       and other organizations regularly reading new works. Send SASE to the above address for a

listing of sources. Applications by individual playwrights or their agents will not be considered.

Available to: Women playwrights of any nationality writing in English
Deadline: Submissions accepted in September only
Apply to: Emilie S. Kilgore, above address


**Bloomington Playwrights Project**
**312 South Washington Street**
**Bloomington, IN 47401**
**E-mail: bppwrite@newsplays.org**
**Web site: http://www.newplays.org**

Ⓓ  The *Reva Shiner Full-Length Play Contest* offers $500, a staged reading, and production for an unpublished, unproduced full-length play suitable for production in a sixty-five-seat theater, with simple sets. There is a $5 reading fee. Write, e-mail, or see the Web site for guidelines.

Available to: No restrictions
Deadline: January 15
Apply to: Above address


**Blue Mountain Center**
**PO Box 109**
**Blue Mountain Lake, NY 12812-0109**

Ⓡ  The Blue Mountain Center offers four one-month residences for writers, from mid-June through the end of October. The residences include free room and board; spouses must apply separately. Send a brief bio, work samples, reviews, and a project description to apply; specify preferred period of stay. There is a $20 application fee.

Available to: Established writers, particularly those whose work shows social and ecological concern
Deadline: February 1
Apply to: Admissions Committee, above address

Ⓡ  The *Richard J. Margolis Award*, of $2,000 plus a month-long residence at Blue Mountain Center, is given annually to a poet, essayist, or journalist "whose work recalls Richard J. Margolis's warmth, humor, and concern for social issues." To nominate a writer, send three copies of at least two samples of work, published or unpublished, of no more than 30 pages total, and a short biographical note.

Available to: No restrictions
Deadline: July 1
Apply to: Richard J. Margolis Award, 101 Arch Street, 9th floor, Boston, MA 02110, attn: Harry S. Margolis


**The Bogliasco Foundation**
**885 Second Avenue, Room 3100**
**New York, NY 10017**
**E-mail: info@bfny.org**
**Web site: http://www.liguriastudycenter.org**

Ⓡ  The Liguria Study Center for the Arts and Humanities, located in the Italian Riviera town of Bogliasco, offers residential fellowships to qualified persons doing advanced creative work or scholarly research in archaeology, architecture, classics, dance, film or video, history, literature, music, philosophy, theater, or the visual arts. Fellowship applicants must demonstrate significant achievement in their disciplines, commensurate with their age and experience. Fellowships are from mid-September to the third week of December and from mid-February to the third week of May, with a typical duration of one month or half a semester. Bogliasco fellows are provided with living quarters and full board; they may be accompanied by spouses or equivalent companions during their stay. See the Web site for application materials.

Available to: See above
Deadline: January 15 for fall/winter; April 15 for winter/spring
Apply to: Above address

**Borderlands Theater**
PO Box 2791
Tucson, AZ 85702
E-mail: bltheater@aol.com
Web site: www.borderlandstheater.org
Fax: 520-882-7406

Ⓓ The *Border Playwrights Project* offers residences to writers of unproduced full-length plays that explore the U. S.-Mexico border and border culture or the concept of other borders, e.g., immigration or issues of class, race, and gender. Plays may be in English and/or Spanish. Playwrights should send a synopsis, and SASE for response.

Available to: No restrictions
Deadline: Inquire
Apply to: Suzi List, Literary Coordinator, above address

**Bordighera Bilingual Poetry Prize**
Box 8G
57 Montague Street
Brooklyn, NY 11201-3356
Web site: www.italianamericanwriters.com/Prize.html

Ⓟ Ⓣ The *Bordighera Bilingual Poetry Prize,* made possible by the Sonia Raiziss-Giop Charitable Foundation, is given annually for a manuscript of poetry written in English by an Italian-American poet and translated into Italian. The winning poet and translator each receive $1,000 and publication by Bordighera, Inc., in a bilingual edition. Poets must be Americans of Italian descent; translators may be of any nationality. Qualified poets may translate their own work. Poets and translators should submit two copies of 10 sample pages of poems in English; the complete work should not exceed 48 manuscript pages. Send SASE for guidelines.

Available to: See above
Deadline: May 31
Apply to: Daniela Gioseffi and Alfredo de Palchi, above address

**Robert Bosch Foundation**
c/o CDS International
871 United Nations Plaza, 15th floor
New York, NY 10017
E-mail: info@cdsintel.org
Web site: http://www.cdsintel.org/rbfpappinfo.pdf
Fax: 212-497-3535

Ⓙ The *Robert Bosch Foundation Fellowship Program* offers journalists and other young professionals from twenty-three to thirty-four years the opportunity to participate in an intensive nine-month work/study program in Germany. Applicants must be U. S. citizens with a graduate degree or at least two years' professional work experience; evidence of outstanding professional performance and/or academic achievement; and the ability to communicate well in German. Fellows receive round trip transportation between their U. S. residence and Germany, a stipend for the duration of the program, tuition and fees for a language course (if needed), limited health and accident insurance, and financial support for an accompanying spouse. Write for additional information and application.

Available to: U. S. citizens
Deadline: October 15
Apply to: Fellowship Program, above address

**Boston Authors Club**
45 Chiltern Road
Weston, MA 02193

Ⓜ The Boston Authors Club makes two annual awards of $500 each, one for an adult book, the other for a children's/young-adult book by authors who live or have lived within 100 miles of Boston. The book must be published in the year prior to the award. Works of fiction, nonfiction, memoir, poetry, and biography are eligible; self-published works are not accepted. Two copies of each book, which will not be returned, should be submitted.

Available to: See above
Deadline: January 1
Apply to: Above address

**The Boston Book Review**
**30 Brattle Street, 4th floor**
**Cambridge, MA 02138**
**Phone: 617-497-0344**
**E-mail: BBR-info@BostonBookReview.org**
**Web site: http://www.bostonbookreview.org**

(IN) The *Boston Book Review Literary Awards*, consisting of the *Fisk Fiction Prize*, given in memory of Lilla Fisk Rand; the *Rea Nonfiction Prize*, given in memory of Anne Rea Jewell; and the *Bingham Poetry Prize*, given in memory of Belinda Bingham Pierce, offer $1,000 each to "celebrate excellent literary accomplishments" published in the calendar year. *By Internal Nomination Only.*

**Boston Review** ✓
**E53-407 MIT**
**Cambridge, MA 02139**

(F) (P) The *Boston Review Short Story Contest* and the *Boston Review Poetry Contest* annually award $1,000 to each contest winner and publication in *Boston Review*, a bimonthly journal of poetry, fiction, reviews, and articles. Fiction writers should submit an unpublished short story of no more than 4,000 words; poets may submit up to five unpublished poems, totaling no more than 10 pages. There is a $15 entry fee, which covers a one-year subscription to the *Review*. Send SASE for guidelines.

Available to: No restrictions
Deadline: June 1 for poetry; September 1 for short stories
Apply to: Short Story Contest or Poetry Contest, above address

**Box Turtle Press**
**184 Franklin Street**
**New York, NY 10013**

(P) The *Mudfish Poetry Prize* annually offers $1,000 and publication in *Mudfish*, a journal of poetry and art. Poets may submit any number of poems; all entries will be considered for publication. The reading fee is $15 for up to three poems, $2 each for more. Send SASE for guidelines.

Available to: No restrictions
Deadline: May 29
Apply to: Mudfish Poetry Prize, above address

**Boyden Residency**
**c/o John Daniel**
**23030 West Sheffler Road**
**Elmira, OR 97437**
**E-mail: Jfd48@aol.com**
**Web site: http://open-spaces.com/article-v2n4-PENNW.php**

(R) The *Margery Davis Boyden Wilderness Writing Residency* is a unique opportunity for a writer or pair of writers seeking a lengthy spell of unparalleled solitude for work and personal refreshment. In exchange for an hour a day of routine caretaking, the resident receives use of a remote but comfortable house in the Rogue River back country of southwestern Oregon and the support of a $2,000 stipend. The residency extends from April through the end of October, entrance and exit dates varying with weather conditions. The program is administered by PEN Northwest, a branch of PEN American Center, in cooperation with Frank and Bradley Boyden, program founders and owners of the property. Writers considering this residence should honestly assess their appetite and tolerance for authentic back country solitude. E-mail or see the Web site for more details.

Available to: See above
Deadline: March 1
Apply to: Above address

**Bread Loaf Writers' Conference**
**Middlebury College**
**Middlebury, VT 05753**
**Web site: http://www.middlebury.edu/~blwc**
**Fax: 802-443-2087**

® The Conference awards fellowships and scholarships to candidates applying to attend a session of the Conference. Candidates for fellowships must have a first original book published within three years of filing their application. Scholarship candidates must have published in major literary periodicals or newspapers. See the Web site for nomination and application procedures.

Available to: See above
Deadline: April 1
Apply to: Above address, or blwc@middlebury.edu

Ⓜ Bread Loaf also offers the *Bakeless Literary Publication Prizes,* an annual competition for new authors of poetry, fiction, and nonfiction. The prizes support emerging writers by sponsoring publication of their first books through Middlebury College/University Press of New England. Winners also receive fellowships to attend the Bread Loaf Writers' Conference. See the Web site for guidelines.

Available to: Emerging writers
Deadline: Manuscripts accepted October 1 through November 15
Apply to: Bakeless Prizes, above address, or bakeless@middlebury.edu

**Bright Hill Press**
**94 Church Street, PO Box 193**
**Treadwell, NY 13846-0193**
**E-mail: wordthur@catskill.net**
**Web site: http://www.nyslittree.org**
**Fax: 607-829-5056**

Ⓟ The *Bright Hill Press Poetry Award* annually offers $500 and publication of a full-length manuscript of poetry. Winners also receive 25 copies of their published book. Poets should submit manuscripts of 48 to 64 pages, with a $17 fee per entry; $10 for Word Thursdays/ Bright Hill Press members. Send SASE or e-mail for guidelines.

Available to: No restrictions
Deadline: November 31
Apply to: Poetry Award, above address

**Bronx Council on the Arts**
**1738 Hone Avenue**
**Bronx, NY 10461**
**Phone: 718-842-3955**
**E-mail: bronxarts@bronxarts.org**
**Web site: http://www.bronxarts.org**

Ⓜ The *BRIO (Bronx Recognizes Its Own) Fellowships* award $2,500 to at least twenty Bronx artists a year; the awards are given in various disciplines, including literary arts, media, performance, and visual arts. The Council provides technical assistance to writers through the Bronx Writers Center, which offers computers, on-line capability, fax machine, copier, resource library, and fiction and poetry collections, and accommodates spoken-word performances, writing workshops, and a literary calendar. Write for guidelines and application.

Available to: Bronx residents over age eighteen who are not full-time matriculated students
Deadline: March 18
Apply to: BRIO Fellowships, above address

Ⓜ The *Van Lier Literary Fellowship and Residency Program* is offered through the Bronx Writers Center. Fellowships of $7,000 each are awarded, over a nine-month period, to writers of fiction, poetry, playwriting, and screenwriting who have not reached their thirtieth birthday by October 1 of the award year. Consult the Web site for more information.

Available to: See above
Deadline: September 1
Apply to: Van Lier Literary Fellowship and Residency Program, above address

**John Carter Brown Library**
**Brown University**
**Box 1894**
**Providence, RI 02912**
**E-mail: JCBL_Fellowships@Brown.edu**
**Web site: http://www.JCBL.org**

Approximately twenty-five *Research Fellowships* are offered annually by the John Carter Brown Library, which houses an outstanding collection of primary materials relating to the discovery, exploration, settlement, and development of the New World. Fellowship recipients are expected to be in continuous residence at the Library and to participate in the intellectual life of Brown University. Preference may be given to applicants able to take up the fellowship during the course of the academic year. Fellowships are of two types:

*Long-Term Fellowships*, supported principally by the National Endowment for the Humanities and the Andrew W. Mellon Foundation, and carrying stipends of $2,800 per month, are available for five months. Applicants must be U. S. citizens or have resided in the United States for three years immediately before the term of the fellowship. Graduate students are not eligible.

*Short-Term Fellowships*, carrying stipends of $1,200 per month, are available for two to four months. Eligible are U. S. and foreign citizens engaged in predoctoral, postdoctoral, or independent research.

Available to: See above
Deadline: January 15
Apply to: Research Fellowships, above address, or e-mail for application

**Bucknell University**
**Stadler Center for Poetry**
**Lewisburg, PA 17837**
**E-mail: stadlercenter@bucknell.edu**
**Web site: http://www.departments.bucknell.edu/stadler_center/**
**Fax: 570-577-3760**

Ⓟ The *Bucknell Seminar for Younger Poets* offers ten fellowships for talented undergraduates to write and receive guidance from established poets during a seminar in June. Readings and workshops are offered. Tuition, room, board, and space for writing are provided.

Available to: Undergraduates from U. S. colleges
Deadline: March 1
Apply to: Send academic transcript, two recommendations, 10-to-12-page portfolio, and letter of presentation to Cynthia Hogue, Director, above address

Ⓡ The *Philip Roth Residence in Creative Writing* provides a studio on the Bucknell University campus, a fully equipped two-bedroom apartment, meals in the University Dining Service, and a stipend of $1,000 for a young writer with some record of accomplishment. The residence coincides with the fall semester, mid-September through late December. In even-numbered years the residence is awarded to a poet, in odd-numbered to a fiction writer. Write for guidelines.

Available to: No restrictions
Deadline: March 1
Apply to: Cynthia Hogue, Director, Philip Roth Residence in Creative Writing, above address

**Radcliffe College**
**Institute for Advanced Study**
**34 Concord Avenue**
**Cambridge, MA 02138**
**Phone: 617-496-1324**
**E-mail: fellowships@radcliffe.edu**
**Web site: http://www.radcliffe.edu**
**Fax: 617-495-8136**

The *Radcliffe Institute for Advanced Study Fellowship Program* supports women scholars, artists, and activists of exceptional promise and demonstrated accomplishment who wish to pursue independent work in academic and professional fields and the creative arts. Appointments are full-time, for September 15-August 15, and require residence in the Boston area during the term. The most recent stipend was $45,000. Applicants should have received their doctorate or appropriate terminal degree at least two years before appointment. Academic applicants without doctorates but with equivalent professional experience will be considered. Applicants in fiction and nonfiction must have a contract for the publication of a book-length manuscript, or must have had at least three short works published; publication in the last five years is highly desirable. Applicants in poetry must have had at least twenty poems or a book of poetry published in the last five years, and be in the process of completing a manuscript. Writers must wait three years to reapply after a previous application. Write, e-mail, or see the Web site for additional information.

Available to: See above
Deadline: October (inquire for exact date)
Apply to: Above address

**Bush Artist Fellows Program**
**E-900 First National Bank Building**
**332 Minnesota Street**
**St. Paul, MN 55101**
**Phone: 800-605-7315**
**Web site: www.bushfoundation.org**

Ⓜ Grants are made to selected artists to enable them to set aside time for concentrating on the development of their artistic talent. Awards are made in seven categories, which rotate in a two-year cycle: visual arts, two-dimensional; visual arts, three-dimensional; choreography/multimedia/performance art; literature (fiction, creative nonfiction, poetry); music composition; scriptworks (playwriting and screenwriting); and film/video. Writers must meet certain prior-publication requirements. Fellowships are for twelve to eighteen months, with a stipend of $44,000. Students are not eligible.

Available to: Minnesota, North Dakota, South Dakota, and western Wisconsin residents, nonstudents, age twenty-five or older, who have been residents of the region for at least twelve of the preceding thirty-six months
Deadline: Inquire
Apply to: Above address

**Witter Bynner Foundation for Poetry**
PO Box 10169
Santa Fe, NM 87504
E-mail: bynnerfounda@aol.com
Fax: 505-986-8222

(P)     The Foundation offers grants in support of poetry translation and the process of translation, developing an audience for poetry, and uses of poetry. Applicants must be sponsored by a nonprofit organization, and a letter of intent must be submitted before an application form can be issued.

Available to: See above
Deadline: February 1 for application; letters of intent accepted August 1 through December 1
Apply to: Above address

**Caldera**
**224 NW 13th Avenue**
**Portland, OR 97209**
**Phone: 503-937-7563**
**E-mail: miriam.feurle@wk.com**
**Web site: www.artistcommunities.org**
**Fax:  503-937-7212**

(R)     Caldera offers free residences of one to five weeks to artists, writers, and creative thinkers on the shore of Blue Lake, near Sisters, Oregon. Applications are accepted for fall, winter, and spring residences. Limited travel grants for those coming from outside the northwest may be available.  Individuals who stay more than fourteen days are strongly encouraged to give an informal presentation about their work. All applicants must submit samples of their work. See the Web site for more information and application.

Available to: No restrictions
Deadline: December 15 for February 15 through June 15 residences; July 15 for September 15 through February 1
Apply to: Miriam Feuerle, Director of Adult Programs, above address

**California Arts Council**
**1300 I Street, Suite 930**
**Sacramento, CA 95814**
**Phone: 916-322-6555**
**E-mail: cac@cwo.com**
**Web site: http://www.cac.ca.gov**
**Fax: 916-322-6575**

(M)     *Artists Fellowships*, given to exemplary California artists in recognition of outstanding artistic achievement, are offered in various disciplines on a rotating basis; the next literature cycle will be 2005-2006. Applicants must be legal residents of California for one year before the application deadline. Write, e-mail, or see the Web site for further information and application.

Available to: See above
Deadline: Inquire
Apply to: Artists Fellowship Program, above address

The *Artists in Residence Program* provides funding for projects that emphasize long-term, in-depth interaction between professional California artists and an organizing group of participants through workshops and classes sponsored by schools, nonprofit organizations, units of government, social institutions, and tribal councils. The Program effectively forges a partnership among artists, sponsors, and the citizens of California. Funding varies according to the nature of the proposed project. Write, e-mail, or consult the Web site for further information and application.

Available to: See above
Deadline: Inquire
Apply to: Artists in Residence Program, above address

**California Library Association**
**717 20th Street, Suite 200**
**Sacramento, CA 95814-3477**
**E-mail: info@cla-net.org**
**Web site: http://www.cla-net.org/groups/beatty/beatty**

© The *John and Patricia Beatty Award* offers $500 for a children's or young-adult book "highlighting California, its culture, heritage and/or future. The California setting must be depicted authentically and must serve as an integral focus for the book." Any children's or young-adult book, fiction or nonfiction, set in California and published in the U. S. during the calendar year preceding the presentation of the award is eligible. Write, e-mail, or see the Web site for submission procedures.

Available to: No restrictions
Deadline: Inquire
Apply to: John and Patricia Beatty Award, above address


**Camargo Foundation**
**125 Park Square Court**
**400 Sibley Street**
**St. Paul, MN 55101-1928**
**E-mail: camargo@jeromefdn.org**
**Web site: www.camargofoundation.org**

® The Camargo Foundation offers fellowships consisting of $3,500 and free residence in fully furnished apartments in Cassis, France. Fellowships are offered to creative writers, photographers and other visual artists, and composers working on independent projects. Fellowships are also offered to scholars engaged in French cultural and/or Francophone cultural studies. Applicants must be working on subjects in the humanities relating to French and/or Francophone culture. Candidates must submit an application form, a CV, and a detailed description of the project they wish to complete in France, together with three letters of recommendation. Applicants in creative writing, photography and other visual art, and music composition must also submit work samples. Write or see the Web site for additional information and application materials. Camargo will not accept any applications electronically. All completed applications must be mailed to the U. S. address above.

Available to: See above
Deadline: February 1
Apply to: Above address


**Cambridge Arts Council**
**51 Inman Street**
**Cambridge, MA 02139**
**E-mail: cac@ci.cambridge.ma.us**
**Web site: http://www.ci.cambridge.ma.us/~CAC/**
**Fax: 617-349-6357**

*Local Cultural Council Grants* are available for high-quality artistic projects that directly benefit the citizens of Cambridge. Grants for which writers may apply are awarded in two categories: Creating and Presenting, for artists to present innovative work in Cambridge; and Education and Access, to teach residents about the arts and to ensure access to the arts for all citizens. Send SASE or e-mail for guidelines and application.

Available to: See above
Deadline: October 15
Apply to: Mary Ann Cicala, Community Arts Administrator, above address


**Campbell Corner**
**Sarah Lawrence College**
**1 Mead Way**
**Bronxville, NY 10708-5999**
**Web site: http://www.slc.edu/campbellcorner**

℗ Ⓝ Campbell Corner, a language-exchange forum on the Sarah Lawrence College Web site named for mythologist Joseph Campbell, sponsors the *Campbell Corner Poetry Prize* and the *Campbell Corner Essay Prize*. Each competition awards $2,500 and publication on the Corner's Literary Exchange. The winner of the poetry prize is invited, along with three finalists, to give a public reading at Sarah Lawrence College. Poets should submit one to three poems "resonating with the transcultural dialogue that Joseph Campbell's writing promotes," and essayists a 1,500-to-5,000-word essay on "transmissions and transgressions of the Holy," in three hard-copy sets and one disk in ASCII text format.

Available to: No restrictions
Deadline: March 15
Apply to: Poetry Contest Director, above address, for poetry prize; Director of Graduate
    Studies, above address, for essay prize

**CANADA**
**The Banff Centre**
**Box 1020, Station 28**
**107 Tunnel Mountain Drive**
**Banff, Alberta TIL 1H5**
**Canada**
**E-mail: arts_info@banffcentre.ca**
**Web site: http://www.banffcentre.ca**
**Fax: 403-762-6345**

Ⓙ Ⓡ The Banff Centre *Creative Nonfiction and Cultural Journalism Program* offers eight established nonfiction writers an opportunity to develop a major essay, memoir, or feature piece in the domain of arts and culture. The program consists of a monthlong residence at the Centre for the selected writers, who work to complete original projects brought to Banff in draft form. Writers receive a $3,000 commission for their work ($1,000 paid on arrival for their first draft, and the balance on completion). There is a processing fee of $50 Canadian. Write, e-mail, or visit the Web site for additional information and application procedures.

Available to: No restrictions
Deadline: March (inquire for exact date)
Apply to: Office of the Registrar, above address

Ⓡ The *Leighton Studios for Independent Residencies* provide residence periods of one week to three months for senior-level writers, composers, and visual artists engaged in the creation of new work. Selection is ongoing. Interested artists are encouraged to apply at least six months before the start of the requested residence. Studio fees are $51 Canadian per day; artists may apply to the Centre for a discount. Write, e-mail, or consult the Web site for additional information.

Available to: Established artists
Deadlines: Ongoing
Apply to: Leighton Studios Registrar, above address

**CANADA**
**Grain Magazine**
**Box 1154**
**Regina, Saskatchewan S4P 3B4**
**Canada**
**E-mail: grain.mag@sk.sympatico.ca**
**Web site: www.skwriter.com**

Ⓜ The *Short Grain Writing Contest* annually offers twelve $500 cash prizes for "postcard" stories (narrative fiction in 500 words or less), dramatic monologue (a self-contained speech given by a single character in 500 words or less), and creative nonfiction (creative prose in 5,000 words or less). The winning works will be published in *Grain*, a quarterly literary journal published by the Saskatchewan Writers Guild. The basic entry fee is $22 Canadian for a maximum of two entries in one category. An additional $5 covers an additional piece in any category. You may enter as many times as you wish, in as many categories as you wish; e-mail entries are not accepted. The entry fee is applied to a one-year subscription to *Grain* (entrants outside Canada should add the equivalent of $4 Canadian for postage). Write, consult the Web site, or e-mail for guidelines.

Available to: No restrictions
Deadline: January 31
Apply to: Short Grain Writing Contest, above address

**CANADA**
**Malahat Review**
**University of Victoria**
**PO Box 1700**
**Victoria, British Columbia V8W 2Y2**
**Canada**
**E-mail: malahat@vvic.ca**
**Web site: http://web.uvic.ca/~malahat/contests.htm**
**Fax: 604-721-7212**

Ⓕ Ⓟ The *Malahat Review Long Poem Prize* of $400 Canadian and *Novella Prize* of $500 Canadian (both of which include payment for publication at the *Review*'s regular rate of $30 for each published page) are given for a long poem and a novella, respectively, in alternate years; the novella is recognized in even-numbered years, poetry in odd-numbered years. The $30 entry fee is payable in U. S. funds and covers a one-year subscription to the *Review*. Send SASE or see the Web site for guidelines.

Available to: No restrictions
Deadline: March 1 for Long Poem Prize; March 1 for Novella Prize
Apply to: Long Poem Prize or Novella Prize, above address

**CANADA**
**Munk Center for International Studies**
**University of Toronto**
**1 Devonshire Place, South House**
**Toronto, Ontario M5S 3K7**
**Canada**
**E-mail: gelberprize.munk@utoronto.ca**
**Fax: 416-946-8915**

Ⓝ The *Lionel Gelber Prize* is a $50,000 award presented annually to the author of the year's most outstanding work of nonfiction in international relations. The award, designed to encourage writers on international relations and to increase the audience for their books, is open to all nationalities. Six copies of each title must be submitted by the publisher. Books must be published during the calendar year under consideration, in English or English translation, and must be distributed or available for sale in Canada. Write or e-mail for additional information.

Available to: No restrictions
Deadline: December 31
Apply to: Prize Manager, above address

**CANADA**
**PRISM international**
**Creative Writing Program**
**University of British Columbia**
**Buch E-462**
**1866 Main Mall**
**Vancouver, British Columbia V6T 1Z1**
**Canada**
**E-mail: prism@interchange.ubc.ca**
**Web site: http://www.arts.ubc.ca/prism**
**Fax: 604-822-3616**

Ⓝ The *Maclean-Hunter Endowment Award for Literary Nonfiction* offers a first prize of $1,500 for the best piece of literary nonfiction no longer than 25 pages. The winning entry will be published in *PRISM international*, the University's literary magazine, and the writer will receive an additional payment of $20 per page. The entry fee of $25 for one piece of nonfiction, $5 for every other piece, covers a one-year subscription to *PRISM*. Canadian residents may use Canadian funds; entrants outside Canada should use U. S. dollars to cover the international mailing costs. E-mail submissions are not accepted. Write, e-mail, or see the Web site for guidelines.

Available to: No restrictions
Deadline: September 30
Apply to: Maclean-Hunter Endowment Award, above address

Ⓕ The *PRISM international Short Fiction Contest* annually awards a $2,000 first prize and five $200 runner-up prizes for short stories no longer than 25 pages. The six winning stories will be published in the summer fiction contest issue; writers will receive an additional payment of $20 per page, plus $10 per page if chosen for the Web site. There is a $22 entry fee for one story, $5 for every other story; the entry fee covers a one-year subscription to *PRISM*. Canadian residents may use Canadian funds; entrants outside Canada should use U. S. dollars to cover the international mailing costs. E-mail submissions are not accepted. Write, e-mail, or see the Web site for guidelines.

Available to: No restrictions
Deadline: Inquire (December or January)
Apply to: Short Fiction Contest, above address

**CANADA**
**Saskatchewan Writers/Artists Colony**
**c/o Saskatchewan Writers Guild**
**PO Box 3986**
**Regina, Saskatchewan S4P 3R9**
**Canada**
**Web site: http://www.skwriter.com/colonies.html**
**Fax: 306-565-8554**

Ⓡ The Saskatchewan Writers/Artists Colony offers residences to writers and visual artists at two retreats in Saskatchewan: St. Peter's Abbey (two weeks in February or six weeks in July/August) and Emma Lake (two weeks in August). The weekly fees are $150-250 Canadian; financial assistance is available. Writers from anywhere are welcome to apply. Write, fax, or see the Web site for additional information and guidelines. Faxed applications are not accepted.

Available to: No restrictions; priority given to Saskatchewan residents
Deadline: December 3 for winter colony; May 1 for summer
Apply to: Above address

**CANADA**
**University of British Columbia**
**Department of Theatre, Film and Creative Writing**
**Buch E-462**
**1866 Main Mall**
**Vancouver, British Columbia V6T 1Z1**
**Canada**
**E-mail: resprize@interchange.ubc.ca**
**Web site: http://www.arts.ubc.ca/crwr/resprize**
**Fax: 604-822-0231**

Ⓓ Ⓡ The *UBC Creative Writing Residency Prize in Stageplay* triennially offers $25,000 and a one-month residence at the University of British Columbia for an original, previously unproduced and unpublished full-length play. The next prize is offered in 2003. While on campus, the winning playwright will mentor creative-writing students, work with theater students and faculty on the development of the play for performance, and deliver the Stageplay Residency Lecture. The winning play will be published in *PRISM international*, UBC's literary magazine, and a public performance will be presented at the campus theater. There is a $50 entry fee, payable in U. S. dollars for entrants outside of Canada. Write, e-mail, or see the Web site for guidelines.

Available to: No restrictions
Deadline: Submissions accepted October 1, 2002-March 31, 2003
Apply to: Prize Coordinator, above address

**Carnegie Fund for Authors**
**1 Old Country Road**
**Carle Place, NY 11514**

The Carnegie Fund offers grants-in-aid to qualified commercially published book authors who have suffered financial emergency as a result of illness or injury (their own or that of spouses or dependent children) or who have suffered some equivalent misfortune. Grant amounts vary according to need.

Available to: See above
Deadline: None
Apply to: Above address

**Carolina Quarterly**
**CB #3520 Greenlaw Hall**
**University of North Carolina**
**Chapel Hill, NC 27599-3520**

Ⓕ Ⓟ The *Charles B. Wood Award for Distinguished Writing* offers $500 for the best poem or short story by an emerging writer published during the year in *Carolina Quarterly*. All poems and short stories by emerging writers are considered.

Available to: *Carolina Quarterly* contributors
Deadline: None
Apply to: Above address

**The Carter Center**
**Mental Health Program**
**One Copenhill**
**Atlanta, GA 30307**
**E-mail: ccmph@emory.edu**
**Web site: http://www.cartercenter.org**

Ⓙ Six *Rosalynn Carter Fellowships for Mental Health Journalism* are awarded annually to print and broadcast journalists to study a selected topic in mental health or mental illness. Fellows receive a grant of $10,000 to cover expenses, including travel, materials, and other incidentals. Fellows make two expense-paid visits to the Carter Center, the first at the beginning of the fellowship year, when fellows meet with advisors to discuss project plans, the second at the end, when fellows present their completed projects. Write, e-mail, or see the Web site for additional information and application procedures.

Available to: Print and broadcast journalists with at least two years' experience
Deadline: May 6
Apply to: Gregory Ficchione, Director, The Carter Center Mental Health Program, above address

**Case Western Reserve University**
**Department of Theater Arts**
**10900 Euclid Avenue**
**Cleveland, OH 44106-7077**
**E-mail: ksg@po.cwru.edu**
**Web site: http://www.cwru.edu/artsci/thtr**
**Fax: 216-368-5184**

Ⓓ The *Marc A. Klein Playwriting Award* offers $500, full production, and an additional $500 during the rehearsal period to defray travel and living expenses, for a previously unpublished, unproduced full-length play, or evenings of thematically related one-acts by a student currently enrolled at a U. S. college or university. Musicals and children's plays are not eligible. Write for additional information and entry form.

Available to: See above
Deadline: May 15
Apply to: Marc A. Klein Playwriting Award, above address

**Catawba College**
**Theatre Arts Department**
**Salisbury, NC 28144**
**E-mail: jepperso@catawba.edu**
**Fax: 704-637-4207**

Ⓓ The *Peterson Emerging Playwright Competition* annually offers $2,000, full production, and transportation and room and board to attend rehearsals and performances for an unpublished, unproduced full-length play by an emerging playwright. Plays for children are not considered. Lodging and food, while in residence, are provided. Playwrights may submit more than one entry. Send SASE or e-mail for guidelines.

Available to: No restrictions
Deadline: February 15
Apply to: Peterson Playwriting Competition, above address

**Cave Canem Foundation, Inc.**
**Box 4286**
**Charlottesville, VA 22905-4286**
**E-mail: cavecanempoets@aol.com**
**Web site: www.cavecanempoets.org**

Ⓟ The *Cave Canem Poetry Prize* awards $500, publication by a distinguished press (most recently, Graywolf Press), and 50 free copies for a manuscript of 50 to 75 poems by an African-American poet who has not yet had a book published professionally. Send SASE for additional information and guidelines, or see the Web site.

Available to: African-American poets
Deadline: May 15
Apply to: Poetry Prize, above address

**CCS Entertainment Group**
**433 North Camden Drive, Suite 600**
**Beverly Hills, CA 90210**
**Web site: http://hollywoodawards.com**

Ⓢ The *Hollywood Screenplay Awards* (formerly known as the Hollywood Columbus Screenplay Discovery Awards) gives first-, second-, and third-place cash prizes for the best unproduced screenplays in competition. The awards seek to bridge the gap between emerging screenwriters and established writers within the industry. One screenplay is selected monthly; all selected screenplays become finalists in the contest. Consult the Web site for guidelines.

Available to: No restrictions
Deadline: December 15
Apply to: Above address

Ⓕ Ⓝ The *Hollywood Book Awards* (formerly known as the Opus Magnum Book Manuscript Discovery Awards) were created to bridge the gap between emerging writers and those established within the industry. First-, second-, and third-place winners receive cash prizes.

Available to: No restrictions
Deadline: December 15
Apply to: Above address

CEC International Partners
12 West 31st Street
New York, NY 10001-4415
Phone: 212-643-1985, ext. 22
E-mail: artslink@cecip.org
Fax: 212-643-1996

*ArtsLink Collaborative Projects* offer grants of up to $10,000 to enable creative artists, including writers and translators, to work with counterparts in Central or Eastern Europe and the Commonwealth of Independent States of the former Soviet Union on projects that will enrich the artists' work and/or create new work that draws inspiration from experience in the country visited. Write for guidelines and application.

Available to: U. S. citizens or permanent residents
Deadline: Inquire
Apply to: ArtsLink, above address


**Centenary College of Louisiana**
**Department of English**
**PO Box 41188**
**Shreveport, LA 71134-1188**

[IN] The *John William Corrington Award for Literary Excellence* offers up to $2,000 and a bronze medal in honor of lifetime achievement. The winner is chosen by a committee of the college's Student Government Association and the English faculty. There is no application process. *By Internal Nomination Only.*


**Center for Book Arts**
**28 West 27th Street, 3rd floor**
**New York, NY 10001**

(P) The *Poetry Chapbook Competition* offers a cash award of $500, a $500 reading honorarium, and publication of a limited-edition chapbook, letterpress-printed and bound by artists at the Center. Poets may submit typescripts of a collection of poems, totaling no more than 500 lines or 24 pages. There is a $15 reading fee for each submission. Send SASE for guidelines.

Available to: No restrictions
Deadline: December 1
Apply to: Poetry Chapbook Competition, above address


**Center for Documentary Studies**
**Duke University**
**1317 West Pettigrew Street**
**Durham, NC 27705**
**Phone: 919-660-3662**
**Web site: http://cds.aas.duke.edu/l-t**

(N) The *Dorothea Lange-Paul Taylor Prize* of $10,000 is given to fund collaborative work between a writer and a photographer in the formative or field work stages of a documentary project. Submissions on any subject are welcome. At the end of one year, prizewinners are invited to the Center to make a public presentation based on their field work. Applications are accepted from collaborators only; individual submissions will not be accepted. More than two people may apply, as long as one is a writer and one a photographer working with black-and-white or color still photography. There is a $15 application fee. Send SASE or see the Web site for guidelines and application.

Available to: See above
Deadline: January 31
Apply to: Dorothea Lange-Paul Taylor Prize Committee, above address

(N) The *John Hope Franklin Student Documentary Awards* provide grants to undergraduates attending any of four area universities (see below) to help them conduct summerlong documentary fieldwork projects. Accepted media include video, photography, and writing.

Students are asked to make a public presentation of their documentary work upon completion of the projects. Applicants should demonstrate an interest in documentary studies and possess the talent and skills necessary to conduct an intensive documentary project, and should be familiar with oral history, photography, film or video, essay or creative writing, journalism, or community service programs. There are restrictions as to the subject matter of the project, but the work should explore an aspect of the human condition, and should expand viewers' understanding of people's lives. Prizewinners may consult with Center staff and associates and use Center facilities while working on the project. Both individual and collaborative proposals are welcome. Contact the Center for more information and application guidelines.

Available to: Registered undergraduate students at Duke University, North Carolina Central University, North Carolina State University, or the University of North Carolina at Chapel Hill
Deadline: March 1
Apply to: John Hope Franklin Student Documentary Awards, Center for Documentary Studies at Duke University, Box 90802, Durham, NC 27708-0802


**Center for Environmental Journalism**
**University of Colorado**
**1511 University Ave, 478 UCB**
**Boulder, CO 80309-0287**
**Phone: 303-492-4114**
**E-mail: cej@colorado.edu**
**Web site: http://campuspress.colorado.edu/CEJ/Scripps.html**

Ⓙ The *Ted Scripps Environmental Fellowship Program* blends classroom and field training at the University of Colorado's Center for Environmental Journalism to help professional journalists acquire knowledge to cover the environment more effectively and enrich public understanding. Five fellowships are awarded each year. Fellows receive tuition, fee payment, and a stipend of $33,000 for the nine-month academic year. Write for additional information.

Available to: U. S. citizens with a minimum of five years' full-time professional journalism experience
Deadline: March 1
Apply to: Environmental Fellowships, above address


**Center Press**
**PO Box 17897**
**Encino, CA 91416-7897**

Ⓜ The *Masters Literary Awards* annually offer a grand prize of $1,000 and possible publication in the Center Press Internet journal. Nominations for honorable mentions are made quarterly in fiction, poetry and song lyrics, and nonfiction. Published and unpublished manuscripts are eligible. There is a $15 reading fee per entry. Send SASE for guidelines and additional information.

Available to: No restrictions
Deadline: Ongoing (nominations made March 15, June 15, September 15, December 15)
Apply to: Masters Literary Awards, above address


**Centrum**
**Fort Worden State Park**
**PO Box 1158**
**Port Townsend, WA 98368**
**E-mail: sally@centrum.org**
**Web site: http//www.centrum.org**
**Fax: 360-385-2470**

Ⓡ *Centrum Residencies,* varying in length from one week to two months, offer an opportunity for reflection and intense creative work. Housing consists of three modest cottages (two or three bedrooms each) and three apartments (two or three bedrooms each), for residences in January through May and September through December. Space is very limited, especially during summer months. There is a $20 application fee. Write or see the Web site for additional information and guidelines.

Available to: No restrictions
Deadline: August 1
Apply to: Above address

**Charlotte Writers Club**
**PO Box 220954**
**Charlotte, NC 28222-0954**

(F)    The *Elizabeth Simpson Smith Award* of $500 is given for the best original unpublished short story of no more than 4,000 words written by a North or South Carolina resident. There is a $10 entry fee. Send SASE for guidelines.

Available to: North and South Carolina Residents
Deadline: April 30
Apply to: Rebecca Schenck, Elizabeth Simpson Smith Award Chair, above address

**Chattahoochee Review**
**Georgia Perimeter College**
**2101 Womack Road**
**Dunwoody, GA 30338-4497**
**Web site: http://www.chattahoochee-review.org**

(N)    The *Lamar York Prize for Nonfiction* offers $1,000 and publication in the *Chattahoochee Review*, a literary magazine, for an essay of up to 5,000 words. Scholarly, critical, and theoretical essays are not eligible; all other approaches and topics are welcome. There is a $10 reading fee. All entries will be considered for publication. Send SASE for guidelines.

Available to: No restrictions
Deadline: Submissions accepted October 1-January 15
Apply to: Lamar York Prize, above address

**Chelsea Award Competition**
**Box 773, Cooper Station**
**New York, NY 10276**

(F) (P)    *Chelsea* awards two annual prizes of $1,000 for the best unpublished work of short fiction (up to 7,500 words) and the best group of four to six unpublished poems (up to 500 lines total) selected in anonymous competitions. Winning entries are published in *Chelsea*; all work entered is considered for publication. The $10 entry fee covers a one-year subscription to *Chelsea*. Send SASE for guidelines.

Available to: No restrictions
Deadlines: June 15 for fiction; December 15 for poetry
Apply to: Above address

**Chesterfield Writers' Film Program**
**1158 26th Street, PMB 544**
**Santa Monica, CA 90403**
**Web site: http://www.chesterfield-co.com**
**Fax: 310-260-6116**

(S)    The *Chesterfield/Writers' Film Project* annually selects up to five writers for a yearlong screenwriting fellowship in Los Angeles, which offers a $20,000 stipend to cover living expenses. Each writer chosen creates two original feature-length screenplays with the advice of professional screenwriters and executive mentors. Writers meet in a workshop setting three to five times a week to consider story ideas, script outlines, and drafts. Current and former writing program students are encouraged to apply. Writers may submit short stories, novels, plays, or screenplays. The application fee is $39.50. Send SASE or see the Web site for application materials.

Available to: No restrictions
Deadline: June 1
Apply to: Writers' Film Project, above address

**The Chicago Reporter**
**332 South Michigan Avenue, Suite 500**
**Chicago, IL 60604**
**Web site: http://www.chicagoreporter.com**
**Fax: 312-427-6130**

Ⓙ The *Chicago Reporter Minority Fellowship in Urban Journalism,* supported by the Robert R. McCormick Tribune Foundation of Chicago, is offered to a talented, aggressive minority journalist to work for a year as a full-time reporter at the *Reporter,* an award-winning investigative monthly. The fellowship offers a competitive salary and benefits, and opportunities for continuing education. Interested candidates should send a résumé and clippings of five published articles. Write or visit the Web site for additional information.

Available to: Minority journalists
Deadline: July 1
Apply to: Alysia Tate, above address

**Chicago Tribune**
**435 North Michigan Avenue, 5th Floor**
**Chicago, IL 60611**

Ⓕ The *Nelson Algren Awards for Short Fiction* offer a first prize of $5,000 and three runner-up prizes of $1,000 each for outstanding unpublished short stories by American writers. The winning stories will be published in the *Tribune*. Stories should be between 2,500 and 10,000 words, typed and double-spaced. Manuscripts will not be returned.

Available to: U. S. citizens
Deadline: Submissions accepted November 1-January 31
Apply to: Nelson Algren Awards, Chicago Tribune Editorial Department, above address

Ⓕ Ⓝ The *Heartland Prizes* award $5,000 each for a novel and a book of nonfiction embodying the spirit of the nation's heartland. Books published between the August 1 preceding the deadline year and July 31 of that year are eligible.

Available to: U. S. citizens
Deadline: July 31
Apply to: Heartland Prizes, Chicago Tribune Editorial Department, above address

**Children's Book Guild of Washington, D.C.**
**c/o Susan Hepler**
**2602 Valley Drive**
**Alexandria, VA 22302**
**Web site: http://www.childrensbookguild.org**

[IN] The *Washington Post/Children's Book Guild Nonfiction Award* offers $2,000 annually to the author of an outstanding body of nonfiction work for children. There is no application process. *By Internal Nomination Only.*

**Children's Literature Association**
**PO Box 138**
**Battle Creek, MI 49016**
**Web site: http://www.ebbs.english.vt.edu/chla**
**Fax: 616-965-3568**

Ⓒ The *Children's Literature Association Research Fellowships and Scholarships,* ranging from $250 to $1,000, support any activity related to serious literary criticism or original scholarship of children's literature that will, presumably, lead to publication and contribute significantly to the field. Awards may be used for transportation, living expenses, or materials, but not for obtaining advanced degrees, researching or writing a thesis or dissertation, writing textbooks, conducting pedagogical projects, or supplementing summer salaries. Write for additional information and guidelines.

Available to: Scholars who have completed an advanced degree program
Deadline: February 1
Apply to: Above address

**Children's Literature Research Collections**
**University of Minnesota**
**Elmer L. Andersen Library**
**222 21st Avenue, South**
**Minneapolis, MN 55455**
**E-mail: clrc@tc.umn.edu**
**Web site: http://www.lib.umn.edu/clrc/awards.html**
**Fax: 612-625-5525**

© The *Ezra Jack Keats/Kerlan Collection Memorial Fellowship* provides $1,500 to a talented aspiring writer and/or illustrator of children's books who wishes to use the Kerlan Collection for furthering his or her artistic development. Special consideration is given to those for whom it would be difficult to finance the visit. The Kerlan Collection contains more than 66,000 children's books, primarily by twentieth-century American writers, and manuscript and illustration material for at least 9,100 titles. Also included are more than 300 periodical and more than 1,200 reference titles, as well as letters, posters, toys, photographs, audiovisuals, publishers' catalogues, and a figurine collection.

Available to: No restrictions
Deadline: May 1
Apply to: Ezra Jack Keats/Kerlan Collection Memorial Fellowship Committee, above address

Ⓝ The *Kerlan Essay Award*, consisting of $300 and a citation, recognizes an outstanding paper of any length written during the preceding school year by a college or university student using the resources of the Children's Literature Research Collections.

Available to: College or university students using the Kerlan Collection for their research
Deadline: June 3
Apply to: Kerlan Essay Award, above address.

**Children's Theatre Foundation of America**
**Box 8067**
**New Orleans, LA 70182**
**Fax: 504-897-5521**

© Ⓓ The *Aurand Harris Children's Theatre Fellowships* offer up to $3,000 to theater artists, including playwrights, to work on specific projects or professional development related to children's theater. Send SASE for guidelines.

Available to: U. S. residents
Deadline: April 30
Apply to: Aurand Harris Fellowships, above address

**Cincinnati Playhouse in the Park**
**Box 6537**
**Cincinnati, OH 45206**
**Web site: http://www.cincyplay.com**

Ⓓ The *Lois and Richard Rosenthal New Play Prize* offers $12,500 and full production in the subsequent season, plus paid travel expenses for a residence in Cincinnati during rehearsals, for an unpublished full-length play that has not been produced professionally. Translations and adaptations are not eligible. Playwrights may submit only one script per year. Submissions should include a two-page synopsis, a character list and playwright bio, and five pages of sample dialogue; cassette tapes or CDs should be submitted for musicals. Materials will not be returned without SASE with correct postage.

Available to: No restrictions
Deadline: Submissions accepted July 1-December 31
Apply to: Rosenthal New Play Prize, above address


**Cintas Foundation**
**c/o William Warren, President**
**Dewey Ballantine LLP**
**1301 Avenue of the Americas, Room 2900**
**New York, NY 10019**

The *Cintas Fellowship Program* offers at least four grants of $10,000 each in architecture, music, literature, and the visual arts for Cuban professional artists living outside Cuba. Fellowships are awarded annually and rotate among genres and disciplines; they may not be used for study programs. Write for additional information and application.

Available to: Cuban citizens or individuals of Cuban descent living outside Cuba
Deadline: March 15
Apply to: Cintas Fellowship Program, above address


**City of Atlanta Bureau of Cultural Affairs**
**City Hall East**
**675 Ponce de León Avenue, 5th floor**
**Atlanta, GA 30308**
**Web site: www.bcaatlanta.org**
**Fax: 404-817-6827**

Ⓜ *Artist Project Grants* are designed to support practicing professional artists, including writers, residing in Atlanta. Grants of up to $3,000 are offered for projects by poets, fiction writers, creative- nonfiction writers, and playwrights who demonstrate a consistent level of high-quality work.

Available to: Atlanta residents
Deadline: December
Apply to: Grants Administrator, above address

Ⓜ The *Mayor's Fellowships in the Arts* annually awards $5,000 to a practicing professional artist who has resided in Atlanta for at least three consecutive years immediately before the deadline. The awards rotate among several artistic disciplines. The most recent literary arts fellowship is awarded in 2002; inquire for next award cycle. Write for guidelines and application.

Available to: Atlanta residents
Deadline: Inquire
Apply to: Grants Administrator, above address


**Civic Education Project**
**1717 Massachusetts Avenue, NW, Suite 506**
**Washington, DC 20036-2001**
**E-mail: cep@osi.hu (CEP Budapest office); cepdc@jhu.edu (CEP Washington office)**
**Web site: www.cep.org.hu**

The *Visiting Faculty Fellowship* and *Local Faculty Fellowship* programs offer teaching fellowships to faculty, retired faculty, recent Ph.D.'s, and advanced postgraduate students, in the social sciences, law and journalism/media studies. CEP fellows teach at partner universities in Central and Eastern Europe, Russia, and Mongolia. Visiting Faculty Fellows are academics from outside the region who teach and mentor for one academic year (two semesters) at a college in a CEP program country; they receive a stipend, roundtrip air travel, accommodation, health insurance, language lessons, and book allowance. Local Faculty Fellows are academics from the region who have a graduate degree from a North American or West European university; CEP supports their efforts to remain in academia in their home country by providing a monthly stipend, teaching materials, and participation in various CEP events and activities. Eligible disciplines include international relations, sociology, political science, law, history, economics, public administration, environmental policy, and journalism/media studies. For guidelines and the list of fellowships, see the CEP Web site.

Available to: See above
Deadline: February 15
Apply to: Above address

**Civil War Institute**
**Gettysburg College**
**233 North Washington Street**
**Gettysburg, PA 17325**
**E-mail: civilwar@gettysburg.edu**
**Web site: http://www.gettysburg.edu**
**Fax: 717-337-6596**

Ⓜ The *Lincoln Prize* annually awards $50,000 for the finest scholarly work on the era of the American Civil War published during the calendar year. Preference is given to work on Lincoln and the Civil War soldier, and work that addresses the literate general public. In rare instances the prize may go to a work of fiction, poetry, drama, or film. Ten copies of the work should be submitted to the Institute. Work that will not be in its final form until the end of the year may be submitted in galley form; copies of the published work must follow as soon as they are available.

Available to: No restrictions
Deadline: November 1
Apply to: Lincoln Prize, above address

**Clackamas Literary Review**
**19600 South Molalla Avenue**
**Oregon City, OR 97045**
**E-mail: clr@clackamaliteraryreview.com**
**Web site: http://www.clackamas.cc.or.us/clr/**

Ⓕ The *Peter and Jean de Maine Award for an Emerging Writer in Fiction* of $1,000 is given annually to a fiction writer with no more than one published book whose work appears in the Spring or Fall issue of the *Review*.

Available to: Authors of stories accepted for publication in *Clackamas Literary Review*
Deadline: Ongoing
Apply to: Above address

Ⓕ Ⓟ The *Willamette Award in Fiction and Poetry* offers $500 in each category and publication in the *Review* for a short story and a poem. Writers should submit one short story of no more than 10,000 words or one to three poems, along with a $10 reading fee. Send SASE or see the Web site for further information.

Available to: No restrictions
Deadline: June 1
Apply to: Willamette Award (specify genre), above address

**Claremont Graduate University**
**Poetic Gallery for the Kate and Kingsley Tufts Poetry Awards**
**160 East 10th Street, Harper Hall B7**
**Claremont, CA 91711**
**Phone: 909-621-8974**
**Web site: www.cgu.edu/tufts**

Ⓟ The *Kate Tufts Discovery Award*, of $10,000, is given for "a first or very early work by a poet of genuine promise." Write for guidelines and entry form before submitting.

(P) The *Kingsley Tufts Poetry Award* offers a $100,000 prize for a book of poems written in English by an emerging poet, "one who is past the very beginning but has not yet reached the acknowledged pinnacle of his or her career." The submitted text must be either published or completed during the calendar year, and may be submitted by the author or, with the author's consent, by a publisher, agent, or other representative. Work scheduled for publication after the deadline may be submitted in the form of typescript or proofs. Write for guidelines and entry form.

Available to: U. S. citizens or legal residents
Deadline: September 15
Apply to: Above address

**Claremont Graduate University**
**School of Religion**
**831 Dartmouth Avenue**
**Claremont, CA 91711**
**Web site: http://religion.cgu.edu**

(N) The *Bross Prize* is given every ten years to the best book-length manuscript that investigates a relationship between any discipline and the Christian religion. The next award will be presented in 2010. At least $15,000 will be given, in one to three prizes. Three typewritten copies of each manuscript must be submitted, or the author will be asked to assume copying costs incurred by the prize committee.

Available to: No restrictions
Deadline: Inquire
Apply to: Bross Prize, above address

**Clauder Competition for Excellence in Playwriting**
**PO Box 383259**
**Cambridge, MA 02238**
**Phone: 617-322-3187**

(D) The *Clauder Competition for Excellence in Playwriting* biennially offers a first prize of $2,500 and full production for full-length plays by young New England playwrights, including students, that have not been produced professionally. Runners-up receive $500 and a staged reading. The next competition will be held in 2003. Send SASE for guidelines.

Available to: See above
Deadline: Inquire
Apply to: Above address

**Cleveland Foundation**
**1422 Euclid Avenue, Suite 1400**
**Cleveland, OH 44115-2001**
**Web site: http://www.clevelandfoundation.org**
**Fax: 216-861-1729**

(M) The *Anisfield-Wolf Book Awards* recognize recent books that have contributed to the understanding of racism or the appreciation of the rich diversity of human cultures. A prize of $10,000 is given each spring for books written in English and published in the preceding calendar year. If multiple winners are chosen in a given year, the $10,000 is divided equally among them. Unfinished manuscripts and self-published books are not eligible. Copies of eligible books should be sent directly to the panel of jurors.

Available to: See above
Deadline: January 31
Apply to: Above address for list of current jurors

**Cleveland Public Theatre**
**6415 Detroit Avenue**
**Cleveland, OH 44102**
**E-mail: cpt@en.com**
**Web site: http://www.cptonline.org**
**Fax: 216-631-2575**

Ⓓ The CPT *New Plays Festival* biennially selects twelve to sixteen new works for three weeks of staged readings. Selected playwrights will be flown to Cleveland for the Festival. The script chosen as "Best of Festival" will receive the *Frank and Janet Levin Award* of $1,000. Write, e-mail, or see the Web site for further information.

Available to: No restrictions
Deadline: Inquire
Apply to: New Plays Festival, above address

**Cleveland State University**
**Poetry Center Prizes**
**Department of English**
**Rhodes Tower, Room 1815**
**1983 East 24th Street**
**Cleveland, OH 44115-2440**
**E-mail: poetrycenter@csuohio.edu**
**Web site: www.csuohio.edu/poetrycenter**

Ⓟ The *Poetry Center Prize* annually awards $1,000 and publication in the CSU Poetry Series for a volume of original poetry in a First Book and Open Competition. Submission should contain a minimum of 40 pages of poetry. Previously published collections, including self-published books, are not eligible. There is a $20 submission fee. Send SASE for guidelines, or e-mail or see the Web site.

Available to: No restrictions
Deadline: Submissions accepted November 1-February 1
Apply to: Poetry Center Prize, above address

**Coalition for the Advancement of Jewish Education**
**261 West 35th Street, floor 12A**
**New York, NY 10001**
**Web site: http://www.caje.org**
**Fax: 212-268-4214**

Ⓕ The *David Dornstein Memorial Creative Writing Contest for Young Adult Writers* offers a $750 first prize and a $250 second prize for a short story of up to 5,000 words on a Jewish theme or topic by a writer age eighteen to thirty-five. (If three winning stories are chosen, the first-place winner will receive $700, the second $200, and the third $100.) CAJE will attempt to publish all winning stories in *Jewish Education News*. Writers may submit one unpublished story of no more than 5,000 words by mail, fax, or e-mail. Send SASE or e-mail for guidelines.

Available to: See above
Deadline: January 31
Apply to: David Dornstein Contest, above address

**Coldwater Community Theater**
**c/o J. Richard Colbeck, Award Chairman**
**89 South Division**
**Coldwater, MI 49036**

Ⓒ Ⓓ The *Robert J. Pickering Award for Playwriting Excellence* annually offers a cash prize plus production in the historic Tibbits Opera House in Coldwater for an unproduced full-length play or musical; plays for children are eligible. Send SASE for guidelines.

Available to: No restrictions
Deadline: December 31
Apply to: Above address

**Colonial Players, Inc.**
**Theater in the Round**
**108 East Street**
**Annapolis, MD 21401**
**Phone: 410-263-0533**

Ⓓ  The biennial *Promising Playwright Award* is given for a full-length play suitable for an arena stage by an aspiring playwright residing in any of the states descended from the original thirteen colonies (Connecticut, Delaware, Georgia, Massachusetts, New Hampshire, New Jersey, New York, North Carolina, Pennsylvania, Rhode Island, South Carolina, Virginia), West Virginia, or Washington, D.C. Plays should be limited to two sets and a cast of ten. The winner is awarded $750 plus production (playwright must be available to attend rehearsals). Send SASE for guidelines.

Available to: See above
Deadline: Submissions accepted September 1-December 31
Apply to: Promising Playwright Award, above address

**Colorado Council on the Arts**
**750 Pennsylvania Street**
**Denver, CO 80203**
**Web site: http://www.coloarts.state.co.us/default.asp**
**Fax: 303-894-2615**

Ⓜ  Several *Artist Fellowship Awards in Literature* of $5,000 are offered annually to acknowledge outstanding achievement by Colorado writers. Fellowships alternate yearly between poetry and playwriting/screenwriting. Write, e-mail, or see the Web site for guidelines and application.

Available to: Colorado residents
Deadline: January 4
Apply to: Artist Fellowship Awards in Literature, above address

**Colorado Review**
**Department of English**
**Colorado State University**
**Fort Collins, CO 80523**
**E-mail: creview@vines.colostate.edu**
**Web site: http://www.coloradoreview.com**

Ⓟ  The *Colorado Prize* offers a $2,000 honorarium and publication by the Center for Literary Publishing and distribution by University Press of Colorado for a book-length collection of poems. There is a $25 reading fee, which covers a one-year, three-volume subscription to *Colorado Review*. Send SASE for guidelines.

Available to: No restrictions
Deadline: Mid-January (inquire for exact date)
Apply to: Colorado Prize, above address

ⒾⓃ  The *"Evil Companions" Literary Award* of $1,000 is given annually to a writer living in, writing about, or having ties to the American West. The award is named for the self-proclaimed "Evil Companions," a group of Denver journalists of the 1950s and 1960s. The winner is chosen by a committee of individuals from *Colorado Review*, the Tattered Cover Bookstore, and the Oxford Hotel. There is no application process. *By Internal Nomination Only*.

**Columbia College**
**Department of Theatre**
**72 East 11th Street**
**Chicago, IL 60605**
**Fax: 312-344-8077**

Ⓓ  The *Theodore Ward Prize for Playwriting* annually awards $2,000 plus production for a professionally unproduced full-length play by an African-American writer. The winner will receive transportation to/from Chicago and housing during the week of rehearsal before the first performance. A second prize of $500 plus a staged reading is also offered. Write for guidelines.

Available to: African-American playwrights
Deadline: Submissions accepted April 1-July 1
Apply to: Theodore Ward Prize for Playwriting, above address

**Columbia University**
**Bancroft Prize Committee**
**Office of the President**
**202A Low Memorial Library**
**Mail Code 4310**
**New York, NY 10027**
**www.columbia.edu/cu/web/eguides/amerihist/bancroft.html**

Ⓝ Two *Bancroft Prizes* are given annually for books in American history (including biography) and diplomacy; "American" refers to North, South, and Central America. The prizes, $4,000 each, are for books first published in the year preceding that of the award. Submissions should include four copies of the book and a nominating letter. Consult the Web site for complete guidelines.

Available to: No restrictions
Deadline: November 1
Apply to: Above address

**Columbia University**
**Graduate School of Journalism**
**2950 Broadway**
**New York, NY 10027**
**Phone: 212-854-5974**
**E-mail: cabot@jrn.columbia.edu (for Maria Moors Cabot Prizes only)**
**Web site: http://www.jrn.columbia.edu**

Ⓙ The *Maria Moors Cabot Prizes* honor the advancement of freedom of the press and distinguished contributions to inter-American understanding. The prizes, awarded annually to two to four professional journalists for the body of their work, consist of a medal, an honorarium of $1,500, and payment of travel expenses to/from the awards ceremony at Columbia University. Greatest consideration is given to sustained work in covering events that affect the Americas. Write, e-mail, or see the Web site for additional information and nomination procedures.

Available to: No restrictions
Deadline: March 31
Apply to: Maria Moors Cabot Prizes, above address

Ⓙ The *Knight-Bagehot Fellowship Program in Economics and Business Journalism* provides a nine-month course of study during the academic year to improve the quality of reporting by expanding participants' understanding of business, finance, and economics. Up to ten fellowships are awarded annually; fellows receive tuition plus a stipend of $28,000 to offset living expenses in New York City. Housing is available in a Columbia-affiliated facility. Applicants must have at least four years' professional experience, not necessarily in business and economics, and must have published work that has appeared regularly in the U. S. or Canada. Write for additional information and application.

Available to: See above
Deadline: March 1
Apply to: Director, Knight-Bagehot Fellowship Program, above address

**Columbia University**
**Charles H. Revson Fellows Program**
**Mail Code 6940**
**New York, NY 10027**
**Phone: 212-280-4023**
**Web site: www.columbia.edu/cu/revson**

The *Revson Fellows Program* awards fellowships to those who have made a significant contribution to New York City or to another large metropolitan center and who can be expected to make even greater contributions in the future, after using Columbia University's instructional, research, and other resources for an academic year. Ten awards, consisting of an $18,000 stipend, four credit courses, and an unlimited number of audited courses, are given each year.

Available to: No restrictions
Deadline: February 1
Apply to: Above address

**Christopher Columbus Fellowship Foundation**
**110 Genesee Street, Suite 390**
**Auburn, NY 13021**
**E-mail: judithmscolumbus@cs.com**
**Web site: www.columbusfdn.org**
**Fax: 315-258-0093**

Four *Frank Annunzio Awards*, of $50,000 each, are given in the following categories: two in Arts/Humanitarianism, and two in Science/Technology. The awards honor living Americans whose innovative thinking has led to creative work, process, product, or other significant achievement that has benefited society. Call, write, or e-mail the Foundation for guidelines.

Available to: U. S. citizens
Deadline: Mid-June (inquire for exact date)
Apply to: Judith M. Shellenberger, Executive Director

**Common Wealth Awards**
**c/o PNC Bank, Delaware, Trustee**
**222 Delaware Avenue**
**PO Box 791**
**Wilmington, DE 19899-0791**

[IN] The *Common Wealth Awards* are available in literature, the dramatic arts, mass communications, science and invention, government, public service, and sociology. Awards are given for a body of work, not for a specific project. Nominations are made by various groups recognized as umbrella organizations in each category. *By Internal Nomination Only.*

**The Commonwealth Club of California**
**595 Market Street**
**San Francisco, CA 94105**
**Phone: 415-597-4846**
**Web site: http://www.commonwealthclub.org**
**Fax: 415-597-6729**

Ⓜ The *California Book Awards* offer $2,000 to each gold medalist and $300 to each silver medalist for the best work published by California writers during the calendar year. Up to ten medals are offered annually in the categories first work of fiction, fiction, nonfiction, poetry, juvenile literature, Californiana, and notable contributions to publishing. Authors must be legal residents of California when their manuscript is submitted for publication. Write, e-mail, or fax for additional information.

Available to: See above
Deadline: December 28
Apply to: Barbara Lane, California Book Awards, above address

**Conference on Latin American History**
**University of Southern Florida**
**4202 East Fowler Avenue**
**SOC 107**
**Tampa, FL 33620**
**E-mail: clah@chuma.cas.use.edu**

Ⓝ The *Bolton-Johnson Prize* offers $1,000 annually for the best book in English, published during the year before the award, on any significant aspect of Latin American history. Sound scholarship, grace of style, and importance of the scholarly contribution are among the criteria for the award. Translations, anthologies of selections by several authors, reprints or new editions of works published previously, or works not primarily historiographical in aim or content are not eligible. An Honorable Mention may be given for an additional distinguished work deemed worthy by the prize committee. Publishers and CLAH members may nominate; each committee member must receive a copy of the nominated book. Inquire for further information and list of committee members.

Available to: See above
Deadline: June 1
Apply to: CLAH Secretariat, above address

**Connecticut Commission on the Arts**
**755 Main Street**
**1 Financial Plaza**
**Hartford, CT 06103**
**Phone: 860-566-4770**
**E-mail: artsinfo@ctarts.org**
**Web site: http://www.ctarts.org**
**Fax: 860-566-6462**

Ⓜ *Artist Fellowships* of $2,500 and $5,000 are offered to Connecticut residents. Grants are on a two-year cycle, with literary arts (poetry, fiction, drama) relevant in even-numbered years. Write for complete guidelines.

Available to: Writers who have lived and worked in Connecticut for at least one year
Deadline: September (inquire for exact date)
Apply to: Artist Fellowships, above address

Ⓜ The Commission on the Arts maintains a roster of performing artists in dance, music, and theater, as well as poets, writers, and storytellers, for public readings. Its *Arts Presentation Program* offers funding support (up to half the artist fee) to organizations for events featuring roster artists. New performing groups and writers are added to the roster every two years.

Available to: Connecticut residents and organizations
Deadline: Inquire
Apply to: Above address

**Converse College**
**Department of English**
**Spartanburg, SC 29302**
**Web site: www.converse.edu.academics/majors/peterkin.htm**

Ⓕ Ⓟ The *Julia Peterkin Award* offers a cash prize of $750, along with payment of expenses for a reading, for poetry in even-numbered years and fiction in odd-numbered years. Fiction writers may submit a single short story or novel excerpt of no more than 20 pages; poets, four or five poems with a maximum of 15 pages total. Work may be published or unpublished. There is a $12 entry fee. Write for additional information and guidelines.

Available to: No restrictions
Deadline: February 15
Apply to: Julia Peterkin Award, above address

**Cooperative Children's Book Center**
**4290 Helen C. White Hall**
**600 North Park Street**
**Madison, WI 53706**
**E-mail: khorning@facstaff.wisc.edu**
**Web site: http://www.education.wisc.edu/ccbc/zolotow.htm**

IN   The *Charlotte Zolotow Award* of $1,000 is given annually for a picture book for young children (through age seven) published during the calendar year. The book may be fiction, nonfiction, or folklore. The recipient is chosen by a committee of children's literature experts. There is no application process. *By Internal Nomination Only.*

**Copper Canyon Press**
**PO Box 271**
**Port Townsend, WA 98368**
**E-mail: poetry@copprcanyonpress.org**
**Web site: http://www.coppercanyonpress.org**

P   The *Hayden Carruth Award for Emerging Poets* offers publication by Copper Canyon Press of a first, second, or third book; a prize of $1,000; and a one-month residence at the Vermont Studio Center. There is a $20 application fee. Send SASE for guidelines and entry form, or download from Web site.

Available to: New and emerging authors
Deadline: Manuscripts accepted in November
Apply to: Hayden Carruth Award, above address

**Cornell University**
**Department of English**
**Goldwin Smith Hall**
**Ithaca, NY 14853**

D  J   The *George Jean Nathan Award for Dramatic Criticism* is given for the best piece of drama criticism published in the U. S. during the theatrical year (July 1-June 30), whether article, essay, treatise, or book. Criticism that has been broadcast on television or radio is also eligible. One award, of $10,000 and a trophy, is given annually. Send SASE for guidelines and selection committee list.

Available to: U. S. citizens
Deadline: September 30
Apply to: George Jean Nathan Award, above address

**Council on Foreign Relations**
**Office of Membership and Fellowship Affairs**
**58 East 68th Street**
**New York, NY 10021**
**E-mail: fellowship@cfr.org**
**Web site: http://www.cfr.org**
**Fax: 212-434-98-01**

J   The *Edward R. Murrow Fellowship,* for a nine-month residence at the Council offices, is available yearly to an American foreign correspondent for "sustained analysis and research" and offers the opportunity to be in residence for nine months at Council headquarters in New York. The stipend equals the journalist's current salary up to $65,000. Write for additional information.

Available to: Correspondents, editors, or producers who have covered international news for radio, television, newspapers or magazines nationally available in the U. S.
Deadline: February 1 for nomination letter; February 28 for complete application
Apply to: Elise Lewis, Vice-President, Membership and Fellowship Affairs, above address

Council for International Exchange of Scholars
3007 Tilden Street, NW, Suite 5L
Washington, DC 20008-3009
E-mail: apprequest@cies.iie.org
Web site: http://www.cies.org
Fax: 202-362-3442

The Council administers the Department of State-sponsored *Fulbright Scholar Program* for advanced research and university lecturing in more than 1,400 countries around the world. Some 800 grants are awarded annually to faculty and professionals in virtually all academic disciplines, including creative writing. Grant benefits vary by country, but usually include international travel, a monthly stipend, and other allowances. Applications are available in March on-line and from the above address.

Available to: U. S. citizens
Deadline: August 1; other deadlines for special programs
Apply to: Box NEWS, above address

A similar program for scholars from abroad for university lecturing and advanced research in the U. S. is administered in this country by the Council. Interested non-U. S. citizens should inquire at the U. S. embassy or Fulbright agency in their home country.

**Crab Orchard Review**
**Department of English**
**Southern Illinois University at Carbondale**
**Carbondale, IL 62901-4503**
**Web site: http://www.siu.edu/~crborchd**

Ⓟ  The *Crab Orchard Award Series in Poetry* offers a $2,000 first prize and a $1,000 honorarium for a reading at Southern Illinois University for an unpublished original collection of poems, 50 to 70 pages long, written in English by a U. S. citizen or resident. The first runner-up will also receive a $1,000 honorarium for a reading, and both books will be published by Southern Illinois University Press. All submissions must be accompanied by a $20 entry fee, which covers a one-year subscription to *Crab Orchard Review*. Send SASE or see the Web site for guidelines.

Available to: U. S. citizens or permanent residents
Deadline: Submissions accepted October 1-November 16
Apply to: John Tribble, Series Editor, Crab Orchard Award Series, above address

Ⓕ Ⓝ  The *Jack Dyer Fiction Prize* and the *John Guyon Literary Nonfiction Prize* each offer $1,000 and publication in *Crab Orchard Review*. Entries must be unpublished original work, not under consideration elsewhere. Writers may submit up to 6,000 words of fiction or up to 6,500 words of literary nonfiction. There is a $10 fee for each entry (one story / essay per entry), which covers a one-year subscription to the *Review*. Write for additional information and guidelines.

Available to: U. S. citizens or permanent residents
Deadline: Submissions accepted February 1-March 15
Apply to: Above address, with envelope marked "Fiction" or "Literary Nonfiction"

**Crane-Rogers Foundation.** *See* **Institute of Current World Affairs**

**The Crescent Review**
**PO Box 7959**
**Charlotte, NC 28470-7959**
**Web site: http://www.thecrescentreview.org**

Ⓕ  The *Chekhov Award for Short Fiction* offers $1,000 and publication in *The Crescent Review* for a short story of up to 7,000 words. A second prize of $400 and a third of $100 are also given. There is a $7 reading fee. Send SASE or, preferably, consult the Web site for guidelines.

Available to: No restrictions
Deadline: Submissions accepted August 15-October 1
Apply to: Chekhov Award for Short Fiction, above address

(F) The *Renwick-Sumerwell Award for Short Fiction* offers $1,000 and publication in *The Crescent Review* for a short story of up to 7,000 words by a writer who has not published short fiction in any publication with a circulation of greater than 500. A second prize of $400 and a third of $100 are also given. There is a $7 reading fee. Send SASE or, preferably, consult the Web site for guidelines.

Available to: See above
Deadline: Submissions accepted April 15-June 15
Apply to: Renwick-Sumerwell Award for Short Fiction, above address

**Cultural Arts Council of Houston/Harris County**
**3201 Allen Parkway**
**Houston, TX 77019**
**Phone: 713-527-9330**
**E-mail: info@cachh.org**
**Web site: http://www.cachh.org**

(M) *Individual Artist Grants* are awarded annually by the Council to Houston or Harris County artists and writers. These include *Artist Fellowship Awards* of $5,000 each and *Emerging Artist Fellowships* of $2,500 each. Write, e-mail, or see the Web site for additional information and application.

Available to: Houston or Harris County residents of at least two years
Deadline: Late fall (inquire for exact date)
Apply to: Individual Artist Grants, above address

**Cumberland Poetry Review**
**PO Box 120128**
**Acklen Station**
**Nashville, TN 37212**

(P) The *Robert Penn Warren Poetry Prize* awards a $500 first place, a $300 second place, and a $200 third place for poems neither previously published nor submitted elsewhere. Prizewinners and honorable mentions will be published in *Cumberland Poetry Review*. Poets may enter as many as three poems of no more than 100 lines each. The $18 reading fee covers a one-year subscription to the *Review*. Write for required entry form.

Available to: No restrictions
Deadline: March 1
Apply to: Above address

**CUNY Dominican Studies Institute**
**City College**
**West 138th Street at Convent Avenue, NAC 4/107**
**New York, NY 10031**

(N) The *Dominican American National Roundtable Annual Contest* awards $1,000, $500, and $250 for the best essays written by Dominican-American high school students. The essays, in English or Spanish, should be from 250 to 400 words; they address a topic that differs every year. (A recent topic was "People or events that have shaped the writer's aspirations for the future.") Winners are guests of honor, with expenses paid, at the Dominican National Roundtable's annual conference.

Available to: Dominican-American high school students
Deadline: November 15
Apply: Above address

**Curbstone Press**
**321 Jackson Street**
**Willimantic, CT 06226**
**Phone: 860-423-5110**
**E-mail: sandy@curbstone.org**
**Web site: www.curbstone.org**

(F) The *Miguel Mármol Prize* offers publication by Curbstone Press and $1,000 advance against royalties for a first book-length work of fiction by a Latina/o writer that reflects a respect for international understanding and fosters an appreciation for human rights and civil liberties. A brief biography of the author must accompany the manuscript. There is a $15 entry fee. Write or consult the Web site for submission procedures.

Available to: See above
Deadline: December 15
Apply to: Above address

**Cushwa Center for the Study of American Catholicism**
**1135 Flanner Hall**
**University of Notre Dame**
**Notre Dame, IN 46556-5611**
**E-mail: cushwa.1@nd.edu**

(N) Two *Publication Awards* are offered by the Cushwa Center and the University of Notre Dame Press for manuscripts dealing with the American Catholic experience or the Irish in America. The award-winning entries will be published by the University of Notre Dame Press, and authors receive a $500 advance on royalties. Manuscripts from the humanities, history, and social studies are considered; unrevised dissertations normally are not. Write for additional information and guidelines.

Available to: No restrictions
Deadline: December 31
Apply to: Publication Awards, above address

**Cyclone Productions**
**Box 148849**
**Chicago, IL 60614**
**Phone: 773-665-7600**
**Web site: http://www.cyclone-entertainment.com**
**Fax: 773-665-7660**

(S) The *Cyclone Productions Screenwriters Project* annually awards grants of up to $5,000 and possible production to writers of diverse backgrounds and varied degrees of writing experience interested in screenwriting careers. Work chosen for production will receive no less than the current minimum established by the Writers Guild of America. Applicants will be evaluated on the basis of a dramatic-writing sample, which may be a completed screenplay, a treatment, or a synopsis for a movie, story, novel, or play. The submission should be adaptable to motion picture or television format. The administration fee varies according to the submission date (see below). Write or consult the Web site for application procedures.

Available to: No restrictions
Deadline: July 1 ($40); August 1 ($45); September 1 ($50)
Apply to: Screenwriters Project, above address

**Dana Awards**
**7207 Townsend Forest Court**
**Browns Summit, NC 27214**
**E-mail: danaawards@pipeline.com**
**Web site: http://danaawards.home.pipeline.com**

(F) (P) The *Dana Awards* recognize work in three categories: the novel, poetry, and fiction, including literary/mainstream short fiction and speculative short fiction (science fiction, fantasy, horror, surrealism). A $1,000 prize is given for an unpublished novel, $1,000 for the best group of five unpublished poems, and $1,000 for a short story. Novelists should submit the first 50 pages only of an unpublished novel, with a $20 entry fee; poets should submit up to five unpublished poems of any length, with a $10 entry fee; and short story writers should submit a story of up to 10,000 words (3,000 words or fewer preferred), with a $10 entry fee. E-mail, consult the Web site, or send SASE for guidelines. E-mail submissions are not accepted.

Available to: No restrictions
Deadline: October 31
Apply to: Above address

**Dart Center for Journalism and Trauma**
**School of Communications**
**Room 102 Communications Building**
**Box 353740**
**University of Washington**
**Seattle, WA 98195-3740**
**Phone: 206-616-3223**
**Web site: www.dartcenter.org**

Ⓙ The *Dart Award* offers a $10,000 prize for the U.S. newspaper entry that "best illustrates the effects of violence on victims and how they cope with emotional trauma," and that treats victims and their experiences with accuracy, insight, and respect. The award is given as a team prize, with entries judged as a total package, including headlines, cutlines, graphics, artwork, and layout. The winning organization is responsible for dividing the prize money among staff members in proportion to individual contributions. Write or see the Web site for guidelines.

Available to: U.S. newspapers
Deadline: February 1
Apply to: Dart Award, above address

The Dart Foundation also offers fellowships to journalists to study emotional trauma, its effect on victims of disaster and violence, and the implications for newsgatherers. Consult the Web site for more information.

**Dashew International Student Center**
**Tom Bradley International Hall**
**University of California, Los Angeles**
**417 Charles E. Young Drive West, Room 106, Box 951397**
**Los Angeles, CA 90095**
**Phone: 310-267-1987**
**E-mail: kperry@saonet.ucla.edu**

Ⓜ The *Harry Kurnitz Award* offers annual prizes of $2,000, $1,000, and $500 to students whose first language is not English, for an outstanding poem, short story, or screenplay. The purpose of the award is to encourage creative writing among international students. Contact the Dashew Student Center for more details.

Available to: Students whose first language is not English
Deadline: Inquire
Apply to: Above address

**Shelby Cullom Davis Center for Historical Studies**
**Princeton University**
**Department of History**
**G-13 Dickinson Hall**
**Princeton, NJ 08544-1017**
**Web site: http://www.princeton.edu/~davisctr/**

*Visiting Davis Fellowships* are available for one semester or a full academic year at the Davis Center at Princeton. Fellows are expected to pursue research related to the current theme of the Center and to participate in its seminar program. The theme for 2001-2003 is "Migration in History." Emphasis is on interdisciplinary approaches and on topics that do not restrict participation to specialists in a single geographical area or period of time.

Support for fellows varies according to the outside grants and sabbatical funds they bring with them; maximum support is $28,000 for a semester and $56,000 for the academic year. Write for additional information and application.

Available to: No restrictions
Deadline: December 1
Apply to: Manager, above address

**Dayton Playhouse**
**1301 East Siebenthaler Avenue**
**Dayton, OH 45414**
**E-mail: futurefest@daytonplayhouse.com**
**Web site: www.daytonplayhouse.com**
**Fax: 937-333-2827**

Ⓓ The *Dayton Playhouse FutureFest* awards $1,000 and production to previously unproduced and unpublished plays. Three full-scale selections, as well as three readers' theater selections, will be presented during FutureFest weekend in July. A $1,000 prize and an opportunity to self-publish are awarded to the winning playwright. Send SASE for guidelines before submitting, or consult the Web site.

Available to: No restrictions
Deadline: Submissions accepted August 1-October 31
Apply to: FutureFest Committee

**Delaware Division of the Arts**
**Carvel State Office Building**
**820 North French Street**
**Wilmington, DE 19801**
**Web site: http://www.artsdel.org**
**Fax: 302-577-6561**

Ⓜ *Individual Artist Fellowships* in the literary arts are available to Delaware residents. Fellowships are $2,000 for emerging professionals, $5,000 for established professionals. Write or consult the Web site for guidelines and application.

Available to: Delaware residents
Deadline: August 1
Apply to: Kristin Pleasanton, Fellowship Coordinator, above address

**Gladys Krieble Delmas Foundation**
**521 Fifth Avenue, Suite 1612**
**New York, NY 10175-1699**
**E-mail: info@delmas.org**
**Web site: http://www.delmas.org**
**Fax: 212-687-8877**

Predoctoral and postdoctoral grants for study in Venice and the Veneto region are awarded annually for historical research on Venice and the former Venetian empire, and for study of contemporary Venetian society and culture. Archaeology, architecture, art, bibliography, economics, history, history of science, law, literature, music, political science, religion, theater, humanities and social science are acceptable areas of study. Applicants must be U. S. citizens or permanent residents and have experience in advanced research at the graduate level or above. Grants range from $500 to $16,500. Funds are for research in Venice and Veneto only, and for transportation to, from, and within Veneto. Consult the Web site for additional information and application.

Available to: U. S. citizens or permanent residents
Deadline: December 15
Apply to: Above address

**Delta Kappa Gamma Society International**
**PO Box 1589**
**Austin, TX 78767-1589**
**E-mail: educatoraward@deltakappagamma.org**
**Web site: www.deltakappagamma.org**
**Fax: 512-478-3961**

Ⓝ The *Educator's Award* of $1,500 annually recognizes "outstanding educational research and writings of women authors whose book may influence the direction of thought and action necessary to meet the needs of today's complex society." The book must be written in English by one or two women and copyrighted during the calendar year prior to the year in which the award is given. Write for additional information and guidelines.

Available to: Women residents of the Society's member countries: Canada, Costa Rica, El Salvador, Finland, Germany, Guatemala, Iceland, Mexico, the Netherlands, Norway, Sweden, the United Kingdom, and the United States (including Puerto Rico)
Deadline: February 1
Apply to: Ruth Diekman, Educator's Award Committee, above address

**Eben Demarest Trust**
**3 Mellon Bank Center, Room 4000**
**Pittsburgh, PA 15259-0001**

The *Eben Demarest Fund* makes one annual grant (never given for scholarship aid) of approximately $16,000 to a mature artist or archaeologist who wishes to concentrate for a time on a chosen field without having to depend entirely on the sale of work or outside employment. The beneficiary is chosen by the Eben Demarest Council. Unsolicited applications from individuals will not be accepted, but applications from organizations or institutions for unusually gifted people will be considered.

Available to: U. S. citizens preferred
Deadline: June 1 for the following calendar year
Apply to: Laurie A. Moritz, above address

**DENMARK**
**Commission for Educational Exchange Between Denmark and the U. S.A.**
**Fiolstraede 24. 3 sal**
**DK 1171 Copenhagen K**
**Denmark**
**Phone: 45-33-12-82-23**
**E-mail: daf-fulb@daf-fulb.dk**
**Web site: www.daf-fulb.dk**
**Fax: 45-33-32-53-23**

The *Binational Commission (Fulbright) Scholarships* for study and research in Denmark are available to university graduates with a specific research program. Grants cover maintenance and travel for graduate students and for postdoctoral or advanced research candidates. See the Web site for more details.

Available to: U. S. citizens
Deadlines: Enrolled students, consult the Web site; Postdoctoral applicants: August 1
Apply to: Predoctoral: Institute of International Education, 809 United Nations Plaza, New York, NY 10017; postdoctoral: Council for International Exchange of Scholars, 3007 Tilden Street, NW, Suite 5L, Washington, DC 20008-3009

**Denver Center Theatre Company**
**1050 13th Street**
**Denver, CO 80204**
**Web site: www.denvercenter.org**
**Fax: 303-825-2117**

Ⓓ The *U. S. West TheatreFest* annually sponsors a development program for new, unproduced full-length plays. Selected plays receive a week of rehearsal with professional actors and directors, culminating in a public reading. Plays chosen for the festival are optioned for

Denver Center Theatre Company production. Selected playwrights receive a $1,000 option fee, transportation to and from Denver, and housing for the festival, rehearsal, and performance period. Send SASE for additional information.

Available to: No restrictions
Deadline: December 31
Apply to: Bruce K. Sevy, Associate Artistic Director, U. S. West TheatreFest, above address

Ⓓ The *Francesca Primus Prize* of $3,000 is given annually for a previously unproduced full-length play by a woman. The winning play receives a rehearsed public reading, with the playwright in residence, as part of the Denver Center Theatre Company U. S. West TheatreFest. The theater retains the option to mount a full production of the work in its next subscription season. Send SASE for additional information and guidelines.

Available to: Women playwrights
Deadline: July 1
Apply to: Bruce K. Sevy, Associate Artistic Director, Francesca Primus Prize, above address

**DePaul University**
**Theatre School**
**2135 North Kenmore**
**Chicago, IL 60614-4111**
**Phone: 773-325-7938**
**Web site: http://theatreschool.depaul.edu/programs/prize.htm**
**Fax: 773-325-7920**

Ⓓ The *Cunningham Commission for Youth Theatre* awards $5,000 annually to encourage the writing of plays for young audiences that "affirm the centrality of religion, broadly defined, and the human quest for meaning, truth and community." Send SASE for guidelines.

Available to: Chicago-area playwrights living within 100 miles of the Loop
Deadline: October 1
Apply to: Cunningham Commission Selection Committee, above address

**descant**
**Department of English**
**Texas Christian University**
**Box 297270**
**Fort Worth, TX 76129**

Ⓕ Ⓟ The *Betsy Colquitt Award for Poetry* offers $500 to the best poem, or series of poems by a single author, published in each volume of *descant*.. The *Frank O'Connor Fiction Award* offers $500 to the best short fiction published in each volume.

Available to: *descant* writers
Deadline: Ongoing
Apply to: Above address

**Walt Disney Studios**
**500 South Buena Vista Street**
**Burbank, CA 91521-0750**
**E-mail: abc.fellowships@abc.com**
**Web site: www.abcnewtalent.disney.com/**

Ⓢ The *Walt Disney Studios Fellowship Program* selects up to eight writers annually to work full-time at developing their craft in the Disney Studios' features or television division. The one-year fellowships, beginning in October, offer a salary of $50,000. Travel expenses and one month's housing will be paid for fellows from outside the Los Angeles area. Applications from minority writers are encouraged. No previous film or television experience is necessary, but writing samples are required. See the Web site for guidelines and application.

Available to: No restrictions
Deadline: Applications accepted June 1-June 22
Apply to: Fellowship Program, above address

**District of Columbia Commission on the Arts and Humanities**
**410 8th Street, NW, Suite 500**
**Washington, DC 20004**
**Web site: http://www.capaccess.org/dccah**
**Fax: 202-727-4135**

Ⓜ The *Artist Fellowship Program* offers fellowships of $5,000 to writers of poetry, fiction, and creative nonfiction who can significantly contribute to and promote the arts in the District of Columbia through artistic excellence. Write for guidelines and application.

> Available to: D. C. residents
> Deadline: Inquire
> Apply to: Artist Fellowship Program, above address

Ⓜ The *Arts Education Projects Program* offers funds from $1,000 to $4,500 for projects that give training and exposure in the arts to young people in the District of Columbia, early childhood through twelfth grade, and that reinforce the importance of the arts in education. Programs providing in-service training and arts curriculum development for teachers and collaborative projects between schools and community facilities are also eligible. Activities may take place in traditional school settings or community facilities. The Commission encourages applicants for projects in schools. Write for guidelines and application.

> Available to: D. C. residents
> Deadline: Inquire
> Apply to: Arts Education Projects Program, above address

Ⓜ The *City Arts Projects Program* offers grants of $1,000 to $4,500 to individuals and grants of $1,000 to $15,000 to organizations for projects that encourage quality arts activities throughout the District of Columbia and that make arts experiences accessible to its residents. Projects must provide exposure to the arts and arts experiences to the broader community or persons traditionally underserved or separated from the mainstream because of location, economic constraints, or disability. Write for guidelines and application.

> Available to: D. C. residents
> Deadline: Inquire
> Apply to: City Arts Projects Program, above address

Ⓜ The *Larry Neal Writers' Competition* awards prizes in poetry, fiction, and dramatic writing to D. C. writers.

> Available to: D. C. residents
> Deadline: Inquire
> Apply to: Larry Neal Writers' Competition, above address

**Djerassi Resident Artists Program**
**2325 Bear Gulch Road**
**Woodside, CA 94062-4405**
**E-mail: drap@djerassi.org**
**Web site: http://www.djerassi.org**
**Fax: 650-747-0105**

Ⓡ The *Djerassi Resident Artists Program* offers one-month residences for writers and other creative artists on a 600-acre ranch south of San Francisco. Living space, studio space, and meals are provided without charge. There are seven thirty-day sessions between late March and mid-November. Send SASE or see the Web site for guidelines and application.

> Available to: Working writers
> Deadline: February 15 for following year
> Apply to: Above address

**Dobie-Paisano Fellowship Project**
**J. Frank Dobie House**
**702 East Dean Keeton Street**
**Austin, TX 78705**
**E-mail: aslate@mail.utexas.edu**
**Web site: www.utexas.edu/ogs/paisano**
**Fax: 512-471-9997**

® The *Dobie-Paisano Writing Fellowships* provide a living allowance of $12,000 and free residence at J. Frank Dobie's ranch, Paisano, fourteen miles west of Austin. Two six-month fellowships, the first beginning in September, the second in March, are awarded. There is a $10 application fee. Write, e-mail, or see the Web site for application and more information.

> Available to: Native Texans, writers previously living in Texas for at least two years, or writers whose published work has Texas as its subject
> Deadline: January 25
> Apply to: Audrey N. Slate, above address

**DOMINICAN REPUBLIC**
**Altos de Chavon**
**La Romana**
**Dominican Republic**
**E-mail: altos@spacelab.net**

® This nonprofit center for the arts offers three fourteen-week residences, beginning in September, February, and June. The majority of residents are visual artists; writers are welcome. Residents pay a $100 registration fee (to cover transportation between the airport and the colony) and a reduced residence rate of $400 a month; they contribute to the community by giving a reading, workshop, performance, or exhibit. Knowledge of Spanish is helpful.

> Available to: No restrictions; preference to creators of work influenced by or involved with Latin America and/or the Caribbean
> Deadline: July 15
> Apply to: Artists in Residence Program, Altos de Chavon, c/o Parsons School of Design, 66 Fifth Avenue, New York, NY 10011; fax 212-229-8988

**Dorland Mountain Arts Colony**
**PO Box 6**
**Temecula, CA 92593**
**E-mail: dorland@ez2.net**
**Web site: http://www.ez2.net/dorland**

® Residences of one to two months are available for writers as well as artists working in other disciplines. Six rustic cabins in a 300-acre nature preserve offer quiet and privacy for concentrated work. A donation of $300 a month is requested at the time of scheduling. Send #10 SASE or see the the Web site for guidelines and application.

> Available to: No restrictions
> Deadlines: September 1; March 1
> Apply to: Above address

**Dorset Colony**
**Box 510**
**Dorset, VT 05251**
**Phone: 802-867-2223**
**E-mail: theatre@sover.net**
**Web site: www.theatredirectories.com**
**Fax: 802-867-0144**

® *Dorset Colony House Residences* are available to writers for intensive work periods, from one week to two months. As many as eight writers are in residence at a time, accommodated in private rooms in a turn-of-the-century historic house in Dorset village, southern Vermont. The requested fee is $120 per week. Send a letter of inquiry.

Available to: No restrictions
Deadline: Variable (fall and spring; inquire for exact dates)
Apply to: John Nassivera, Executive Director, above address

**Dow Jones Newspaper Fund**
**PO Box 300**
**Princeton, NJ 08543-0300**
**E-mail: newsfund@wsj.dowjones.com**
**Web site: http://www.dj.com/newsfund**
**Fax: 609-520-5804**

Ⓙ The *Dow Jones Newspaper Fund Business Reporting Program* offers up to twelve summer internships to minority college students. After a one-week training program, interns work as business reporters at a daily newspaper, where they are paid regular wages. Upon returning to school, they receive a scholarship of $1,000. Write for additional information and application.

Available to: Minority college sophomores and juniors
Deadline: November 1
Apply to: Business Reporting Program, above address

Ⓙ The *High School Journalism Teacher of the Year* program selects one teacher of the year and four distinguished advisors from candidates across the country. They may be nominated by newspapers, press associations, colleges, or high school principals for their outstanding abilities as journalism teachers. The teacher of the year then selects the best journalism student attending his or her high school, who receives a $1,000 scholarship to study journalism in college. A $500 scholarship is awarded to each of the students selected by the distinguished advisors.

Ⓙ Candidates for the *High School Workshop Writing Competition* must be nominated by directors of High School Journalism Workshops for Minorities. Up to eight scholarships, of $1,000 each, will be awarded for the freshman year in college; all are renewable for the sophomore year, pending continued interest in a journalism career, adequate grades, and financial need. Students do not apply for these scholarships.

Available to: Teacher of the Year, see above; minority students slated to study journalism as college freshmen who attend High School Workshop
Deadline: Teacher of the Year, July 1; High School Workshop, none
Apply to: Program Director, above address, for nomination forms for Teacher of the Year and information on Workshop

**Drama League of New York**
**165 West 46th Street, Suite 601**
**New York, NY 10036**
**E-mail: info@dramaleague.org**
**Web site: http://www.dramaleague.org**
**Fax: 212-302-2254**

Ⓓ The Drama League's *New Directors/New Works* program is designed to foster artistic collaboration. Applications must be submitted by directors who are developing a project with a writer or artistic collaborator. The program offers selected teams the unique opportunity to explore new material in workshop without the pressure of producers and critics. Each team is awarded a stipend of $1,000 for production expenses, and up to four weeks' use of a rehearsal space in New York City during the summer. Write or see the Web site after December 1 for application and guidelines.

Available to: U. S. citizens or permanent residents age twenty-one and over
Deadline: Usually February (projects accepted once a year; inquire for exact date)
Apply to: Artistic Director, above address

**Dubuque Fine Arts Players**
**1686 Lawndale**
**Dubuque, IA 52001**
**Web site: http://iowa.com**

Ⓓ The *National One-Act Playwriting Contest* awards a $600 first prize, a $300 second prize, and a $200 third prize for unproduced, unpublished one-acts. Musicals and children's plays are not eligible. The three winning plays may be produced. Writers should submit two copies, a $10 entry fee, and a completed entry form. Send SASE for guidelines and entry form.

Available to: No restrictions
Deadline: January 31
Apply to: One-Act Playwriting Contest Coordinator, above address

**Dumbarton Oaks**
**1703 32nd Street, NW**
**Washington, DC 20007**
**Web site: www.doaks.org**

Contact Dumbarton Oaks for application procedures for the following:

The *Bliss Prize Fellowship in Byzantine Studies* is intended to provide encouragement, assistance, and training to outstanding college seniors who plan to enter the field of Byzantine studies. The fellowship covers graduate school tuition and living expenses for two academic years, as estimated by the graduate school in which the successful candidate enrolls. It also covers travel (up to $5,000) for the intervening summer to/from areas important in Byzantine civilization and culture. Candidates must be in their last undergraduate year or have a recently awarded B.A., must be proficient in ancient or medieval Greek, and must be applicants to a doctoral program in any field or area of Byzantine studies. Students already enrolled in graduate programs are not eligible.

*Fellowships* are awarded to scholars who hold a doctorate (or appropriate final degree) or have established themselves in their field and wish to pursue research in Byzantine or pre-Columbian studies or landscape architecture. A stipend of $24,325 plus housing is available annually.

*Junior Fellowships*, with a stipend of $13,900 plus housing, are available to advanced graduate students who have completed course work for their doctorate and wish to pursue their dissertation or final project at Dumbarton Oaks.

*Summer Fellowships*, with a maintenance allowance of $215 per week plus housing, are available to scholars at any level.

Available to: See above
Deadline: November 1
Apply to: Associate Director, above address

**Dungannon Foundation**
**West Church Hill Road**
**Washington, CT 06794**

ⓘⓝ The *Rea Award for the Short Story* offers $30,000 annually to "a writer who has made a significant contribution to the short story." The award, established in 1986 by Michael M. Rea, is sponsored annually by the Dungannon Foundation. Recipients are nominated and selected by a jury. *By Internal Nomination Only*.

**Earhart Foundation**
**2200 Green Road, Suite H**
**Ann Arbor, MI 48105**
**Phone: 734-761-8592**
**Web site: www.arts.edu/faculty/spons/E0000157.HTM**

*Fellowship Research Grants* are awarded to individuals who have established themselves professionally in such social science and humanities disciplines as economics, philosophy, international affairs, and government/politics. Applicants must be associated or affiliated with educational or research institutions and must have a Ph.D. and several years' teaching experience; the effort supported should lead to the advancement of knowledge through teaching, lecturing, or publication. Recent grants have ranged from $850 to $35,000. Write for additional information and guidelines.

Available to: See above
Deadline: Ongoing
Apply to: Fellowship Research Grants, above address

**Early Childhood Resources and Information Center of The New York Public Library**
**66 Leroy Street**
**New York, NY 10014**
**Phone: 212-929-0815**
**Web site: www.ezra-jack-keats.org/programs/NYPL_Awards.htm**

© The *Ezra Jack Keats New Writer Award* of $1,000 is given annually to a promising new writer of children's picture books who has published no more than five children's books "that reflect the tradition of Ezra Jack Keats, a Caldecott Medal winner whose books often featured multicultural settings and portrayed strong family relationships." The book(s) must appeal to children ages nine and under. Publishers may submit books published during the calendar year. Established writers who have written for young adults or adults but have not published work for children are not eligible. Write for guidelines.

Available to: See above
Deadline: Inquire
Apply to: Ezra Jack Keats New Writer Award, above address

**East-West Center**
**1601 East-West Road**
**Honolulu, HI 96848**
**E-mail: seminars@eastwestcenter.org**
**Web site: http://www.eastwestcenter.org**
**Fax: 808-944-7600**

Ⓙ The *Jefferson Fellowship Program* twice yearly makes available, for six American and six Asian and Pacific mid-career and senior-level print and broadcast journalists, awards for an immersion course on cultures and current issues in Asian Pacific countries. The program takes place in April/May and in September/October, with fellows spending the first part of the program at the Center and the second in the field (Asia/Pacific fellows visit the U. S. mainland, American fellows go to Asia/Pacific destinations). Write, e-mail, or see the Web site for additional information.

Available to: See above
Deadlines: January for first session; June for second
Apply to: EWC Media Program, above address

**Eastern Frontier Society**
**342 Pine Brook Road**
**Bedford, NY 10506**
**E-mail: wedmaster@easternfrontier.com**
**Web site: www.easternfrontier.com**

® The *Eastern Frontier Residency Program* annually offers ten residences of up to four weeks during July to selected artists and writers, in the picturesque setting of Norton Island, Maine, for developing their work. There is a $10 tax-deductible application fee. Send writing samples with application. See the Web site for more information and application.

Available to: No restrictions
Deadline: April 1
Apply to: Above address

Eaton Literary Agency
PO Box 49795
Sarasota, FL 34230-6795
E-mail: info@eatonliterary.com
Web site: http://www.eatonliterary.com/award.htm
Fax: 941-365-4679

Ⓕ Ⓝ  The *Eaton Literary Award* offers a $2,500 prize for a book-length work of fiction or nonfiction and a $500 prize for a short story or article. Write, e-mail, or see the Web site for guidelines.

Available to: No restrictions
Deadline: August 31 for the book-length prize; March 31 for the short story/article prize
Apply to: Above address


Eckerd College Review
4200 54th Avenue South
St. Petersburg, FL 33711
Web site: www.eckerd.edu

Ⓟ  The *Eckerd College Review Poetry Contest* offers $500 and publication for a poem. Second- and third-place winners each receive $50 and publication; all contest entries will be considered for publication. There is a $7 entry fee for three poems; $3 for each additional poem. Send SASE or e-mail for guidelines.

Available to: U. S. citizens
Deadline: December 1
Apply to: Poetry Contest, above address


Education Writers Association
1331 H Street, NW, Suite 307
Washington, DC 20005
E-mail: ewa@ewa.org
Web site: http://www.ewa.org
Fax: 202-637-9707

Ⓙ  The *National Awards for Education Reporting* honor the best education reporting in the print and broadcast media during the calendar year. A $250 cash prize is awarded in each of twenty categories, and a $1,000 grand prize is given for the best of these. A $35 entry fee is required. Write for rules and entry forms.

Available to: Education journalists
Deadline: Mid-January (inquire for exact date)
Apply to: National Awards for Education Reporting, above address

Ⓙ  The *National Fellowships in Education Reporting* offer an eight-week program of investigative study and travel for education journalists. The fellowships support up to twelve reporters for two months in pursuing special projects in education. Fellows receive half-salary for the study period; paid travel expenses; access to expert sources; editing assistance, if desired; the opportunity to work with other reporters at EWA regional meetings and national seminar; and consultation with EWA staff about progress and problems during the project. Fellowships are open to full-time print or broadcast journalists who have been covering education at least two years, who have the endorsement of their employers, and who can show a likely outlet for the product of their study. Freelance writers may apply if they write about education a substantial portion of their time and have an agreement with a media organization to publish or air stories resulting from the fellowship. Write for guidelines.

Available to: See above
Deadline: Early May (inquire for exact date)
Apply to: National Fellowships in Education Reporting, above address

**Eisenhower Center for American Studies**
923 Magazine Street
New Orleans, LA 70130
Web site: www.uno.edu/~eice/
Fax: 504-539-9563

(N)  The *Forrest C. Pogue Prize* (formerly $1,500; stipend may change) is awarded annually to scholarly historical work about the U. S. Army in World War II. Three copies of nominated work(s) published within the calendar year, along with a cover letter of introduction, should be sent to the Center. Write for additional information.

   Available to: No restrictions
   Deadline: February 15
   Apply to: Kevin Willey, Assistant Director, above address


**Electronic Literature Organization**
c/o UCLA Department of English
2225 Rolfe Hall, Box 951530
Los Angeles, CA 90095-1530
Phone: 310- 206-1863
Web site: www.eliterature.org
Fax: 310-206-5093

(F) (P)  The *Electronic Literature Awards* offer two $10,000 prizes annually for electronic fiction and poetry. The awards are designed not only "to recognize the pioneers who are already creating innovative literature in the electronic media," but "to inspire writers and artists who are only beginning to explore the amazing creative opportunities this field offers." See the Web site for more details.

   Available to: No restrictions
   Deadline: Inquire
   Apply to: Above address


**Emporia State University English Department**
Box 4019
Emporia State University
Emporia, KS 66801-5087
Web site: http://www.emporia.edu/bluestem/index.htm
Fax: 316-341-5547

(P)  The annual *Bluestem Award* offers $1,000 plus publication for a book-length collection of poems (at least 48 pages) by a U. S. author. Manuscripts may include poems published previously in periodicals or anthologies but not in full-length single-author volumes. There is a $15 reading fee.

   Available to: U. S. citizens
   Deadline: March 1
   Apply to: Bluestem Award, above address


**Maurice English Foundation for Poetry**
c/o Helen W. Drutt English
2222 Rittenhouse Square
Philadelphia, PA 19103-5505

(P)  The *Maurice English Poetry Award* of $3,000 is offered to an author in or beyond his or her sixth decade of life for a distinguished book of poems published during the preceding calendar year. The award honors Maurice English, whose work did not appear in book form until his fifty-fifth year. Contact the Foundation for information.

   Available to: See above
   Deadline: Inquire
   Apply to: Above address

**The English-Speaking Union**
**139 East 44th Street**
**New York, NY 10016-0914**
**E-mail: info@english-speakingunion.org**
**Web site: www.english-speakingunion.org**

[IN] The *Ambassador Book Awards* of $1,000 are given to writers who have made "an exceptional contribution to the interpretation of life and culture in the United States." The Union distributes books by winning authors throughout its libraries and facilities in Great Britain and forty other countries. There is no application process. *By Internal Nomination Only.*

**Ensemble Studio Theatre**
**549 West 52nd Street**
**New York, NY 10019**
**E-mail: sloanproject@ensemblestudiotheatre.org**
**Web site: www.ensemblestudiotheatre.org**
**Fax: 212-664-0041**

(D) The *Ensemble Studio Theatre/Alfred P. Sloan Foundation Science & Technology Project* is designed "to stimulate artists to create credible and compelling work exploring the worlds of science and technology and to challenge existing stereotypes of scientists and engineers in the popular imagination." The Project commissions and develops new theater pieces and presents the results, at various levels of production, in its annual First Light Festival. Playwrights interested in a commission should submit a one-page written proposal, consisting of a project description and a simple outline or synopsis, and a résumé or biography. Commission payments range from $500 to $10,000. Write, see the Web site, or e-mail for additional information.

Available to: No restrictions
Deadline: October 1
Apply to: EST/Sloan Science & Technology Project, above address

**Willard R. Espy Literary Foundation**
**PO Box 614**
**Oysterville, WA 98641**
**Web site: www.espyfoundation.org**
**E-mail: wrelf@willapabay.org**
**Fax: 360-665-5224**

(R) The Willard R. Espy Literary Foundation offers residences for the months of February, June and October in Oysterville, on Washington's southwest coast. Three chosen writers share accommodations in a bay-front cottage; they receive a weekly stipend for food. Emerging as well as established writers whose work reflects a Pacific Northwest background are eligible. Write or see the Web site for additional information.

Available to: See above
Deadline: December 1 for February residence; April 1 for June residence; August 1 for October residence
Apply to: Above address

(M) The *Willard R. Espy Award* of $1,000 is given annually to a writer who has not yet published a book, for a work-in-progress set in the Pacific Northwest. The award applies to genres from year to year, including fiction, memoir, and poetry/light verse; fiction will be awarded in 2003.

Available to: See above
Deadline: May 15
Apply to: Above address

**Experimental Television Center**
**109 Lower Fairfield Road**
**Newark Valley, NY 13811**
**E-mail: etc@experimentaltvcenter.org**
**Web site: http://www.experimentaltvcenter.org**

The *Electronic Arts Grant Program* annually awards grants of up to $1,000 to New York state artists involved in the creation of audio, video, or computer-generated time-based works. Funds must be used to complete a work in progress. Eligible forms include film; single- or multiple-channel audio and video; computer-based moving-imagery and sound works; installations and performances; and works for CD-ROM, multimedia technologies, and the Internet. Work must be innovative and creative, and must approach the various media as art forms; all genres are eligible, including experimental, narrative, and documentary. Write, e-mail, or see the Web site for guidelines and application.

Available to: New York State residents
Deadline: March 15
Apply to: Electronic Arts Grant Program, above address

**F&W Publications, Inc.**
**1507 Dana Avenue**
**Cincinnati, OH 45207**
**E-mail: tarab@fwpubs.com**
**Web site: www.writersdigest.com**

Ⓢ The *International Screenplay Competition*, sponsored by the American Screenwriters Association and *Writer's Digest*, offers six prizes for six outstanding screenplays. The grand prize winner receives $5,000, presented at the Hollywood Screenwriters Conference in Los Angeles. Other prizes range from $2,500 to $100. All winners receive a free one-year membership in the American Screenwriters Association. The entry fee is $40 per script for ASA members, $50 for nonmembers. Consult the Web site for more details.

Available to: No restrictions
Deadline: October 1
Apply to: Above address or e-mail address

**Fellowship of Southern Writers**
**Arts & Education Council**
**PO Box 4203**
**Chattanooga, TN 37405**
**Web site: www.artsedcouncil.org**

ⓘ Eight biennial awards of $1,000 each are given in recognition of distinguished achievement in southern writing: the *Robert Penn Warren Prize for Fiction*, the *Hillsdale Prize for Fiction*, the *Hanes Prize for Poetry*, the *Cleanth Brooks Medal for Distinguished Achievement in Southern Letters*, the *Bryan Family Foundation Award for Drama*, the *Fellowship's Award for Nonfiction*, the *Fellowship's New Writing Award*, and the *James Still Award for Writing*. Eligible are writers who were born and brought up in the South, or who have resided there for a significant part of their lives, or whose works, in character or spirit, embody aspects of the southern experience. *By Internal Nomination Only*.

**Fence Books**
**14 Fifth Avenue, #1A**
**New York, NY 10011**
**Web site: www.fencemag.com**

Ⓟ The *Alberta Prize*, sponsored by Fence Books in conjunction with the Alberta duPont Bonsal Foundation, awards $5,000 and publication for a first or second full-length book of poetry by a woman poet writing in English. See the Web site for further information.

Available to: Women poets
Deadline: Inquire
Apply to: Above address

(P)    The *Fence Modern Poets Series,* sponsored by Fence Books and Saturnalia Books, offers $1,000 and publication for a book by a poet writing in English at any stage in his or her career. For more details, see the Web site.

>     Available to: No restrictions
>     Deadline: Inquire
>     Apply to: Above address

**Final Draft**
**1600 Ventura Boulevard #800**
**Encino, CA 91436**
**E-mail: info@finaldraft.com**
**Web site: http://www.finaldraft.com**
**Fax: 818-995-4422**

(S)    The annual *Final Draft International Screenwriting Competition* recognizes the best work by young screenwriters. The first-prize winner receives $10,000, roundtrip airfare to Los Angeles, and three nights' hotel accommodations, and will meet studio executives and agents. The second-prize winner receives $3,000, and the third-prize winner $1,000. There is a $50 entry fee. See the Web site for more information.

>     Available to: No restrictions
>     Deadline: March 15
>     Apply to: International Screenwriting Competition, above address

**Fine Arts Work Center in Provincetown**
**24 Pearl Street**
**Provincetown, MA 02657**
**E-mail: Info@fawc.org**
**Web site: www.fawc.org**

(R)    The Center seeks to help emerging artists and writers at a critical stage of their careers by giving them the opportunity "to work independently in a congenial and stimulating environment." Fiction writers, poets, and visual artists are eligible; fellows are admitted on the basis of work submitted. Grants-in-aid are awarded. The program extends from October 1 through May 1. Send SASE for information and application, or see the Web site.

>     Available to: No restrictions
>     Deadline: December 1
>     Apply to: Writing Coordinator, above address

(R)    The *Fine Arts Work Center Summer Workshop* offers weeklong and weekend courses in creative writing and the visual arts. A limited number of scholarships are offered annually to people of racial and ethnic minorities, New Jersey schoolteachers, and people who are HIV-positive. See the Web site for more specifics.

>     Available to: See above
>     Deadline: Late spring (inquire for exact date)
>     Apply to: Above address

**FINLAND**
**Finnish Literature Information Center**
**Mariankatu 7 A 2**
**00170 Helsinki**
**Finland**
**Phone: 358-(0)9-131-231**
**E-mail: hanna.kjellberg@finlit.fi**
**Web site: http://www.finlit.fi**
**Fax: 358-(0)9-13123-220**

(T)    Translation grants are offered annually for translators and publishers, authors of critical works, and regular contributors to literary magazines published outside Finland. Applications should specify the amount of grant required, describe the project it will be used for and the expected duration, and the name of the prospective publisher. Projects should be concerned with the advancement of Finnish, Finnish-Swedish, and Sámi pro Lapp literature abroad. Applications for grants for scientific and scholarly translations (journals, dissertations, textbooks, technical literature) will not be considered.

Available to: See above
Deadline: April 1 and November 1
Apply to: Director, above address

**F. Scott Fitzgerald Literary Conference**
**Rockville City Hall**
**111 Maryland Avenue**
**Rockville, MD 20560-2364**

Ⓕ The *F. Scott Fitzgerald Literary Conference Short Story Contest* annually awards $1,000, and an invitation to read at the Conference, for an unpublished short story of 3,000 words or less by District of Columbia, Maryland, or Virginia writers. Three $100 runner-up prizes will also be awarded. Send SASE for guidelines.

Available to: District of Columbia, Maryland, or Virginia residents
Deadline: July (inquire for exact date)
Apply to: Short Story Contest, above address

**Five Points**
**Georgia State University**
**University Plaza**
**Atlanta, GA 30303-3083**
**Web site: www.webdelsol.com/Five_Points/info.htm**

Ⓕ The *Paul Bowles Prize* awards $1,000 for the best piece of fiction published in *Five Points*, preferably around 7,500 words. The winner is selected annually by the editors of the journal. See the Web site for guidelines.

Available to: Authors of works published in *Five Points*
Deadline: Ongoing for submissions to the journal; for award, inquire
Apply to: Above address

Ⓟ The *James Dickey Prize for Poetry* awards $1,000 and publication in *Five Points* for a previously unpublished collection of up to three poems, no more than 50 lines each. Poets may submit up to five poems. The $15 reading fee covers a one-year subscription to the journal. Send SASE for guidelines.

Available to: No restrictions
Deadline: November 30
Apply to: James Dickey Prize, above address

**Florida Division of Cultural Affairs**
**Department of State**
**The Capitol**
**Tallahassee, FL 32399-0250**
**Web site: http://www.dos.state.fl.us**
**Fax: 850-922-5259**

Ⓜ *Individual Fellowships* of $5,000 are given to Florida writers in poetry, fiction, children's literature (through the literature program), and playwriting (through the theater program). Applicants must reside in the state at the time of application and for the duration of the fellowship period. Write for guidelines.

Available to: Florida residents
Deadline: Mid-January (inquire for exact date)
Apply to: Above address

**Florida Playwrights' Process**
**PACT Institute for the Performing Arts**
**1111 McMullen-Booth Road**
**Clearwater, FL 33759**
**E-mail: flplaypro@yahoo.com**
**Web site: http://www.rutheckerdhall.net**
**Fax: 727-791-7449**

(D)   The *Florida Playwrights' Process* offers $400 plus a travel stipend of $250 and production for an unproduced, unpublished full-length play with a cast limit of six, simple props and sets, and a maximum length of 2 hours. The selected Florida playwright must be available for workshops, readings, and performances as scheduled by the artistic director. The Florida Playwrights' Process offers a similar program for high school and middle school playwrights from Pinellas, Hillsborough, Polk, Hernando, and Pasco counties. Send SASE or e-mail for additional information and guidelines for either program.

Available to: Florida playwrights
Deadline: November 8 (adults), December 14 (students)
Apply to: Above address

**The Florida Review**
**University of Central Florida**
**Department of English**
**Orlando, FL 32816**
**Web site: www.pegasus.cc.ucf.edu/~english/floridareview/home.htm**

(M)   The *Florida Review Editors' Awards*, of $1,000 each, are offered in fiction, memoir, and poetry for previously unpublished work. Winning works will be published in the *Review*. Fiction and memoir submissions should be no longer than 10,000 words. Poets may submit three to five poems, each with a maximum of 40 lines. A reading fee of $12 for each submission covers a one-year subscription to the journal. Send SASE for guidelines.

Available to: No restrictions
Deadline: Submissions accepted January 1-April 12
Apply to: Editors' Awards, above address

**Florida Studio Theatre**
**1241 North Palm Avenue**
**Sarasota, FL 34236**
**E-mail: Fstchris@aol.com**
**Web site: www.fst2000.org**
**Fax: 941-955-4127**

(D)   The *Barbara Anton Playwriting Award*, established to recognize excellence in playwriting, includes a stipend of $1,000 and a residence at Florida Studio Theatre. This is the first of a number of awards aimed at developing new plays and playwrights, which FST plans to present during the next several years.

Available to: No restrictions
Deadline: Inquire
Apply to: Above address

**Folger Shakespeare Library**
**201 East Capitol Street, SE**
**Washington, DC 20003**
**Phone: 202-544-4600**
**Web site: http://www.folger.edu**
**Fax: 202-544-4623**

The Folger Institute Programs offer *Consortium Funds* for participation in seminars to advanced graduate students and faculty from the Institute's affiliated universities: American, Amherst, Boston, Catholic, Columbia, CUNY Graduate School and University Center,

Delaware, Duke, Emory, Fordham, George Mason, George Washington, Georgetown, Harvard, Howard, Johns Hopkins, Maryland-Baltimore County, Maryland-College Park, Massachusetts-Amherst, New York, North Carolina, North Carolina State, Notre Dame, Pennsylvania, Pennsylvania State, Princeton, Rochester, Rutgers, St. Andrews, South Carolina, SUNY at Buffalo, Syracuse, Vanderbilt, Virginia, West Virginia, William and Mary, and Yale.

Available to: See above
Deadlines: June 1 for fall-term seminars and yearlong programs; September 1 for spring-term seminars
Apply to: Folger Institute, above address

The Folger Library offers a limited number of six-to-nine-month residential fellowships to advanced scholars who have made substantial contributions in their fields and whose research projects are appropriate to the collection of the Library. *Long-Term Fellowships* are supported by the Andrew W. Mellon Foundation, the National Endowment for the Humanities, and the Folger Library. The two *Mellon Postdoctoral Research Fellowships* carry stipends of $45,000 and $30,000. The three *National Endowment for the Humanities Fellowships* carry maximum stipends of $30,000. Mellon Fellowships and Folger Long-Term Fellowships are open to scholars from any country; NEH Fellowships are restricted to U. S. citizens or foreign nationals who have been living in the U. S. for at least three years.. *Short-Term Fellowships* offer up to $1,800 a month for one to three months to postdoctoral scholars, and are available from July to June yearly. Write, e-mail, or see the Web site for further information and application.

Available to: See above
Deadlines: March 1 for short-term; November 1 for long-term
Apply to: Fellowships Coordinator, above address

IN The *O. B. Hardison, Jr., Poetry Prize* of $2,000 is awarded annually by a panel of judges to an American poet whose art and teaching "exemplify great imagination and daring, and fine scholarship, in the spirit of the life and work of O. B. Hardison, Jr., former director of the Folger Shakespeare Library." *By Internal Nomination Only.*

**The Formalist**
**320 Hunter Drive**
**Evansville, IN 47711**

P The annual *Howard Nemerov Sonnet Award* offers $1,000 and publication in *The Formalist* for an original, unpublished sonnet. Writers may enter as many sonnets as they wish, with a $3 fee per sonnet. Eleven other finalists will be published. Send SASE for rules.

Available to: No restrictions
Deadline: June 15
Apply to: Howard Nemerov Sonnet Award, above address

**Foundation for Contemporary Performance Arts**
**820 Greenwich Street**
**New York, NY 10014**

IN Individual artist grants, of $25,000 each, are awarded annually to artists in poetry, dance, music, theater/performance art, and visual arts. Grant recipients are selected on the basis of merit, innovative work, and the effect such recognition and support might have now in their careers. Grants are given to emerging as well as established artists. In 2000, eleven grants were given. Unsolicited nominations are not accepted. *By Internal Nomination Only.*

The Foundation awards a limited number of discretionary grants to artists who need modest support for emergency situations related to their work. Grants are made for unexpected expenses when projects are close to completion or for sudden work-related opportunities. No funds are available for personal or medical emergencies. Requests should be made in the form of a letter to the Foundation by artists of demonstrated accomplishment..

**Foundation for Iranian Studies**
**4343 Montgomery Avenue, Suite 200**
**Bethesda, MD 20814-4401**
**Fax: 301-657-4381**

The Foundation offers an annual prize of $1,000 for the best Ph.D. dissertation in Iranian studies. Students completing dissertations between July 1, 2002, and June 30, 2003, are eligible for the 2003 prize. Dissertations must be nominated by the author's advisor and submitted with the dissertation committee's letter of acceptance.

Available to: Ph.D. candidates in Iranian studies
Deadline: August 1
Apply to: Above address


**Four Way Books**
**PO Box 535**
**Village Station**
**New York, NY 10014**
**Web site: http://www.fourwaybooks.com**

(P) Four Way Books annually awards a cash prize and publication for a book-length collection of poems. The award changes from year to year. In 2002, the press offered the *Intro Prize in Poetry* for authors who have not published a full-length book of poetry, which consisted of $1,000 and a monthlong residence at the Fine Arts Work Center in Provincetown. There is a $20 entry fee. Send SASE for guidelines and entry form, or consult the Web site.

Available to: U. S. poets
Deadline: March 31
Apply to: above address


**French-American Foundation**
**519 Madison Avenue, Suite 310**
**New York, NY 10022**
**E-mail: info@frenchamerican.org**
**Web site: http://www.frenchamerican.org**
**Fax: 212-829-8810**

(T) The *French-American Foundation Translation Prize* of up to $10,000 is awarded annually for the best translation of a work from French into English published in the United States in the current year. All categories of prose are eligible, except technical, scientific, and reference works and children's literature. Translations must be submitted by publishing houses, not individual translators.

Available to: No restrictions
Deadline: July 6
Apply to: Above address


**Friends of American Writers**
**c/o Jane Larson**
**400 East Randolph #2123**
**Chicago, IL 60601**

The *Friends of American Writers Literary Adult Awards* offer a first prize of $1,600 and a second prize of $1,000 for the best book published during the calendar year. Write for additional information.

(C) The *Friends of American Writers Young People's Literature Awards* annually offer two prizes of $900 each for the best books for young people from toddler to high school age published during the calendar year. Write for additional information.

Available to: U. S. writers
Deadline: December 15
Apply to: Above address

**Friends of New Netherland**
c/o New Netherland Project
New York State Library
CEC, 8th floor
Albany, NY 12230
E-mail: gehring@mail.nysed.gov
Web site: www.nnp.org
Fax: 518-573-0472

Ⓝ The *Hendricks Manuscript Award* offers $1,500 for the best manuscript, published or unpublished, focusing on any aspect of the Dutch colonial experience in North America. The winning manuscript, if not otherwise obligated, will be considered for publication by Syracuse University Press. Write for additional information and guidelines.

Available to: No restrictions
Deadline: February 15
Apply to: Hendricks Manuscript Award Committee, above address

**Robert Frost Foundation**
90 Mount Vernon Street
Lawrence, MA 01843
Web site: www.frostfoundation.org

Ⓟ The *Robert Frost Poetry Award* annually offers $1,000 to a poet from New England who has not yet published a full-length book of poetry. The award winner will be a featured reader at the Robert Frost Festival, held in Lawrence, Massachusetts. There is a $10 reading fee.

Available to: See above
Deadline: September 1
Apply to: Robert Frost Poetry Award, above address

**Fund for Investigative Journalism**
PO Box 60184
Washington, DC 20039-0184
E-mail: Fundfij@aol.com
Web site: http://www.fij.org

Ⓙ The Fund gives grants, ranging from $500 to $10,000, to reporters working without the protection and backing of major news organizations. These grants are limited to journalists seeking help for investigative pieces involving corruption, malfeasance, incompetence, and societal ills in general, as well as for media criticism. There is no tuition support.

Available to: Anyone with a publisher's or producer's commitment
Deadline: February 1; June 1; October 1
Apply to: Peg Lotito, Executive Director, above address

The Fund's *FIJ Prize*, of up to $10,000 for books and other investigative projects, is decided at each of its tri-annual board meetings. At the final meeting of the year, the Fund awards either an additional $15,000 to a proposal already selected or a $25,000 prize for a new and compelling entry. The prize is usually awarded only to an author who has found a publisher unwilling or unable to support a project as fully as it demands; the Fund will, however, consider proposals that might need its endorsement before a publisher agrees to an advance. Write or see the Web site for guidelines and application.

Available to: See above
Deadline: Inquire
Apply to: Peg Lotito, Executive Director, above address

**Fund for UFO Research**
PO Box 277
Mount Rainier, MD 20712
Web site: http://www.fufor.org

Ⓙ The *Donald E. Keyhoe Journalism Award* of $1,000 is given for the best investigative reporting on UFO research by a professional mainstream journalist or freelance author in one or more of three categories: newspaper/magazine, radio broadcast, TV broadcast. Print entries must have appeared in a newsstand magazine or newspaper other than one devoted exclusively to reporting on UFOs. Write or see the Web site for additional information.

Available to: No restrictions
Deadline: February 15
Apply to: Donald E. Keyhoe Journalism Award, above address

**George Washington University**
**Department of English**
**801 22nd Street, NW, Suite 760**
**Washington, DC 20052**
**Web site: http://www.gwu.edu/~english**

Ⓜ    The *Jenny McKean Moore Writers Program* at George Washington University engages a creative writer (usually a poet or fiction writer, occasionally a writer of creative nonfiction) to teach two semesters at the university (a tuition free community workshop and a class to GWU students) at a salary of approximately $50,000. SASE with writing sample and résumé must accompany application. The visiting lecturer must live in or near Washington, D. C., during the academic year (late August to early May).

Available to: No restrictions
Deadline: November 15
Apply to: Faye Moskowitz, Chair, above address

✓    **Georgia State University Review**
**Georgia State University**
**Campus Box 1894**
**Atlanta, GA 30303-3083**
**Phone: 404-651-4804**
**E-mail: kchaple@emory.edu**

Ⓕ Ⓟ    The *Review*'s *Writing Contest* offers a $1,000 prize and publication in the *Review* for an unpublished story and for an unpublished poem. Short story manuscripts should not exceed 7,500 words. Poets may submit up to three poems, none longer than two pages. The reading fee is $10 for each story or group of three poems. Send SASE or e-mail for guidelines.

Available to: No restrictions
Deadline: January 31
Apply to: Writing Contest, above address

**German Marshall Fund of the United States**
**11 Dupont Circle, NW, Suite 750**
**Washington, DC 20036**
**E-mail: info@gmfus.org**
**Web site: http://www.gmfus.org**
**Fax: 202-265-1662**

*Research Fellowships* are available to established U. S. scholars and Ph.D. candidates for advanced study that seeks to improve the understanding of significant contemporary economic, political, and social developments relating to Europe, European integration, and relations between Europe and the United States. Projects should involve a comparative analysis of a topic in more than one country or the exploration of a topic in a single country in ways that will likely be relevant for other countries. Applicants must be graduate students, recent Ph.D.'s, or more senior scholars. Awards of up to $40,000 will be made for senior scholars; of up to $20,000 for graduate students. Write or e-mail for information and application.

Available to: U. S. citizens
Deadline: November 15
Apply to: Above address

**GERMANY**
**Art Society (Künstlergilde)**
**Hafenmarkt 2**
**D-73728 Esslingen**
**Germany**

Ⓜ The *Andreas Gryphius Prize* is given for the best essay, novel, or poem dealing with particular problems of German culture in Eastern Europe. Two awards (of DM 25,000 and DM 7,000 in 2000) are available annually. *(PEN was unable to confirm the information for this edition but believes it is current. Inquire before applying.)*

Available to: No restrictions
Deadline: Inquire
Apply to: Andreas Gryphius Prize, above address

Ⓟ The *Nikolaus Lenau Prize,* established in 1985 in memory of Nikolaus Lenau (1802-1850), is given for the best poem dealing with particular problems of German culture in Eastern Europe. An award (of DM 11,000 in 2000) is given annually. *(PEN was unable to confirm the information for this edition but believes it is current. Inquire before applying.)*

Available to: No restrictions
Deadline: Inquire
Apply to: Nikolaus Lenau Prize, above address

**GERMANY**
**Stadt Buxtehude**
**Kulturabteilung**
**Stavenort 5**
**D-21614 Buxtehude**
**Germany**

IN The *Buxtehude Bulle* is awarded for the best young people's book (for ages twelve to eighteen) published in Germany during the preceding year. One prize (DM 10,000 in 2001) is awarded annually. *By Internal Nomination Only.*

**GERMANY**
**DAAD (German Academic Exchange Service)**
**Markgrafenstrasse 37**
**10117 Berlin**
**Germany**
**E-mail: BKP.berlin@daad.de (Berlin); daadny@daad.org (New York)**
**Web site: http://www.berliner-kuenstlerprogramm.de**

The *Artists-in-Berlin Program* (*Berliner Künstlerprogramm*) invites some fifteen to twenty internationally known artists, writers, composers, and filmmakers to spend twelve months in Berlin, where they have the opportunity to work undisturbed and to participate actively in the city's cultural life. Invited artists receive monthly grant installments for living costs and rent, travel expenses for themselves and accompanying family staying in Berlin for the duration of the invitation, and health and accident insurance. Write, e-mail, or see the Web site for guidelines and application. Forms may be obtained also by writing the Artists-in-Berlin Program, German Academic Exchange Service, 950 Third Avenue, New York, NY 10022.

Available to: See above
Deadline: December 31
Apply to: Artists-in-Berlin Program, above address

DAAD awards short-term grants for study and research visits to Germany for scholars and Ph.D. candidates. For information, contact DAAD at the New York address listed above.

**GERMANY**
**German Academy for Language and Literature**
**Alexandraweg 23**
**64287 Darmstadt**
**Germany**
**E-mail: sekretariat@deutscheakademie.de**
**Web site: www.deutscheakademie.de**

[IN] The *Friedrich Gundolf Prize* is given to individuals who have distinguished themselves in disseminating German culture abroad. A brochure can be requested from the address above. One award of 12,500 euros is available annually. *By Internal Nomination Only.*

[IN] The *Johann Heinrich Voss Prize for Translation* recognizes an outstanding lifetime achievement in translation into German. One award of 15,000 euros is available annually. *By Internal Nomination Only.*

**GERMANY**
**Goethe Prize of the City of Frankfurt**
**Römerberg 23**
**60311 Frankfurt am Main**
**Germany**
**Web site: www.kultur.inm.de**

[IN] The *Goethe Prize* (DM 100,000 as of 2000) is given every three years to a writer whose creative work demonstrates a continuation of Goethe's ideals and thoughts. *By Internal Nomination Only.*

**GERMANY**
**Institut für Europäische Geschichte**
**Alte Universitätsstrasse 19**
**D-55116 Mainz**
**Germany**
**E-mail: ieg2@inst-euro-history.uni-mainz.de**
**Web site: http://www.inst-euro-history.uni-mainz.de**

Grants are offered for advanced study and research in Germany in modern and contemporary European history and the history of European religion with regard to the Reformation. Candidates must be university graduates. Write, e-mail, or see the Web site for further information and application procedures.

Available to: No restrictions
Deadline: Inquire
Apply to: For European history: Professor Heinz Duchhardt, Abteilung Universalgeschichte, above address; for history of European religion: Professor Gerhard May, Abteilung Religionsgeschichte, above address

**Getty Grant Program**
**1200 Getty Center Drive, Suite 800**
**Los Angeles, CA 90049-1685**
**Phone: 310-440-7320**
**E-mail: researchgrants@getty.edu**
**Web site: www.getty.edu/grants/index.html**
**Fax: 310-440-7703**

*Postdoctoral Fellowships* provide support to scholars who have obtained their doctorates within the six years previous to the award, to pursue interpretive research for projects that will contribute substantially and originally to the understanding of art and its history. A maximum of fifteen non-residential fellowships with stipends of $40,000 each are awarded for twelve-month periods.

Available to: See above
Deadline: November 1
Apply to: Dr. Nancy Micklewright, Program Officer, Postdoctoral Fellowships, above address

*Collaborative Research Grants* provide opportunities for teams of scholars to collaborate on interpretive research for projects that offer new explanations of art and its history. Teams may consist of two or more art historians, or of an art historian and one or more scholars from other disciplines. Funding is also available for researching and planning scholarly exhibitions; teams for these projects should include scholars from both museums and universities. Grant periods and stipends vary according to needs, but generally support research periods of one to two years.

   Available to: See above
   Deadline: November 1
   Apply to: Dr. Joan Weinstein, Senior Program Officer, Collaborative Research Grants, above address

*Curatorial Research Fellowships* support the professional scholarly development of curators by providing them with time off from regular museum duties to undertake short-term research or study projects. Fellowships, which provide stipends of $3,500 per month and up to $3,000 for travel and research materials, are reserved for full-time curators with at least three years' professional experience who are employed at museums with art collections. Fellowships provide stipends for research periods of one to three months.

   Available to: See above
   Deadline: November 1
   Apply to: Dr. Nancy Micklewright, Program Officer, Curatorial Research Fellowships, above address

**The Gilder Lehrman Center for the Study of Slavery, Resistance, and Abolition**
**34 Hillhouse Avenue**
**New Haven, CT 06520-8206**
**E-mail: gilder.lehrman.center@yale.edu**
**Web site: http://www.cis.yale.edu/glc/**
**Fax: 203-432-6943**

Ⓝ   The *Frederick Douglass Book Prize* awards $25,000 for an outstanding book published in English during the calendar year on slavery and/or abolition and antislavery movements. The book may deal with any geographic area or time period; works related to the Civil War are eligible only if their primary focus relates to slavery or emancipation. Send SASE or e-mail for guidelines.

   Available to: No restrictions
   Deadline: February 1
   Apply to: Frederick Douglass Book Prize, above address

**Gilman School**
**5407 Roland Avenue**
**Baltimore, MD 21210**
**Phone: 410-323-3800**
**Web site: http://www.gilman.edu/**

Ⓕ Ⓟ   The *Reginald S. Tickner Writing Fellowship* is awarded annually to a serious poet or fiction writer for an academic year. Responsibilities include teaching creative writing, directing a speakers' series, advising a literary magazine, and working individually with students on their writing. This part-time teaching position provides the fellow with a competitive compensation ($18,000 base in 2002-2003). Gilman is an independent boys' school that coordinates classes with Bryn Mawr School and Roland Park Country School. Send SASE for guidelines.

   Available to: No restrictions
   Deadline: January (inquire for exact date)
   Apply to: Meg Tipper, above address

**Gival Press**
PO Box 3812
Arlington, VA 22203
E-mail: givalpress@yahoo.com
Web site: http://www.givalpress.com

(P)  The *Gival Press Poetry Competition* annually awards $500 and 10 copies of a limited-edition publication by this independent house for a collection of poems, 50 to 80 pages, on any theme, in any style. There is a $15 reading fee. Send SASE or consult the Web site for complete guidelines.

Available to: No restrictions
Deadline: December 15
Apply to: Poetry Competition, above address

✓  **Glimmer Train Press**
710 SW Madison Street #504
Portland, OR 97205
Web site: http://www.glimmertrain.com
Fax: 503-221-0837

(F)  The *Fiction Open* offers a first prize of $2,000 and publication in *Glimmer Train*, a second prize of $1,000, and third of $600, for previously unpublished fiction of any length, on any theme. There is a $15 reading fee per story. Send SASE for guidelines.

Available to: No restrictions
Deadline: Submissions accepted May-June
Apply to: Fiction Open, above address

(P)  The *Poetry Open* offers a first prize of $500 and publication in *Glimmer Train*, a second prize of $250, and a third of $100, for a poem of any length, form, and theme. There is a reading fee of $10 for each submission of up to three previously unpublished poems. Send SASE for guidelines.

Available to: No restrictions
Deadline: Submissions accepted in April
Apply to: Poetry Open, above address

(F)  Twice yearly, the *Short Story Award for New Writers* offers $1,200 and publication in *Glimmer Train* for a short story of no more than 8,000 words, by a writer whose fiction has appeared in a nationally distributed publication with a circulation above 5,000. The first runner-up receives $500. All applicants receive the issue of *Glimmer Train* with the winning story. There is a $12 reading fee per story. Send SASE for guidelines.

Available to: See above
Deadline: Submissions accepted February-March for spring award; August-September for fall
Apply to: Short Story Award for New Writers, above address

(F)  Twice yearly, the *Very Short Fiction Award* offers $1,200 and publication in *Glimmer Train* for a previously unpublished "short-short," not to exceed 2,000 words. The first runner-up receives $500. There is a $10 reading fee per story. Send SASE for guidelines.

Available to: No restrictions
Deadline: Submissions accepted May-July for summer award; November-January for winter
Apply to: Very Short Fiction Award, above address

**Dick Goldensohn Fund Projects**
PO Box 20374
New York, NY 10009
E-mail: grants@dickgoldensohn.org
Web site: www.dickgoldensohn.org/html/apply.html

(J)  The *Dick Goldensohn Fund* annually awards grants (normally $1,500, although larger and smaller requests are considered) to reporters, editors, freelance writers, and others working on innovative journalistic projects. The Fund's goal is "to foster journalistic undertakings that investigate abuses of the public trust, spotlight overlooked aspects of contemporary life, or promote social, political, and economic justice." There is a $5 application fee. Send SASE for further details.

Available to: No restrictions
Deadline: August 30
Apply to: Above address

**Goshen College**
**1700 South Main Street**
**Goshen, IN 46526**
**E-mail: douglc@goshen.edu**

Ⓓ The *Goshen College Peace Playwriting Contest*, offered biennially, seeks unproduced, unpublished one-acts exploring a contemporary peace theme. The winning playwright will be awarded $500, production, and room and board to attend rehearsals and/or production. Second place entails a cash award of $100. Plays should be 20 to 50 minutes long. Include a one-paragraph synopsis and current résumé with script submission.

Available to: No restrictions
Deadline: December 31 of odd-numbered years
Apply to: Doug Caskey, Director of Theatre, above address

**Great American Book Contest**
**417 North Sangamon Street**
**Chicago, IL 60622**
**E-mail: greatamericanbk@aol.com**
**Web site: http://bookdealsinc.com/page5.html**
**Fax: 312-491-8091**

Ⓕ Ⓝ The *Great American Book Contest* annually awards a grand prize of $3,000 and an honorable mention of $750 to unpublished book-length prose manuscripts—fiction or nonfiction— with American settings. The contest seeks to discover American authors of exceptional talent whose work equals or surpasses the finest of the country's past and future. The winner is offered an editorial meeting with an editor from a leading New York publisher, and a film development meeting with a feature film scout. See the Web site for more information.

Available to: No restrictions
Deadline: December 31
Apply to: Above address

**Great Lakes Colleges Association**
**535 West William, Suite 301**
**Ann Arbor, MI 48103**
**Web site: http://www.glca.org**

Ⓕ Ⓟ The *New Writer Awards* recognize the best first books of poetry and fiction published during the previous year. Winning authors will visit GLCA colleges as soon as possible after publication, and will participate in promotional activities the colleges arrange. Authors receive from each of the schools visited an honorarium of at least $300, room and board, and payment of transportation costs. Entries may be submitted by publishers only, with a limit of one entry each in poetry and in fiction.

Available to: No restrictions
Deadline: February 28
Apply to: Daniel Bourne, Director, New Writers Awards, English Department, The College of Wooster, 1189 Beall Avenue, Wooster, OH 44691-2363

**The Griffin Trust for Excellence in Poetry**
**6610 Edwards Boulevard**
**Mississauga, Ontario L5T 2V6**
**Canada**
**Phone: 905-565-5993**
**E-mail: info@griffinpoetryprize.com**
**Web site: www.griffinpoetryprize.com**
**Fax: 905-564-3645**

(P)     The *Griffin Poetry Prizes*, of C$40,000 each, are awarded annually for two collections of poetry in English published during the preceding year. One prize is given to a living Canadian poet or translator, the other to a living poet or translator from any country, which may include Canada. To be eligible for the latter, publishers should submit four copies of a book of poetry published in the calendar year of submission, written or translated into English, by a poet or translator of any nationality. See the Web site for more information and entry form.

Available to: See above
Deadline: December 31
Apply to: Ruth Smith, Manager, above address

**The Harry Frank Guggenheim Foundation**
**527 Madison Avenue**
**New York, NY 10022-4304**
**Web site: http://www.hfg.org**
**Fax: 212-644-5110**

*Research Grants*, ranging from $15,000 to $35,000 a year for periods of one or two years, are available to postdoctoral scholars working on projects in any of the natural or social sciences or the humanities that "promise to increase understanding of the causes, manifestations, and control of violence, aggression, and dominance." Requests will be considered for salaries, employee benefits, research assistantships, computer time, supplies and equipment, fieldwork, secretarial and technical help, and other essentials for the completion of the project. Write or consult the Web site for additional information and application procedures.

Available to: No restrictions
Deadline: August 1
Apply to: Above address

The Foundation awards a small number of *Dissertation Fellowships* to individuals who will finish writing their dissertation within the award year. These fellowships, $10,000 each, are designed to assist doctoral candidates in completing their theses in a timely manner. Applications are evaluated in comparison with one another and not in competition with postdoctoral research proposals. Applicants may be citizens of any country, studying at colleges or universities in any country.

Available to: No restrictions
Deadline: February 1
Apply to: Above address

**John Simon Guggenheim Memorial Foundation**
**90 Park Avenue**
**New York, NY 10016**
**Phone: 212-687-4420**
**E-mail: fellowships@gf.org**
**Web site: http://www.gf.org**
**Fax: 212-697-3248**

(M)     Fellowships are given annually to advanced professionals with a significant record of publication for research in any field of knowledge or creative work in any of the arts. Candidates should already have demonstrated exceptional capacity for productive scholarship or exceptional creative ability in the arts. The awards are given for a minimum of six months and a maximum of one year. In 2001, the average fellowship grant was $36,000. Write, e-mail, or consult the Web site for additional information and application.

Available to: U. S. and Canadian citizens or permanent residents
Deadline: October 1
Apply to: Above address

**Guideposts**
**16 East 34th Street**
**New York, NY 10016**
**Web site: http://www.guideposts.org**

The *Guideposts Young Writers Contest* offers to high school juniors and seniors a first prize of $10,000, a second of $8,000, a third of $6,000, a fourth of $4,000, a fifth of $3,000, sixth through tenth of $1,000, and eleventh through twentieth of $250 gift certificates for college supplies, for true first-person stories about memorable or moving experiences. First through tenth prizes are awarded as scholarships to the accredited colleges or schools of the winners' choice. Submissions should not exceed 1,200 words. Write or consult the Web site for guidelines.

Available to: High school juniors and seniors
Deadline: November (inquire for exact date)
Apply to: Young Writers Contest, above address

**Gulf Coast**
**University of Houston**
**English Department**
**Houston, TX 77204-3012**
**Web site: www.gulfcoast.uh.edu**

Ⓕ Ⓟ The *Gulf Coast Poetry and Short Story Prizes* award $300 and publication in *Gulf Coast* for a winning poem and short story. Fiction writers may submit one story, poets up to five poems totaling no more than 10 pages. The reading fee of $15 covers a one-year subscription to *Gulf Coast*. All submissions will be considered for publication. Send SASE for guidelines.

Available to: No restrictions
Deadline: February 15
Apply to: Poetry Prize or Short Story Prize, above address

**Hadassah Magazine**
**50 West 58th Street**
**New York, NY 10019**
**E-mail: Hadamag@aol.com**
**Web site: http://www.hadassah.org/**
**Fax: 212-446-9521**

Ⓕ The *Harold U. Ribalow Prize* is given annually for an outstanding work of fiction on a Jewish theme, published in English in the calendar year preceding the prize year. The prize consists of $1,000 and publication of an excerpt in *Hadassah*.

Available to: No restrictions
Deadline: March 31
Apply to: Harold U. Ribalow Prize, above address

**Hall Farm Center for Arts and Education**
**392 Hall Drive**
**Townshend, VT 05353**
**Phone: 802-365-4483**
**Web site: www.hallfarm.org**

Ⓡ The Center, located on a 221-acre former farm in the Vermont countryside, offers residences to writers and other artists, working at any stage of their careers. There is no cost for a residence, which may range from a few days to several weeks; artists are responsible for transportation to and from the Center. See the Web site for application.

Available to: No restrictions
Deadline: March 1
Apply to: Above address

**Hambidge Center**
PO Box 339
Rabun Gap, GA 30568
E-mail: hambidge@rabun.net
Web site: http://www.rabun.net/~hambidge
Fax: 706-746-9933

Ⓡ    Residency fellowships of two weeks to two months are available to artists in all fields. The
     Center awards some ninety fellowships annually, from May through November. Weekly
     fees are $125. See the Web site for further information and application.

     Available to: No restrictions
     Deadline: November 1 and May 1
     Apply to: Residence Program, above address


**Harvard University Press**
79 Garden Street
Cambridge, MA 02138

Ⓝ    The *Robert Troup Paine Prize* of $3,000 is given every four years to the best manuscript on a
     designated subject that has been accepted for publication by Harvard University Press in
     the preceding four years. The current period is January 1, 2002-December 31, 2005; inquire
     for the designated subject. Authors will be paid royalties as well as the $3,000 prize.

     Available to: Harvard University Press authors who qualify
     Deadline: December 31, 2005
     Apply to: Robert Troup Paine Prize, above address


✓  **Headlands Center for the Arts**
   944 Fort Barry
   Sausalito, CA 94965
   E-mail: staff@headlands.org
   Web site: http://www.headlands.org
   Fax: 415-331-3857

Ⓡ    The Headlands Center for the Arts is located in several restored historic military buildings in
     the breathtaking Marin Headlands, part of the Golden Gate National Recreation area.
     Live-in residences of four weeks to three months are available to artists from the U. S.
     and abroad; live-out residences of eleven months are available to Bay Area artists only.
     Live-in residences include studio, housing, stipend, and meals; live-out include studio,
     stipend, and some meals. Residents are encouraged to interact with fellow residents, the
     environment, and the greater San Francisco community. Among the public programs are
     three open houses each year, interdisciplinary panels, performances and informal
     presentations by residents and other artists.

     Available to: California, New Jersey, North Carolina, and Ohio artists; residents of other
          states by invitation
     Deadline: June for the following year (inquire for exact date)
     Apply to: Above address


**HEArt Quarterly**
PO Box 81038
Pittsburgh, PA 15217
Web site: http://trfn.clpgh.org/heart
Fax: 412-244-0120

Ⓕ Ⓟ  The *HEArt Quarterly Poetry and Short Fiction Contest* annually awards a $500 prize for a poem
     and for a short story. Submissions must be previously unpublished work concerning social
     justice as well as racial, sexual, gender, and class discrimination. Poets may submit up to
     three poems, with a 5-pages maximum; fiction writers may submit one story of up to
     7,000 words. There is a $15 entry fee, which covers a one-year subscription to the *Quarterly*.
     Current subscribers' entry fees may be used to purchase gift subscriptions for others.
     Send SASE or see the Web site for guidelines.

Available to: No restrictions
Deadline: Submissions accepted October 1-December 31
Apply to: HEArt Quarterly Contest, above address

**Hedgebrook**
**2197 East Millman Road**
**Langley, WA 98260**
**Web site: www.hedgebrook.org**

® Residences of one week to two months are available to women writers of diverse cultural backgrounds in six individual cottages on thirty wooded acres on Whidbey Island, near Seattle. Residence includes free room and board. Travel scholarships and a stipend program to aid low-income writers are available. Applicants need not be published authors. The required application form is available from the Web site. Do not send submission before receiving an application.

Available to: Women writers
Deadline: October 1 for winter and spring; April 1 for summer and fall
Apply to: Above address

**Heinz Family Foundation**
**3200 CNG Tower**
**Pittsburgh, PA 15222**
**E-mail: awards@heinz.org**
**Web site: http://www.awards.heinz.org**

[IN] The *Heinz Award*s, $250,000 each, recognize significant and sustained contributions in five categories: arts and humanities; the environment; the human condition; public policy; and technology, the economy, and employment. There is no application process. *By Internal Nomination Only.*

**Helicon Nine Editions**
**3607 Pennsylvania Avenue**
**Kansas City, MO 64111**
**Web site: http://www.heliconnine.com**
**Fax: 816-753-1090**

Ⓕ The *Willa Cather Fiction Prize* offers a $1,000 award and publication by Helicon Nine for an original, unpublished manuscript of fiction (a novella or short story collection) between 150 and 300 double-spaced pages. Work that has appeared in magazines or anthologies is eligible. There is a $20 reading fee. Send SASE or see the Web site for guidelines.

Available to: No restrictions
Deadline: May 1
Apply to: Literary Prizes, above address

Ⓟ The *Marianne Moore Poetry Prize* offers a $1,000 award and publication by Helicon Nine for an original, unpublished poetry manuscript of at least 48 pages. Work that has appeared in magazines or anthologies is eligible. There is a $20 reading fee. Send SASE or see the Web site for guidelines.

Available to: No restrictions
Deadline: May 1
Apply to: Literary Prizes, above address

**Lorian Hemingway Short Story Competition**
**PO Box 993**
**Key West, FL 33041**
**E-mail: calico2419@aol.com**
**Web site: www.shortstorycompetition.com**

Ⓕ The *Lorian Hemingway Short Story Competition* offers a $1,000 first prize, a $500 second prize, and a $500 third prize for short stories of any form or style, maximum 3,000 words. The competition is open to writers whose fiction has not appeared in a nationally distributed publication with circulation above 5,000. For guidelines, send SASE, e-mail, or consult the Web site.

Available to: No restrictions
Deadline: May 15
Apply to: Above address

**Hemingway Western Studies Center**
**Boise State University**
**1910 University Drive**
**Boise, ID 83725**
**E-mail: ttrusky@boisestate.edu**
**Fax: 208-426-4373**

The *Rocky Mountain Artists/Eccentric Book Competition* offers $500 and standard sales royalties for multiple-edition works (100 to 1,000 copies) relating to such public concerns as race, religion, gender, and the environment. The annual contest seeks to "encourage the creation of beautiful, terrifying, intriguing and ingenious, as well as inexpensive, books." Works with special relevance to Rocky Mountain audiences are preferred. Authors and artists may submit sample copies, dummies, or publication proposals, with SASE for return of materials. Proposals specifying offset, copier, or silkscreen printing on commercial papers will be favored. Works may consist of text and/or visual content. Send SASE, fax, or e-mail for further information.

Available to: U. S. writers
Deadline: Inquire
Apply to: Rocky Mountain Artists/Eccentric Book Competition, above address

**The Heritage Foundation**
**214 Massachusetts Avenue, NE**
**Washington, DC 20002**
**Phone: 202-546-4400**
**Web site: http://www.heritage.org/media_center/LWflyer.pdf**
**Fax: 202-546-8328**

ⓙ The *Lawrence Wade Journalism Fellowship* is awarded annually to a journalism student or student journalist who best exemplifies the high ideals and standards of the late Lawrence Wade. The winning fellow receives a ten-week salaried internship at the Foundation and a $1,000 scholarship. Applicants must be enrolled full-time in an accredited college or university, and working toward an undergraduate or graduate degree, but need not be studying or majoring in journalism or a related communications field. Write or consult the Web site for guidelines. Applications are not accepted by e-mail.

Available to: See above
Deadline: March 1
Apply to: Selection Committee, Lawrence Wade Journalism Fellowship, Center for Media and Public Policy, above address

**Highlights for Children**
**Editorial Headquarters**
**803 Church Street**
**Honesdale, PA 18431**
**Phone: 570-253-1080**
**E-mail (for information only): emberger@highlights-corp.com**
**Web site: http://www.highlights.com/about/contribFiction.html**
**Fax: 570-251-7847**

© *Highlights for Children* sponsors an annual *Fiction Contest*. Previously unpublished short stories (for readers age nine to twelve, a maximum of 900 words; for readers through age eight, a maximum of 500) will be judged for three cash prizes of $1,000 each. All entries will be considered for regular publication with payment at regular rates. Stories should not include violence. Send SASE for further information.

Available to: No restrictions
Deadline: Submissions accepted January 1-February 28
Apply to: Fiction Contest, above address

**The Highlights Foundation**
**814 Court Street**
**Honesdale, PA 18431**
**Phone: 570-253-1192**
**E-mail: contact@highlightsfoundation.org**

© The *Highlights Foundation Scholarship Program* provides financial support to qualified candidates wishing to attend the annual Highlights Foundation Writers Workshop at Chautauqua. Individuals with a serious interest in writing for children and an established financial need are invited to apply. Scholarship awards are granted at the discretion of the Foundation Scholarship Committee. Send SASE for guidelines. For more information, contact Jenny Blanchard, Program Director, above address.

Available to: Prospective first-time attendees of the Writers' Workshop at Chautauqua
Deadline: March 15.
Apply to: Selection Committee, Highlights Foundation Scholarship Program, PO Box 686, Honesdale, PA 18431

**Sidney Hillman Foundation**
**c/o UNITE!**
**1710 Broadway**
**New York, NY 10019-5299**
**Phone: 212-332-9365**
**Web site: www.uniteunion.org**

Ⓙ Ⓝ The *Sidney Hillman Foundation Prize Awards* are given for outstanding contributions related in theme to the ideals of Sidney Hillman, including "the protection of individual civil liberties, improved race relations, a strengthened labor movement, the advancement of social welfare and economic security, greater world understanding." Contributions may be in nonfiction, daily or periodical journalism, or radio and television journalism, and must have been published or produced in the previous year. Several prizes of $2,000 each are awarded annually.

Available to: No restrictions
Deadline: January 31
Apply to: Susan Cowell, Executive Director, above address

**Historic New Orleans Collection**
**533 Royal Street**
**New Orleans, LA 70130-2179**
**E-mail: WRC@hnoc.org**
**Web site: http://www.hnoc.org**
**Fax: 504-598-7108**

Ⓝ The *Kemper and Leila Williams Prize in Louisiana History* is given annually for the best work of nonfiction dealing with Louisiana history or culture published during the calendar year. The prize consists of a cash award of $1,500 and an engraved plaque. All submissions must be made in quadruplicate. Write, e-mail, or see the Web site for additional information.

Available to: No restrictions
Deadline: January 15
Apply to: Chair, Kemper and Leila Williams Prize Committee, above address

History of Science Society
University of Washington
Box 351330
Seattle, WA 98195
E-mail: hssexec@u.washington.edu
Web site: http://www.hssonline.org
Fax: 206-685-9544

(N)    The *Watson Davis and Helen Miles Davis Prize* of $1,000 is given to the best book on the history
       of science in English (original language or translation) directed to a wide readership and
       published during the preceding three years.

       Available to: No restrictions
       Deadline: April 1
       Apply to: Robert J. Malone, Executive Director, above address

(N)    The *History of Women in Science Prize* of $1,000 is given to a book in odd-numbered years, and
       to an article in even-numbered years, on the subject of women and science published
       during the preceding four years.

       Available to: No restrictions
       Deadline: April 1
       Apply to: Robert J. Malone, Executive Director, above address

(N)    The *Pfizer Award* of $2,500 and an inscribed medal is given for the best book on the history of
       science in English (original language or in translation) published during the preceding
       three years.

       Available to: No restrictions
       Deadline: April 1
       Apply to: Robert J. Malone, Executive Director, above address

(N)    The *Henry and Ida Schuman Prize* awards $500 annually for an original essay by a graduate
       student on the history of science and its cultural influences. Up to $500 in travel costs to
       attend the HSS annual meeting is also available.

       Available to: Graduate students
       Deadline: April 1
       Apply to: Robert J. Malone, Executive Director, above address


Herbert Hoover Presidential Library Association
PO Box 696
West Branch, IA 52358-0696
Phone: 319-643-5327
E-mail: info@hooverassociation.org
Web site: http://www.hooverassociation.org
Fax: 319-643-2391

The *Herbert Hoover Presidential Travel and Grant Program* annually awards grants, normally
ranging from $500 to $1,500, to researchers to pay for trips to the Hoover Library. The
Association considers larger requests for extended graduate and postdoctoral research. All
funds must be used for research at the Library. Applicants should consult with the archival
staff about their topic before submitting a request; archivists can be reached at 319-643-5301
or at library@hoover.nara.gov. Write for additional information and application.

Available to: No restrictions
Deadline: March 1
Apply to: Chairman, Fellowship and Grant Committee, above address


The Horn Book
56 Roland Street
Boston, MA 02129
E-mail: lraece@hbook.com
Web site: http://www.hbook.com

©    The *Boston Globe-Horn Book Awards for Excellence in Children's Literature* are offered by the

Boston Globe Newspaper Company and *The Horn Book* to foster and reward excellence in text and illustration of children's books. Three awards, of $500 each, are offered for fiction and poetry, nonfiction, and picture books; reprints and textbooks are not considered. Publishers may submit up to eight books per juvenile imprint, from any of the three categories; submissions must be sent directly to the judges. Write or consult the Web site for names and addresses of current judges. Awards are made each autumn at the New England Library Association conference.

Available to: Authors of children's books published in the U. S. between June 1 and the following May 31; book submissions not accepted before February
Deadline: May 15
Apply to: Boston Globe-Horn Book Awards, above address


**George A. and Eliza Gardner Howard Foundation**
**Box 1867**
**Brown University**
**Providence, RI 02912**
**E-mail: Howard_Foundation@brown.edu**
**Web site: http://www.brown.edu/Divisions/Graduate_School/howard**

The Foundation seeks to support people in the middle stages of their careers whose work to date is evidence of their promise and achievement. Nominees normally should have the rank of assistant or associate professor or a nonacademic equivalent. Support is intended to augment paid sabbatical leaves.

A limited number of fellowships are awarded annually, with stipends of $20,000 for one-year terms for independent projects. Awards are granted in a sequence, one year devoted to the arts, the next to the social sciences. In 2002-2003, awards will be given in playwriting (excluding film), in theater arts (including theory and criticism; excluding production and direction), and in music and musicology; in 2003-2004, in history, including the history of science, and political science; in 2004-2005, in creative writing in English including novels, short stories, poetry, playwriting, essays, and creative nonfiction; and in 2005-2006, in literary criticism, film criticism, and translations. Fellowships are not available for work leading to an academic degree or for private study. Candidates must be nominated by a representative of an affiliated college or university, a professional critic or editor, or the director of a professional association. Write, e-mail, or see the Web site for further information and application procedures.

Available to: See above
Deadline: Mid-October for nominations; late November for applications with supporting materials
Apply to: Professor Henry F. Majewski, Administrative Director, above address


**L. Ron Hubbard's Writers of the Future Contest**
**PO Box 1630**
**Los Angeles, CA 90078**
**E-mail: contests@authorservicesinc.com**
**Web site: http://www.writersofthefuture.com**

Ⓕ The *L. Ron Hubbard Writers of the Future Contest* is an international search for new and amateur writers of science fiction or fantasy short stories or novelettes (under 17,000 words). A first prize of $1,000, a second of $750, and a third of $500 are offered quarterly. The quarterly first-prize winners compete for an annual grand prize of $4,000. Submissions must be unpublished; no entry fee is required. Entrants retain all rights. Send SASE, e-mail, or visit the Web site for guidelines.

Available to: Writers who have not professionally published a novel or short novel, more than three short stories, or more than one novelette
Deadline: December 31, March 31, June 30, September 30
Apply to: Above address

**Hudson River Classics**
**PO Box 940**
**Hudson, NY 12534**
**Fax: 518-828-1480**

Ⓓ The *W. Keith Hedrick Playwriting Contest* offers $500 and a staged reading of a previously unpublished or unproduced play between 60 and 90 minutes in length. There is a $5 processing fee.

Available to: Playwrights from the Northeast
Deadline: Submissions accepted February 1-May 1
Apply to: W. Keith Hedrick Playwriting Contest, above address

**Hudson Valley Writers' Center**
**300 Riverside Drive**
**Sleepy Hollow, NY 10591**

Ⓟ The *Slapering Hol Press Chapbook Competition* offers $500, publication, and a reading at the Center for poets who have not published a book or a chapbook. Poets should submit a manuscript of 16 to 20 pages, on which their name does not appear; a separate cover sheet should give title, poet's name, address, phone number, brief bio, and acknowledgments. There is a $10 reading fee. Send SASE for guidelines.

Available to: See above
Deadline: May 15
Apply to: Slapering Hol Press Chapbook Competition, above address

**Hugo Scholarship Committee**
**University of Montana**
**Department of English**
**Missoula, Montana 59812**
**Web site: www.umt.edu**

Ⓟ The *Richard Hugo Memorial Scholarship* honors the memory and the work of the poet whose character and personality shaped a strong and unusual creative-writing program at the University of Montana. The scholarship is solely for graduate students accepted into the University's MFA program in poetry. There is no application process; poems submitted with applicants' MFA applications will automatically be considered in awarding the scholarship.

Available to: See above
Deadline: February 1
Apply to: MFA program

**Humanitas Prize**
**17575 Pacific Coast Highway, PO Box 861**
**Pacific Palisades, CA 90272**
**E-mail: humanitasp@aol.com**
**Web site: http://www.humanitasprize.org**

Ⓢ The *Humanitas Prize* is given for excellence in writing for film and television with a focus on human values. Awards are made in eight categories: feature film; 90-minute-or-longer program on PBS or cable; 90-minute-or-longer program on network television; 60-minute television program; 30-minute television program; children's live-action program; children's animated program; and in cooperation with the Sundance Institute, independent feature film. The first three categories offer a $25,000 prize each; the remaining five offer $10,000 each. To be eligible, work must have been aired or screened between April 1 of the year preceding the deadline and April 1 of the award year. Write or e-mail for required application.

Available to: No restrictions
Deadline: April 1
Apply to: Above address

**Humboldt State University**
**English Department**
**Arcata, CA 95521**
**Web site: www.humboldt.edu/~carver**

(F)  The *Raymond Carver Short Story Contest* annually awards $1,000 plus publication in *Toyon*, the university literary journal, for an unpublished short story of up to 6,000 words. Writers should submit two copies of their manuscript, only one with cover page and author's name, and a $10 reading fee. Send SASE for guidelines.

>  Available to: U. S. residents
>  Deadline: December 31
>  Apply to: Raymond Carver Short Story Contest, above address

**Humboldt State University**
**Department of Theatre Arts**
**Arcata, CA 95521**
**E-mail: mtk3@axe.humboldt.edu**
**Web site: http://www.humboldt.edu/~mtk3**
**Fax: 707-826-5494**

(D)  The *National New Play Award* triennially offers $1,000, full production, and a two-week residence for the writer of an unproduced, unpublished full-length play. The next award will be given in 2005. Write, e-mail, or see the Web site for updated information.

>  Available to: No restrictions
>  Deadline: January 30
>  Apply to: National New Play Award, above address

**Hurston/Wright Foundation**
**PO Box 77287**
**Washington, DC 20013**
**Phone: 301-422-0152**
**E-mail: hurstonwright@aol.com**
**Web site: hurston-wright.org**

(F)  The *Hurston/Wright Award* of $1,000 is given annually to honor excellence in fiction writing by African-American students enrolled full-time in a U. S. college or graduate school. Two finalists each receive $500. Writers may submit an unpublished short story or an excerpt from a novel, no longer than 25 pages. Send SASE for guidelines, or see the Web site.

>  Available to: See above
>  Deadline: December 31
>  Apply to: Hurston/Wright Award, above address

(M)  The Hurston/Wright Foundation, in collaboration with Borders Books and Music, has also established the *Hurston/Wright Legacy Award*, to be given annually to recognize black writers for works of booklength nonfiction, fiction, and "debut fiction." The winner receives $10,000, and two finalists each receive $5,000. See the Web site for more information.

**ICARUS**
**PO Box 1232**
**Kill Devil Hills, NC 27948**
**Phone: 252-441-6584**
**Web site: www.icarusinternational.com/entries.html#poetry**

(P)  The *ICARUS Poetry Competition* offers $500 for an unpublished poem or prose poem, with a 100-line limit, on a specific theme related to flight (the theme for 2002 is "One Small Step"). The winning and finalist works will be published in a chapbook that will be given to all entrants. There is a $10 reading fee. Send SASE for guidelines.

>  Available to: No restrictions
>  Deadline: July 2
>  Apply to: Poetry Competition, above address

ICELAND
Ministry of Education, Science and Culture
Solvholsgötu 4
150 Reykjavik
Iceland
E-mail: postur@mrn.stjr.is
Web site: http://www.mrn.stjr.is
Fax: 354-1-562-3068

Several scholarships are offered for advanced study and research in the language, literature, and history of Iceland at the University of Iceland. Grants are for a period of eight months, and cover tuition plus a cash stipend (currently $600 a month).

    Available to: U. S. citizens
    Deadline: Inquire
    Apply to: Institute of International Education, U. S. Student Programs Division, 809 United Nations Plaza, New York, NY 10017


ICELAND
Sigurdur Nordal Institute
PO Box 1220
122 Reykjavik
Iceland
E-mail: ulfarb@hi.is or nordals@hi.is
Web site: http://www.nordals.hi.is
Fax: 354-1-562-6263

Ⓣ    The *Snorri Sturluson Icelandic Fellowships* are granted to writers, translators, and scholars in the humanities to enable them to stay in Iceland for at least three months, to improve their knowledge of the language, culture, and society. The amount of each fellowship covers travel expenses to and from Iceland, plus living expenses while in the country. Applicants should submit a brief but thorough account of the purpose of their stay, specifying the anticipated duration, as well as a curriculum vitae.

    Available to: See above; not for university students
    Deadline: October 31
    Apply to: Snorri Sturluson Icelandic Fellowships, above address


Idaho Commission on the Arts
Box 83720
Boise, ID 83720-0008
E-mail: cconley@ica.state.id.us
Web site: http://www.state.id.us/arts/
Fax: 208-334-2488

Ⓜ    The Idaho Commission on the Arts offers three grant programs for writers. *Fellowships* of $3,500 are awarded for artistic excellence (one per lifetime), with disciplines rotating on a three-year cycle (fellowships for visual arts are available in 2002; for performance art in 2003). *Writer-in-Residence* awards of $8,000 are given for highest artistic excellence (one per lifetime); these are available in 2004. During a three-year term, the writer gives twelve community readings in the state, with travel and other expenses covered. *QuickArt$* funds are awarded quarterly for specific projects and professional development. The maximum for QuickArt$ projects is $1,000; for professional development, $400. These grants are available only to Idaho residents of at least one year before application. Write, e-mail, or see the Web site for guidelines and further requirements.

    Available to: Idaho residents
    Deadline: For QuickArt$, August 5 and November 3, 2002, and February 3, 2003; inquire for others
    Apply to: Literature Director, above address

Illinois Arts Council
James R. Thompson Center
100 West Randolph, Suite 10-500
Chicago, IL 60601
E-mail: info@arts.state.il.us or susan@arts.state.il.us
Web site: http://www.state.il.us/agency/iac
Fax: 312-814-1471

(M)   *Artists' Fellowships* are offered annually to Illinois writers of poetry and prose, and of plays and screenplays. A limited number of $700 *Finalist Awards* are also given yearly. Write, e-mail, or see the Web site for guidelines before submitting.

Available to: Illinois writers
Deadline: September 1 for playwriting/screenwriting; December 1 for poetry and prose
Apply to: Above address

(R)   The *Arts-in-Education Program* provides support for Illinois artist residences in schools and communities statewide, for periods ranging from one week to six months. Residences may involve primary and secondary educational institutions, community colleges, and local arts and community organizations, as well as four-year colleges and universities if the residence involves the local K-12 student population. To be considered for the program, writers must apply for inclusion in an artists' roster. Applications are reviewed every two years (the next round in 2003). Roster artists receive a stipend of $800 per week. Write, e-mail, or see the Web site for additional information.

Available to: Illinois writers
Deadline: June 1, 2003, for roster inclusion; February 15 for residence
Apply to: Arts-in-Education Program, above address

The *Illinois Artstour Program* links the state's performing artists, including writers who have given public readings, with presenters in the state. Writers may offer their work and conduct workshops, master classes, residences, and lecture/demonstrations sponsored by Illinois presenters. To be considered, writers apply for inclusion in the Artstour roster. Write for additional information.

Available to: Illinois writers
Deadline: Inquire
Apply to: Illinois Artstour Program, above address

(M)   *Literary Awards* are given annually to previously unpublished Illinois writers publishing new work in nonprofit literary magazines with editorial offices in the state whose primary mission is to showcase contemporary poetry, fiction, and creative nonfiction, analytical, scholarly, or journalistic works; interviews and reviews are ineligible. Companion awards of $1,000 each are given to thirteen writers publishing new work in similar literary magazines.

Available to: See above
Deadline: March 1
Apply to: Above address

The *Short-Term Artist Residencies (STAR) Program* provides funding for Illinois organizations to work with Illinois professional artists to develop and implement residence programs that bring arts activities into the community. Each residence lasts from one to five days. The Arts Council will support half of the artist's fee; the local sponsor must provide the remaining half and cover other expenses. Writers are encouraged to seek sponsors to initiate programs. Write, e-mail, or see the Web site for additional information.

Available to: Illinois nonprofit organizations
Deadline: Ongoing
Apply to: STAR Program, above address

(M)   *Special Assistance Grants* are available to Illinois writers as the budget allows. They aim to support artists in promoting professional growth, gaining access to artistic venues, or resolving specific artistic problems. Write, e-mail, or see the Web site for additional information.

Available to: Illinois writers
Deadline: Ongoing
Apply to: Above address

Illinois State University
English Department
Stevenson Hall
Campus Box 4240
Normal, IL 61790-4240
Phone: 309-438-3667
E-mail: rccruz@ilstu.edu

Ⓕ Ⓟ The *Charles Johnson Awards for Fiction and Poetry* offer $500 in each genre to U. S. ethnic-minority college students and college students "whose work freshly explores the experience/identity of a minority or marginalized culture." Eligible writers may submit one short story of up to 25 pages, or three to five poems totaling up to 6 pages. Manuscripts are not returned. Send SASE or e-mail for further information. *(As this edition goes to press, PEN was unable to confirm this information, but believes it is accurate.)*

Available to: See above
Deadline: February 1
Apply to: Ricardo Cortez Cruz, above address (e-mail submissions are not accepted)


Independent Publisher Book Awards
Jenkins Group
400 West Front Street, 4A
Traverse City, MI 49684
Phone: 800-706-463
E-mail: jimb@bookpublishing.com
Web site: www.independentpublisher.com
Fax: 231-933-0448

Ⓜ The *Independent Publisher Book Awards* recognize excellence in independent publishing. Independents, university and small presses, and self-publishers throughout North America may submit entries. Ten awards of $500 each are presented at BookExpo America in Chicago. All books must have been published in the year preceding the award year. Entry fee is $60 per title, per category. For more information see the Web site.

Available to: No restrictions
Deadline: April 16
Apply to: Above address


Indiana Review
Ballantine Hall 465
1020 East Kirkwood Avenue
Bloomington, IN 47405-7103
Web site: http://www.indiana.edu/~inreview/ir.html

Ⓕ The *Indiana Review Fiction Prize* offers $500 and publication for a short story in any style and on any subject, up to 15,000 words. Contestants may enter multiple times under separate cover; name, address, and phone number should appear on a cover letter only. There is a fee of $12 per entry; all entrants receive a copy of the prize issue of the review. Send SASE with submission for notification. Manuscripts will not be returned.

Available to: No restrictions
Deadline: October 2002 (send SASE for 2003 guidelines)
Apply to: Fiction Prize, above address


Indiana University-Purdue University at Indianapolis
425 University Boulevard #309
Indianapolis, IN 46202
E-mail: dwebb@iupui.edu
Web site: http://www.iupui.edu/~comstudy/playsym/symwork.html
Fax: 317-278-1025

Ⓓ The *National Youth Theatre Playwriting Competition*, sponsored in odd-numbered years by the Department of Communication Studies at Indiana University-Purdue University and the

Indiana Repertory Theatre, awards cash prizes to ten semifinalists for professionally unproduced plays for audiences age six through eighteen. Four finalists receive awards of $1,000 each, and playwrights are provided a week of development at the Indiana Repertory Theatre with the support of a director, dramaturg, and actors, culminating in a showcase of readings at the National Youth Theatre Symposium. Send SASE or see Web site for guidelines and entry form.

Available to: No restrictions
Deadline: Submissions must be postmarked between August 2 and 31, and received no later than September 9, of even-numbered years
Apply to: Dorothy Webb, National Youth Theatre Playwriting Competition, above address

**Inkwell Magazine**
**Manhattanville College**
**2900 Purchase Street**
**Purchase, NY 10577**
**Web site: http://www.mville.edu/inkwell_mag/contests.htm**

(P) The *Inkwell Poetry Competition* offers in even-numbered years a grand prize of $1,000 and two honorable mentions of $50 each for an unpublished poem no longer than 40 lines. Winning entries and top finalists will be published in *Inkwell*. The entry fee is $10 for the first poem and $5 for each additional, up to five total. Send SASE for guidelines.

Available to: No restrictions
Deadline: October 30
Apply to: Poetry Competition, above address

(F) The *Inkwell Short Fiction Contest* offers in even-numbered years a grand prize of $1,500 for a previously unpublished short story of up to 2,500 words. The winning entry and top finalists will be published in *Inkwell*. The entry fee is $15 per story. Send SASE for guidelines.

Available to: No restrictions
Deadline: October 30
Apply to: Short Fiction Contest, above address

**Institute for Humane Studies**
**George Mason University**
**3301 North Fairfax Drive, Suite 440**
**Arlington, VA 22201-4432**
**E-mail: ihs@gmu.edu**
**Web site: http://www.theihs.org**
**Fax: 703-993-4890**

The *Hayek Fund for Scholars* awards up to $1,000 to students and untenured faculty who would like to participate in professional activities. Applicants must explain how participation will advance their careers and their understanding of the classical liberal tradition. Write, e-mail, or see the Web site for additional information.

Available to: Students and untenured faculty members
Deadline: Ongoing
Apply to: Hayek Fund for Scholars, above address

The *Humane Studies Fellowships* offer up to $12,000 in tuition and stipend for an academic year to approximately eighty graduates and undergraduates who have a clearly demonstrated interest in the classical liberal/libertarian tradition of individual rights and market economies, and who wish to apply the principles of this tradition in their work. Write, e-mail, or see the Web site for additional information and application.

Available to: Full-time graduate students, and junior or senior undergraduates
Deadline: December 31
Apply to: Humane Studies Fellowships, above address

(M) *IHS Film & Fiction Scholarships* offer up to $10,000 in tuition and stipend to talented graduate students pursuing an MFA in film, fiction writing, or playwriting who have demonstrated an interest in classical liberal ideas and their place in contemporary society. Write, e-mail, or see the Web site for additional information and application.

Available to: See above
Deadline: January 15
Apply to: Film & Fiction Scholarships, above address

Ⓜ The *IHS Young Communicators Fellowships* assist appropriate candidates in taking advantage of short-term opportunities to pursue careers involving the communication of ideas. Each fellowship consists of a stipend of up to $2,500 for a twelve-week period, and housing and travel assistance up to $2,500 if required. Fellowships cannot be used for tuition or living expenses associated with pursuing a degree. Eligible are college juniors or seniors, graduate students, or recent graduates who have clearly demonstrated interest in the classical liberal tradition of individual rights and market economies and who are intent on a career in journalism, film, writing (fiction or nonfiction), publishing, or market-oriented public policy; they must also have arranged or applied for an internship, training program, or other short-term position related to their intended career. Write, e-mail, or see the Web site for additional information.

Available to: See above
Deadline: March 15 for summer positions; at least ten weeks in advance for others
Apply to: Young Communicators Fellowships, above address

Ⓙ The *Felix Morley Journalism Competition* awards a first prize of $2,500 to an outstanding young writer whose work demonstrates an appreciation of classical liberal principles. These include inalienable individual rights; their protection through private property, contract, and rule of law; voluntarism in human relations; and the self-ordering market, free trade, free migration, and peace. Applicants must be full-time students (college, university, or high school), or be twenty-five or younger, and must submit a clipping or legible copy of three to five separate examples of their work—editorials, op-eds, articles, essays, reviews—along with an entry form. Write, e-mail, or visit the Web site for additional information and application.

Available to: See above
Deadline: December 1
Apply to: Morley Journalism Competition, above address

**Institute for the Study of Diplomacy**
**Edmund A. Walsh School of Foreign Service**
**Georgetown University**
**Washington, DC 20057-1025**
**Web site: http://data.georgetown.edu/sfs/programs/isd/**
**Fax: 202-965-5811**

Ⓙ The *Edward Weintal Prize for Diplomatic Reporting* offers a cash award to recognize initiative, hard digging, and bold thinking in the coverage of American diplomacy and foreign policy, among print and broadcast media journalists. There is no entry form. Nominations should include clippings (print media) or cassettes and transcripts (broadcast), a cover letter, and biographical material on the nominee.

Available to: No restrictions
Deadline: Mid-January (inquire for exact date)
Apply to: Weintal Prize, Institute for the Study of Diplomacy, 1316 36th Street, NW, Washington, DC 20007

**Institute of Current World Affairs**
**Crane-Rogers Foundation**
**4 West Wheelock Street**
**Hanover, NH 03755**
**E-mail: icwa@valley.net**
**Web site: http://www.icwa.org**
**Fax: 603-643-9599**

One or two fellowships per year are awarded to help talented individuals develop a deep understanding of a topic, country, or region outside the U. S. and share that understanding with interested segments of the English-speaking public. Candidates should be under thirty-six and should demonstrate initiative, character, communications skills, seriousness of purpose, and enthusiasm for their fields. Full support, including living and traveling expenses, is provided for the duration of the fellowship, which is normally two years. Awards are not made to support work toward academic degrees or to underwrite specific programs of research as such, but are aimed at providing the opportunity to acquire a thorough comprehension of the chosen area. Interested persons send a letter of intent to the executive director before submitting a formal application. Write, e-mail, or see the Web site for further information.

Available to: See above
Deadline: March 15 and August 15 for letter of intent; April 1 and September 1 for application
Apply to: Peter B. Martin, Executive Director, above address


**Institute of International Education**
**U. S. Department of State Fulbright Program**
**U. S. Student Programs Division**
**809 United Nations Plaza**
**New York, NY 10017**

The *U. S. Department of State Fulbright* and other grants for graduate study abroad are available in academic fields and the creative and performing arts. Among the requirements is proficiency in the language of the country to be visited. Grants cover the costs of international travel, tuition, living, and health insurance.

Available to: U. S. citizens
Deadline: October 25
Apply to: U. S. Department of State Fulbright Program, above address


**Institute on the Arts & Civic Dialogue**
**Harvard University**
**69 Dunster Street**
**Cambridge, MA 02138-5908**
**E-mail: dialogue@arts-civic.org**
**Web site: http://www.arts-civic.org**
**Fax: 617-495-9121**

® The Institute offers residences to professional artists in all disciplines for a six-week summer program, in order to support works that address contemporary issues and examine how those works can engage audiences of various economic, social, and intellectual and cultural backgrounds. Of special interest are artists whose work deals with food and hunger, the environment, and reproductive rights and genetics. Selected artists are provided with funds, facilities, travel, and accommodations to facilitate the development of new work.

Available to: No restrictions
Deadline: Inquire
Apply to: Above address

**Inter American Press Association Scholarship Fund**
**2911 NW 39th Street**
**Miami, FL 33142**
**Phone: 305-285-7205**
**E-mail: zulaydominguez@aol.com**
**Web site: http://www.sipiapa.org**
**Fax: 305-635-2272**

ⓙ Five scholarships of $13,000 each are available annually to U. S. and Canadian print journalists, ages twenty-one through thirty-five, for nine months' advanced study and research in Latin America. Candidates must be fluent in Spanish or Portuguese and have a well-defined program that will enable them to return to promote freedom of the press and understanding between the Americas. The scholarship also provides airfare for the trip. The program brings Latin American journalists to study in the U. S and Canada as well.

Available to: Natives of the Western Hemisphere
Deadline: December 31
Apply to: Scholarship Fund, above address

ⓙ Several *IAPA Grand Prizes for Press Freedom* are given for outstanding work in defense of freedom of the press in the Americas. Published news items, articles and series, photographs, and cartoons can be considered for the award. Work submitted should be accompanied by a brief note from the editor and/or author explaining how it was done, why, what repercussions it had and any other factor relevant for appraisal by the judges. Books, essays, theses, and any other work that has not been published as a news article in a newspaper, periodical, or magazine are not eligible.

Available to: See above
Deadline: February 1
Apply to: Press Freedom Prizes, above address

**Intermedia Arts**
**2822 Lyndale Avenue South**
**Minneapolis, MN 55408**
**E-mail: allstaff@intermediaarts.org**
**Web site: http://www.intermediaarts.org**

The *Minnesota McKnight Fellowship for Interdisciplinary Artists* annually awards four fellowships, of $25,000 each, to artists working in interdisciplinary forms who "exhibit a sustained commitment to exploring the changing relationships among artistic disciplines, diverse cultural forms, and/or traditional expressions;" writing may be one of those disciplines. Applicants must reside in Minnesota. An additional $2,000 is available for travel and/or presentation of work during the two-year fellowship period. Send SASE or see the Web site for guidelines and application.

Available to: Minnesota Residents
Deadline: March 1
Apply to: Minnesota McKnight Fellowship for Interdisciplinary Artists, above address

Ⓡ The *National McKnight Fellowship for Interdisciplinary Artists* awards $10,000 to an artist for a four-week residence at Intermedia Arts, which may be in consecutive or nonconsecutive weeks. Up to $4,000 is available for travel, lodging, and daily expenses related to the residence; a maximum of $2,000 in organizational support and/or materials will be available for creating or presenting artwork and/or leading an educational activity during the residence. The fellowship seeks to support outstanding work by artists who "exhibit a sustained commitment to exploring the changing relationships among artistic disciplines, diverse cultural forms, and/or traditional modes of expression," and to broaden understanding of interdisciplinary arts. Applicants must demonstrate an accomplished body of interdisciplinary work and have teaching and/or mentoring experience. Judges will pay close attention to the artist's impact on the local artistic community. Send SASE for guidelines. The next fellowship is 2004.

Available to: No restrictions
Deadline: Inquire
Apply to: National McKnight Fellowship for Interdisciplinary Artists, above address

**INTERNATIONAL**
Arvon Foundation
42A Buckingham Palace Road, 2nd Floor
London SW1W 0RE
England
Phone: 44-20-7931-7611
E-mail: london@arvonfoundation.org
Web Site: www.arvonfoundation.org
Fax: 44-20-7963-0961

(P)  The *Daily Telegraph/Arvon International Poetry Competition* is offered in even-numbered years. The last competition awarded first, second and third prizes of £5,000, £2,500 and £1,000, respectively, with three further prizes of £500 each. Winning entries are published in an anthology. Write or consult the Web site for further information and guidelines.

Available to: No restrictions
Deadline: August 16
Apply to: International Poetry Competition, above address


**INTERNATIONAL**
Simone and Cino del Duca Foundation
10, rue Alfred de Vigny
75008 Paris
France

(IN)  The *Cino del Duca World Prize* (of 200,000 French francs in 2001) is awarded yearly in October to encourage a writer of any nationality whose work constitutes a message of modern humanism. The author's work should be of a scientific or literary nature. *By Internal Nomination Only.*


**INTERNATIONAL**
Fédération Internationale des Traducteurs
Peter Krawutschke, Secretary General
3711 Winding Way
Kalamazoo, MI 49004
E-mail: info@fit-ift.org
Web site: http://www.fit-ift.org

(T)  The Pierre-François Caillé-FIT Foundation offers grants to affiliated translators to enable them to spend time in a country in which their target language is the national language and to establish contact with translators or interpreter circles in that country.

Available to: Translators affiliated with a member society of FIT (in the U. S., the American Translators Association)
Deadline: Ongoing
Apply to: Above address

The following international translation prizes are awarded by FIT. American translators must apply through the American Translators Association.

(T)  The *Aurora Borealis Prize for Outstanding Translation of Fiction Literature* and the *Aurora Borealis Prize for Outstanding Translation of Nonfiction Literature*, sponsored by the Norwegian Association of Nonfiction Writers and Translators, are given either for a single translation of outstanding quality or for the entire body of a translator's fiction and nonfiction work. Applicants must belong to an FIT member society; in the United States, this is the American Translators Association.

(T)  The *Pierre-François Caillé Memorial Medal* is awarded once every three years, during FIT congresses, for promoting the standing of the translating profession internationally." The recipient must belong to an FIT member society; in the U. S., this is the American Translators Association.

(T)  The *Karel Capek Medal* is awarded once every three years, during FIT congresses, to "promote the translation of literary works written in languages of limited diffusion." The recipient must belong to an FIT member society; in the U. S., this is the American Translators Association.

(T)　The *Astrid Lindgren Translation Prize* is awarded once every three years, during FIT congresses, for promoting the translation of works written for children.

> Available to: Translators sponsored by a member society of FIT
> Deadline: Six months before an FIT congress (query American Translators Association for date)
> Apply to: American Translators Association, 225 Reinekers Lane #590, Alexandria, VA 22314, attn: Walter Bacak; or e-mail ata@atanet.org

**INTERNATIONAL**
**Premio Feltrinelli**
**c/o Accademia Nazionale dei Lincei**
**Palazzo Corsini**
**Via Lungara 10**
**00165 Rome**
**Italy**

(IN)　The *Antonio Feltrinelli International Prize* or *Premio Feltrinelli* (100 million Italian lire in 2001), is awarded to persons distinguishing themselves in the arts and sciences. The prize is given annually to citizens of any country, in alternating fields: moral and historical sciences; physical, mathematical, and natural sciences; medicine; fine arts; and literature. *By Internal Nomination Only.*

**INTERNATIONAL**
**Fundación Cultural Lya y Luis Cardoza y Aragón**
**Callejón de las Flores 1**
**Barrio del Niño Jesús, Coyoacán**
**0400 Mexico, D.F.**
**Mexico**
**E-mail: elrio@mail.internet.com.mx**
**Fax: 52-5-554-4010**

(N)　The *Premio Anual de Ensayo Literario Hispanoamericano Lya Kostakowsky,* of $25,000, is given annually for an unpublished essay written in Spanish on a given theme (the theme for 2001 was "What does it mean to be Latin American?"). Entries must be no longer than 50 pages. Write, fax, or e-mail for guidelines and current theme.

> Available: Writers whose language of composition is Spanish
> Deadline: October 15
> Apply to: Above address

**INTERNATIONAL**
**IMPAC**
**37 Dame Street**
**Dublin 2**
**Ireland**
**E-mail: dub.award@iol.ie**
**Web site: http://www.i-m-p-a-c.com or http://www.impacdublinaward.ie**
**Fax: 353-1-671-5385**

(F)　The *International IMPAC Dublin Literary Awards* annually offer 100,000 euros for "a work of fiction that makes a lasting contribution to world literature." This, the world's richest prize for a single work of fiction, is sponsored by IMPAC, a management-productivity engineering company, and the Dublin municipal government. The award is given to a work of fiction written and published in English, or written in another language and published in English translation, during the calendar year. If the winning book is originally in English, the prize is awarded solely to the author; if the winning work is a translation, the author receives 75,000 euros and the translator 25,000 euros. The Dublin City Public Libraries invite libraries around the world to nominate any number of titles, which must then be submitted by the publishers. Individual authors may not submit work directly. Write for additional information. The prize is which is awarded to the author if the book is written in English.

Available to: No restrictions
Deadline: Mid-November for library nominations
Apply to: International IMPAC Dublin Literary Contest, Awards Office, above address

**INTERNATIONAL**
**International Academy of Poetry and Poetics**
**Frauenhoferstrasse 3**
**97076 Würzburg**
**Germany**

[IN] The *International Rainer Maria Rilke Prize for Poetry* of $20,000 is given every five years to honor the lifetime work of a writer who has published poetry in more than one European language. There is no application process. (This prize was last given in 1999.) *By Internal Nomination Only.*

**INTERNATIONAL**
**International League of Antiquarian Booksellers**
**Bibliography Prize Secretary**
**Konrad Meuschel**
**Hauptstrasse 19A**
**53604 Bad Honnef**
**Germany**
**Fax: 49-2224-5642**
**E-mail: kmeuschel@aol.com**

(N) The *International League of Antiquarian Booksellers Bibliography Prize* is awarded to the author of the best work, published or unpublished, of learned bibliography or research into the history of the book or of typography, book of general interest on the subject. One prize of $10,000 is given every four years. Entries must be submitted in a language that is commonly understood around the world. The next award will be given in 2006.

Available to: No restrictions
Deadline: December 31, 2004
Apply to: Above address

**INTERNATIONAL**
**The Irish Times**
**10-16 D'Olier Street**
**Dublin 2**
**Ireland**
**Web site: http://www.booktrust.org.uk/prizes/irishtimes.htm**

[IN] The *Irish Times Irish Literature Prizes* are awarded biennially, with the cash amount of 27,500 Irish pounds shared among the winners in the following categories: international fiction, Irish fiction, Irish nonfiction, Irish poetry, and Irish language. Candidates are nominated by literary editors and critics in Ireland, the United Kingdom, and the U. S. *By Internal Nomination Only.*

**INTERNATIONAL**
**Jerusalem International Book Fair**
**PO Box 775**
**Jerusalem 91007**
**Israel**
**E-mail: jer_fair@netvision.net.il**
**Web site: http://www.jerusalembookfair.com**
**Fax: 972-2-624-3144**

[IN] The *Jerusalem Prize* of $5,000 is awarded annually to a writer whose work expresses the theme of the freedom of the individual in society. The prize is presented each year at the Jerusalem International Book Fair. Recipients are chosen by the Book Fair jury. There is no application process. *By Internal Nomination Only.*

The *Jerusalem Fellowship Program* provides an opportunity for emerging editors to meet with Israeli authors, attend the awarding of the Jerusalem Prize, learn about the history of Hebrew literature, and meet with publishers from around the world at the Jerusalem International Book Fair. Editorial fellows exchange ideas and information about a broad range of authors and books. For more information, consult the Web site or contact the Jerusalem International Book Fair.

Available to: No restrictions
Deadline: Inquire
Apply to: Above address


**INTERNATIONAL**
**Journalists in Europe**
**4, rue du Faubourg Montmartre**
**75009 Paris**
**France**
**E-mail: europmag@europmag.com**
**Web site: http://europmag.com**
**Fax: 33-1-48-24-40-02**

Ⓙ Ⓡ  *Journalists in Europe* programs give journalists the opportunity to acquire firsthand experience of European countries, to explore the ties among them and between Europe and the rest of the world, and to see how the European Union and its institutions work. Three programs are offered each year; journalists may apply for all three simultaneously. Candidates must be between twenty-five and thirty-five years of age, must be currently employed journalists with at least four years' full-time experience, and should have a working knowledge of English and French. Write or see the Web site for complete information.

Available to: See above
Deadline: January 31
Apply to: Above address


**INTERNATIONAL**
**Lontar Foundation**
**Jl.Danau Laut Tawar No. 53**
**Pejompongan, Jakarta 10210**
**Indonesia**
**Phone: 62-21-574-6880**
**E-mail: lontar@attglobal.net**
**Web site: http://www.lontar.org/home/index/php**
**Fax:  62-21-572-0353**

Ⓜ  The *Lontar Foundation Literary awards* present three cash prizes (5 million, 3 million, and 2 million rupiahs, respectively) for books published in the field of Indonesian literature. The first-prize book will be translated into English and published by the Lontar Foundation. Categories include novels, plays, literary anthologies, literary collections (short stories, poetry, and essays), memoirs, and travelogues. Books must have been published_self-published or by a commercial or noncommercial publisher_in the year preceding that of the award. Lontar employees and members of their families are not eligible.

Available to: See above
Deadline: May 1
Apply to: Above address


**INTERNATIONAL**
**Maison Internationale de la Poésie**
**Chaussée de Wavre, 150**
**1050 Brussels**
**Belgium**
**Web site: http://www.maison-int-poesie.cfwb.be**
**Fax: 32-2-511-52-83**

ⒾⓃ  The *Grand Prix des Biennales* (150,000 Belgian francs in 2001) is awarded by an international jury in even-numbered years to a poet chosen for the worldwide significance of his or her work. *By Internal Nomination Only*.


INTERNATIONAL
**The Mitchell Prizes**
**The Burlington Magazine**
**14-16 Duke's Road**
**London WC1H 9AD**
**England**
**Phone: 44-020-7388-1228**
**E-mail: editorial@burlington.org.uk**
**Fax: 44-020-7388-1230**

Ⓝ The *Eric Mitchell Prize* and the *Mitchell Prize for the History of Art*, both $10,000, are awarded in even-numbered years to the authors of, respectively, an outstanding exhibition catalogue and a book in English that has made an outstanding and original contribution to the study and understanding of the visual arts. Write for additional information.

Available to: No restrictions
Deadline: April 30
Apply to: Above address


INTERNATIONAL
**Alexander S. Onassis Public Benefit Foundation**
**7, Eschinou Street**
**105 58 Athens**
**Greece**
**Phone: 3010-371-3000**
**E-mail: pubrel@onassis.gr**
**Web site: http://www.onassis.gr**

Ⓓ The *Onassis International Prize* is given for a new and original theatrical play written in English, French, German, Greek, Italian, or Spanish. A first prize of $150,000, a second of $100,000, and a third of $75,000 are awarded. The next prizes will be given in 2005. For complete information, contact the Foundation or see the Web site.

Available to: No restrictions
Deadline: June 30, 2003
Apply to: Above address

*Foreigners' Fellowships Program* gives research grants for stays in Greece and educational scholarships to non-Greek full members of national academies, university professors of all levels, researchers-Ph.D. holders, artists, translators of Greek literature, elementary and secondary school teachers of Greek as a foreign language, postgraduate students and Ph.D. candidates. The program includes the following fields and sections of research: humanistic sciences: philology, literature, translation, linguistics, theology, history, archaeology, philosophy, educational studies, psychology; political science: sociology, anthropology, public administration, international relations, mass media; law; economics; architecture; arts: visual arts, music, dance, theater, photography, film studies. Persons not of Greek nationality are eligible; persons of Greek descent (second generation and further) are also eligible, if they permanently reside and work outside Greece, or are enrolled in foreign universities. Consult the Web site for further eligibility information.

Available to: See above
Deadline: January 31
Apply to: Secretariat, above address

INTERNATIONAL
**Juan Rulfo Award**
**Comisión de Premiación**
**Avenida Alemania 1370**
**Guadalajara, Jalisco 44190**
**Mexico**
**E-mail: premios@fil.com.mx**
**Fax: 52-3-810-0379**

Ⓜ The *Juan Rulfo Award for Latin American and Caribbean Literature* offers $100,000 for lifetime achievement to a native of Latin America or the Caribbean who writes in Spanish, Portuguese, or English; or a native of Spain or Portugal who writes in Spanish or Portuguese. Any writer who has produced noteworthy work in poetry, drama, the novel, the short story, or the essay is eligible. The prize is funded by a group of Mexican government agencies, universities, and businesses. Nominations may be made by cultural or educational institutions, associations, or groups interested in literature. Nominators should send the writer's vita and supporting documents.

Available to: See above
Deadline: June 17
Apply to: Awards Committee, above address, or contact David Unger, U. S. Coordinator, Guadalajara International Book Fair, Division of Humanities NAC 5225, City College of New York, New York, NY 10031

INTERNATIONAL
**Amaury Talbot Fund**
**Barclays Bank Trust Company Ltd**
**Osborne Court**
**Gadbrook Park, Northwich**
**Cheshire CW9 7UE**
**England**

Ⓝ The *Amaury Talbot Fund Annual Prize*, of approximately £600, is given for the most valuable work of anthropological research relating to Africa published in the calendar year for which the prize is being awarded. First preference is given to works relating to Nigeria, second to works relating to West Africa as a whole, and then to works relating to the rest of Africa. Two copies of the work in question must be submitted; these will not be returned.

Available to: No restrictions
Deadline: March 31, for work published in the previous calendar year
Apply to: Above address, reference WO844

INTERNATIONAL
**UNESCO**
**Division of Creativity, Cultural Industries and Copyright**
**1, rue Miollis**
**75732 Paris Cedex 15**
**France**
**E-mail: m.bulos@unesco.org**
**Web site: http://www.unesco.org/culture/toleranceliterature**
**Fax: 33-1-45-68-55-95**

Ⓒ The *UNESCO Prize for Children's and Young People's Literature in the Service of Tolerance* awards $8,000 biennially for works for the young that best embody the concepts of tolerance and peace and promote mutual understanding based on respect for other people and cultures. The works may be novels, collections of short stories, or picture books, in two categories: for children up to age twelve and for young people thirteen to eighteen. Entries must have been published in the two years before the award deadline (2002 and 2003 for the 2005 prize). All submissions should be accompanied by a summary in English or French. Publishers should send three copies of each book, with a limit of one title per age category, to their respective countries' National Commission for UNESCO. Write for additional information.

Available to: No restrictions
Deadline: Inquire
Apply to: Maha Bulos, above address

**INTERNATIONAL**
**UNESCO**
**International Fund for the Promotion of Culture (IFPC)**
**1, rue Miollis**
**75732 Paris Cedex 15**
**France**
**E-mail: s.berriche@unesco.org**
**Web site: http://www.unesco.org/culture/ifpc/**
**Fax: 33-1-45-68-55-99**

Ⓡ The *UNESCO-Aschberg Bursaries for Artists Program* covers round-trip travel expenses and provides residences at host and partner institutions around the world for younger artists in various disciplines. Eligibility and application procedures vary according to the host institution; for most bursaries, applicants must be under the age of thirty-five. For 2002-2003, the program will offer 57 bursaries from 51 partner institutions in 27 countries. Contact the IFPC in Paris for current information and application.

Available to: No restrictions
Deadline: April 30
Apply to: UNESCO-Aschberg Bursaries for Artists, above address

**INTERNATIONAL**
**UNESCO/Françoise Gallimard Prize**
**c/o Béatrice Mennechet**
**5, rue de Lille**
**Paris 75007**
**France**
**Web site: http://www.unesco.org**
**Phone/Fax: 33-0-1-42-60-61-52**

Ⓕ The *UNESCO/Françoise Gallimard Prize* is given to writers under age forty who seek "to express the tensions and hopes of our time and to reflect them in a literary work, thus helping to build a better world." Two awards, one of $20,000 for a work written in French and one of $10,000 for a work written in another language and translated into French, are given for novels or short story collections published in the two years preceding the award year. The competition is reserved for candidates from a different group of countries every year. Fax a letter of request for a list of eligible countries and additional information.

Available to: See above
Deadline: Inquire
Apply to: Above address

**INTERNATIONAL**
**World Prize for Mystical Poetry**
**Jorge Juan, 82, 1° 6**
**28009 Madrid**
**Spain**
**Phone: 34-915-75-40-91**
**E-mail: frielo@adenle.es**
**Web site: www.rielo.com**

Ⓟ The *World Prize for Mystical Poetry* recognizes poetry expressing the significance of humanity's spiritual values. Previously unpublished works, of 600 to 1,300 lines, originally written in either Spanish or English or translated into one of these languages, are eligible. The entry may be a single poem or a collection. The award consists of a cash prize of 6,000 euros and publication of the entry. See the Web site for more details.

Available to: No restrictions
Deadline: October 15
Apply to: Above address

**International Center for Journalists**
**1616 H Street, NW, 3rd floor**
**Washington, DC 20006-4999**
**E-mail: editor@icfj.org**
**Web site: http://www.icfj.org**
**Fax: 202-737-0530**

☺    The *Worth Bingham Prize* of $10,000 honors newspaper or magazine investigative reporting on stories of national significance about circumstances in which the public interest is being ill served. Entries may include a single story, a series of related stories, or up to three unrelated stories; columns and editorials are also eligible. Individual stories must have been published during the calendar year preceding the deadline; in the case of a series, at least half the stories must have been published during the contest year. Write or e-mail susan@icfj.org for guidelines and entry form.

     Available to: No restrictions
     Deadline: January 7 for entries published during the previous calendar year
     Apply to: Worth Bingham Prize, above address

☺    The *Arthur F. Burns Fellowship* offers young print and broadcast journalists from the U. S. and Germany the opportunity to work and report from abroad. Ten journalists from each country are selected annually to work at counterpart news organizations in the foreign country. Travel expenses and a stipend are provided. Applicants must be working journalists in any news media, under age thirty-five, with demonstrated talent and an interest in U. S.-European affairs. Proficiency in German for U. S. journalists is not required but is regarded favorably in the selection process. Write, e-mail, or see the Web site for application requirements.

     Available to: See above
     Deadline: March 1
     Apply to: Burns Fellowship, above address, or e-mail burns@icfj.org

☺    The *Ford Environmental Journalism Fellowships* annually send two U. S. environmental reporters overseas to train journalists and report on environmental matters. Fellows are posted for up to three months in their country of choice; preference is given to countries or regions in the developing world or with new democracies. On assignment, fellows work closely with host organizations, conducting workshops, seminars, and lectures, and consult with local media organizations. Travel expenses and a stipend are provided. Write, e-mail, or see the Web site for further information.

     Available to: Environmental journalists
     Deadline: November 6
     Apply to: Ford Environmental Journalism Fellowships, above address, or e-mail ford@icfj.org

☺    The *Senator John Heinz Fellowship in Environmental Reporting* combines the training of overseas journalists with reporting on international environmental matters. One fellow per year is posted for up to three months in the country of his or her choice; preference is given to countries or regions in the developing world or with new democracies. While on assignment, the fellow works closely with a host organization, conducting workshops, seminars, and lectures, and consulting with local media organizations. Travel expenses and a stipend are provided. Write, e-mail, or see the Web site for further information.

     Available to: U. S. journalists
     Deadline: November 6
     Apply to: Senator John Heinz Fellowship, above address, or e-mail heinz@icfj.org

☺    The *ICJF-KKC Journalism Fellowship in Japan*, sponsored by the Keizai Koho Center (Japan Institute for Social and Economic Affairs) allows five American journalists to travel to Japan for a two-week program in the fall that includes visits to Japanese news media, business leaders, and government officials. The second week of the program is devoted to independent research and reporting projects designed by each participant. Applicants should have at least five years' media experience and no substantial previous travel to Japan. Write, e-mail, or consult the Web site for application requirements and forms.

     Available to: U. S. journalists
     Deadline: July 1
     Apply to: ICJF-KKC Fellowship, above address, or e-mail ken@icfj.org

Ⓙ The *Knight International Press Fellowships*, sponsored by the John S. and James L. Knight Foundation, annually support some twenty-two American journalists and news executives. Fellows spend from two to nine months abroad in a variety of teaching, training, consulting, and assistance roles, usually working in conjunction with an overseas media center. Travel expenses and a stipend are provided. Write for guidelines and application.

Available to: U. S. journalists
Deadline: January 15 and July 15
Apply to: Knight Fellowships, above address, or e-mail knight@icfj.org

Ⓙ The *McGee Journalism Fellowship in Southern Africa* is given annually to a U. S. journalist who is posted to southern Africa for three to four months. While in Africa, the fellow consults in newsrooms, leads workshops, or teaches at a university. Upon returning, the fellow shares his or her experiences through lectures, seminars, and published articles. The fellowship, which provides an honorarium and covers expenses for assignments, is open to print or broadcast professionals, as well as journalism educators. Contact the Center or see the Web site for detailed program and application guidelines.

Available to: U. S. journalists and journalism educators
Deadline: April 16
Apply to: mcgee@icfj.org or above address

**The International Consortium of Investigative Journalists**
**The Center for Public Integrity**
**910 17th Street, NW, 7th floor**
**Washington, DC 20006**
**E-mail: info@icij.org**
**Web site: http://www.icij.org**
**Fax: 202-466-1102**

Ⓙ The *ICIJ Award for Outstanding International Investigative Reporting* offers a first prize of $20,000, and $1,000 to five finalists, for individual investigative work or single-subject series on a transnational topic of world significance. The investigative work must involve reporting in at least two countries. The award is open to any professional journalist or team of journalists of any nationality. Send SASE, e-mail, or see the Web site for guidelines.

Available to: No restrictions
Deadline: July 15
Apply to: ICIJ Award, above address

**International Quarterly**
**PO Box 10521**
**Tallahassee, FL 32303-0521**
**E-mail: vbrock@mailer.fsu.edu**
**Web site: http://mailer.fsu.edu/~vbrock**
**Fax: 904-224-5127**

Ⓜ The *Crossing Boundaries Writing Awards* consist of two prizes of $1,000 each, with publication in *International Quarterly*, for poetry, fiction, nonfiction, and "crossing boundaries," a category that includes "atypical work and innovative or experimental writing." Translations into English are accepted. There are no length requirements for poetry; the maximum number allowed is five. Writers in other categories should submit a manuscript of no more than 5,000 words. There is a $15 entry fee. Send SASE for guidelines. *(As this edition goes to press, PEN was unable to confirm this information, but believes it is accurate.)*

Available to: No restrictions
Deadline: March 1
Apply to: Crossing Boundaries Writing Awards, above address

**International Reading Association**
**PO Box 8139**
**Newark, DE 19714**
**Fax: 302-731-1057**

© The *International Reading Association Children's Book Awards* recognize authors whose early work shows unusual promise for a career in children's literature. The awards are given for a first or second book of fiction or nonfiction of high literary quality, published during the calendar year, in any country and in any language. Six prizes, of $500 each, are presented annually, for fiction and nonfiction, in three categories: primary (ages preschool to eight), intermediate (ages nine to thirteen), and young adult (ages fourteen to seventeen).

Available to: No restrictions
Deadline: November 1
Apply to: Children's Book Awards, Executive Offices, above address

© ℗ The *IRA Lee Bennett Hopkins Promising Poet Award* offers $500 every three years to a promising new writer of children's poetry (for children and young adults up to twelfth grade) who has published no more than two books. Write for guidelines.

Available to: See above
Deadline: December 1
Apply to: Hopkins Award, Executive Offices, above address

Ⓝ The *Outstanding Dissertation of the Year Award* of $1,000 is given annually for dissertations in reading or related fields. Studies using any research approach (ethnographic, experimental, historical, survey, etc.) are accepted. Each dissertation will be assessed in the light of its particular approach, the scholarly qualification of its results, and its significant contribution to knowledge within the reading field.

Available to: Doctoral candidates
Deadline: October 1
Apply to: Outstanding Dissertation Award, Research Division, above address

The *Helen M. Robinson Award* of $1,000 is given annually to assist doctoral students at the early stages of their dissertation research. Applicants must be members of the International Reading Association.

Available to: IRA members
Deadline: January 15
Apply to: Robinson Award, Research Division, above address

© The *Paul A. Witty Short Story Award* offers $1,000 to the author of an original short story that encourages young people to read periodicals. Stories must have been published for the first time in a periodical for children during the calendar year.

Available to: No restrictions
Deadline: November 1
Apply to: Witty Award, Executive Offices, above address

**International Research and Exchanges Board (IREX)**
**1616 H Street, NW**
**Washington, DC 20006**
**E-mail: irex@irex.org**
**Web site: http://www.irex.org**
**Fax: 202-628-8189**

Individual advanced research grants are available in all disciplines, with an emphasis on projects in the humanities and social sciences. Grants are awarded to predoctoral and postdoctoral scholars for a period of one to twelve months for research in Central and Eastern Europe and Eurasia. U. S. scholars in policy research and development and in cross-disciplinary studies are strongly urged to apply. Fellowships are also awarded for U. S. specialists, doctoral candidates, and senior scholars to conduct advanced social science and humanities research in Mongolia for periods of one to four months. Normally candidates must be U. S. citizens or permanent residents, have advanced-graduate-student status or a Ph.D., and possess sufficient command of the host-country language for advanced research. Grants and stipends vary according to country of study and academic level. Write, e-mail, or consult the Web site for additional information.

Available to: See above
Deadline: Varies depending on type of project and country where project will be conducted
Apply to: Above address

**International Women's Media Foundation**
**1726 M Street, NW, Suite 1002**
**Washington, DC 20036**
**E-mail: IWMF@aol.com**
**Web site: http://www.IWMF.org**
**Fax: 202-496-1977**

(J) The *Courage in Journalism Award* of $2,000 recognizes women journalists of any nationality who have demonstrated extraordinary qualities while pursuing their work under difficult or dangerous circumstances.

Available to: Women journalists
Deadline: March 15
Apply to: Amy Johnson, Director of Programs, above address, or e-mail ajohnson@iwmf.org

**Intersection for the Arts**
**446 Valencia Street**
**San Francisco, CA 94103**
**E-mail: info@theinterseciton.org**
**Fax: 415-626-1636**

(M) The *Joseph Henry Jackson Award* is given to the author of an unpublished work-in-progress of fiction, nonfiction, short fiction, or poetry. One award, of $2,000, is given annually. Send SASE for guidelines and application.

Available to: Northern California or Nevada residents for three consecutive years before deadline date, twenty to thirty-five years old
Deadline: January 31
Apply to: Above address

(M) The *James D. Phelan Award* is given for an unpublished work-in-progress of fiction (novel or collection of short stories), nonfiction, poetry, or drama. One award, of $2,000, is given annually. Send SASE for guidelines and application.

Available to: Native Californians twenty to thirty-five years old
Deadline: January 31
Apply to: Above address

The *Tanenbaum Award for Nonfiction* is given for an unpublished work-in-progress of nonfiction. One award, of $2,000, is given annually. Send SASE for guidelines and application.

> Available to: Northern California or Nevada residents for three consecutive years before deadline date, twenty to thirty-five years old
> Deadline: January 31
> Apply to: Above address

**The Iowa Review**
**308 EPB**
**University of Iowa**
**Iowa City, IA 52242**
**Web site: http://www.uiowa.edu/~iareview**

The *Iowa Award* of $1,000 and the *Tim McGinnis Memorial Award* of $500 are given annually by *The Iowa Review*. The former honors the best work of the year in any genre; the latter is for work with a light touch and a distinctive comic vision. There is no separate application process; all work published in the *Review* during the previous year is considered for the awards.

> Available to: Contributors to *The Iowa Review*

**Iowa State University**
**Department of English**
**203 Ross Hall**
**Ames, IA 50011-1201**
**E-mail: englgrad@iastate.edu**
**Fax: 515-294-6814**

The *Pearl Hogrefe Fellowship* is granted once each year to support beginning graduate study in creative writing at Iowa State University. The fellowship, for a nine-month academic period, covers the cost of tuition and includes a stipend of $1,087 a month. Write for application guidelines.

> Available to: No restrictions
> Deadline: January 31
> Apply to: Above address

**IRELAND**
**Fish Publishing**
**Durrus, Bantry**
**County Cork**
**Ireland**
**E-mail: info@fishpublishing.com**
**Web site: http://www.fishpublishing.com**

Ⓕ The *Fish Short Story Prize* annually awards $1,200, or 1,500 euros, for an unpublished short story not exceeding 5,000 words. A second prize, of a week's residence at the Anam Cara Writers and Artists Retreat in Eyeries, West Cork, is also offered. The top eighteen stories are published in a yearly anthology. There is a $12 entry fee for one story, an additional $8 is required for another story submitted in the same envelope. Winning stories will be read by London literary agents. Write, e-mail, or see the Web site for additional information.

> Available to: No restrictions
> Deadline: November 30
> Apply to: Fish Short Story Prize, above address

**IRELAND**
**Tyrone Guthrie Centre**
**Annaghmakerrig**
**Newbliss**
**County Monaghan**
**Ireland**
**E-mail: thetgc@indigo.ie**
**Web site: www.tyroneguthrie.ie**
**Fax: 353-47-54380**

® The Tyrone Guthrie Centre offers one-week to three-month residences throughout the year to writers who have shown "evidence of sustained dedication and a significant level of achievement." Overseas writers are expected to pay the cost of residence; the Centre does offer assistance in obtaining grants from cultural institutions in the writer's home country. Write, e-mail, or fax for guidelines.

Available to: Established writers
Deadline: None
Apply to: Above address


**Irish American Cultural Institute**
**One Lackawanna Place**
**Morristown, NJ 07960**
**E-mail: irishwaynj@aol.com**
**Web site: http://www.irishaci.org**
**Fax: 973-605-8875**

IN The *Irish American Cultural Institute Literary Awards* are given to encourage excellence among Irish writers in Irish or English. Any writer resident in Ireland who has published works of fiction, poetry, or drama is eligible. A total of $15,000 in prizes is awarded annually. *By Internal Nomination Only.*

The *Irish Research Fund* offers grants of up to $5,000 for research on the Irish experience in America. Applications are accepted from all disciplines. Write, e-mail, or fax for additional information.

Available to: No restrictions
Deadline: October 1
Apply to: Irish Research Fund, above address


**The Christopher Isherwood Foundation**
**PO Box 650**
**Montrose, AL 36559**
**E-mail: james@isherwoodfoundation.org**
**Web site: www.isherwoodfoundation.org**

Ⓕ The Foundation offers several grants in the amount of $3,000 to fiction writers who have published at least one book. See the Web site for more details.

Available to: Published writers
Deadline: November 1
Apply: James P. White, Director, above address

Ⓝ Scholarly grants in the amount of $2,000, administered in collaboration with the W. M. Keck Foundation, are available to scholars writing about Isherwood and his circle.

Available to: Inquire
Deadline: Inquire
Apply to: Robert C. Ritchie, W. M. Keck Foundation Director of Research, The Huntington, 1151 Oxford Road, San Marino, CA 91108

Ⓕ The *William Goyen-Doris Roberts Fellowship* of $3,000 is awarded to a fiction writer. See the Web site for more details.

> Available to: Inquire
> Deadline: Inquire
> Apply to: Above address

Ⓕ The *James C. McCormick Fellowship* of $3,000 is awarded to a fiction writer. See the Web site for more details.

> Available to: Inquire
> Deadline: Inquire
> Apply to: Above address

**Isle Royale National Park**
**800 East Lakeshore Drive**
**Houghton, MI 49931-1895**
**Web site: www.nps.gov/isro**
**Fax: 906-482-8753**

Ⓡ The Isle Royale *Artist-in-Residence Program* offers two-to-three-week residences from early June to mid-September to writers, journalists, and artists. Isle Royale is an island wilderness on Lake Superior, where residents are offered a rustic cabin with basic cooking equipment, fuel, pit toilet, and a canoe for transportation; there is no electricity or running water. Send SASE for guidelines and application.

> Available to: No restrictions
> Deadline: February 15
> Apply to: Artist-in-Residence Program, above address

**Italian Americana**
**University of Rhode Island**
**College of Continuing Education**
**80 Washington Street**
**Providence, RI 02903**

Ⓟ The *John Ciardi Lifetime Achievement Award in Poetry* annually offers $1,000 and announcement in *Italian Americana*, a biannual journal of poetry, fiction, historical articles, book reviews, and memoirs of the Italian-American experience. Poets who have published at least one book of poetry, not including chapbooks, are eligible. Submit a list of published books. Two awards totaling $500 are also offered for the best fiction published in *Italian Americana* each year.

> Available to: See above
> Deadline: Ongoing
> Apply to: John Ciardi Lifetime Achievement Award in Poetry, above address

**ITALY**
**Harvard University Center for Italian Renaissance Studies**
**Villa I Tatti**
**Via di Vincigliata 26**
**50135 Firenze (FI)**
**Italy**
**E-mail: Vitatti@tin.it**
**Web site: http://www.vit.firenze.it**

The Harvard University Center for Italian Renaissance Studies offers up to fifteen fellowships each academic year, available to postdoctoral scholars doing advanced research in any aspect of the Italian Renaissance. Normally fellowships are reserved for scholars in the early stages of their careers, and for those whose projects require their presence in Florence. The maximum grant is $40,000; most grants are considerably less.

> Available to: No restrictions
> Deadline: October 15

Apply to: Villa I Tatti, Harvard University, University Place, 124 Mount Auburn Street, Cambridge, MA 02138-5762 (send original letter of application to the address in Italy above, and a duplicate to the Villa I Tatti office in Cambridge)

**ITALY**
**Italian Cultural Institute**
**686 Park Avenue**
**New York, NY 10021-4009**
**Web site: http://www.italcultny.org/transgrants.htm**
**Fax: 212-861-4018**

(T) In order to encourage the circulation of Italian works abroad, *Italian Government Translation Prizes and Grants* are awarded for the translation of Italian literary and scientific works into English. Prizes are awarded only to previously translated and published works. Grants are available for translation projects, though monies are remitted only after publication of the translated work and upon receipt of a copy of the published book. Write or see the Web site for further information.

Available to: No restrictions
Deadline: March 31 and September 30
Apply to: Above address

**Jacksonville State University**
**Department of English**
**700 Pelham Road North**
**Jacksonville, AL 36265-1602**
**E-mail: swhitton@jsucc.jsu.edu**
**Fax: 256-782-5441**

(D) The *Southern Playwrights Competition* annually awards $1,000 and production for a full-length play or solo piece by a resident or native of Alabama, Arkansas, Florida, Georgia, Kentucky, Louisiana, Mississippi, North Carolina, South Carolina, Tennessee, Texas, Virginia, or West Virginia. Plays must be unpublished, original works that deal with the southern experience and that have not received Equity production. Send SASE for guidelines and entry form.

Available to: See above
Deadline: February 15
Apply to: Southern Playwrights Competition, above address

**Rona Jaffe Foundation**
**c/o Beth McCabe**
**HC 30, Box 38**
**Barnet, VT 05821**

(IN) The *Rona Jaffe Foundation Writers' Awards* offer several grants, up to a maximum of $8,500, to emerging women writers of fiction, poetry, and creative nonfiction. The Foundation does not accept unsolicited nominations or applications. *By Internal Nomination Only*.

**Alice James Books**
**University of Maine at Farmington**
**238 Main Street**
**Farmington, ME 04938**
**Web site: http://www.umf.maine.edu/~ajb**

(P) The *Beatrice Hawley Award* annually offers $2,000 and publication by Alice James Books for a book of poetry. There is a $20 entry fee. Send SASE or see the Web site for guidelines.

Available to: No restrictions
Deadline: December 1
Apply to: Beatrice Hawley Award, above address

Ⓟ     The *Jane Kenyon Chapbook Award* offers $500 and publication in odd-numbered years by Alice James Books. There is a $12 reading fee. Send SASE or see the Web site for guidelines.

Available to: U. S. residents
Deadline: June 15
Apply to: Jane Kenyon Chapbook Award, above address

Ⓟ     The *New England/New York Award* annually offers publication by Alice James Books for original books of poetry. Two winners each receive $2,000 and a monthlong residency at Vermont Studio Center. The award carries a three-year work commitment with the cooperative, which consists of attending four or five meetings per year, helping judge future book contests, and mentoring a new member through the publishing process. There is a $20 entry fee, which will cover the cost of one book or cassette ordered from the Alice James backlist. Send SASE or see the Web site for guidelines.

Available to: Poets living in New England or New York state
Deadline: September 1
Apply to: New England/New York Award, above address

**JAPAN**
**Association of International Education**
**2079 Aomi**
**Koto-ku**
**Information Center**
**Tokyo 135-8630**
**Japan**
**Web site: http://www.aiej.or.jp**

The *Monbukagakusho Scholarships*, tenable in Japan, are given to university graduates, with preference to candidates in the fields of Japanese culture and science, or those for whom study in Japan will enhance the value of their specific program. Grants for up to two years, covering tuition, transportation costs, and a stipend of ¥185,500 per month, are available annually.

Available to: U. S. citizens
Deadline: Varies; contact Japanese embassy or nearest consulate
Apply to: Nearest consulate general of Japan; information from Japan Information Center, Consulate General of Japan, 299 Park Avenue, 18th floor, New York, NY 10171

**JAPAN**
**The Japan Foundation**
**152 West 57th Street, 39th floor**
**New York, NY 10019**
**Web site: http://www.jfny.org/jfny/**
**Fax: 212-489-0409**

Fellowships are offered to writers and other artists who wish to pursue creative projects in Japan with Japanese counterparts. Fellowships are tenable in Japan for periods of two to six months during the Japanese fiscal year (April 1-March 31) and are not renewable. The Japan Foundation also offers research and doctoral fellowships for periods up to fourteen months. Artist and research fellows receive stipends of ¥370,000 to ¥430,000 per month during their stay in Japan; doctoral fellows receive ¥310,000; additional allowances are made for accompanying dependents, health insurance, and research/cultural activities for a maximum of ¥140,000 per month. A full-fare, economy-class air ticket for travel to and from Japan, and settling-in and departure allowances are also provided. Write for further information and application procedures.

Available to: U. S. citizens and permanent residents
Deadline: December 1 for artist fellowships; November 1 for research and doctoral
Apply to: Above address (New York) or nearest consulate general of Japan for artist fellowships

Ⓜ     *Visiting Professor Grants* assist American academic institutions wishing to invite guest scholars or artists-in-residence, including writers, from Japan to teach at their institutions. The grant covers roundtrip airfare and up to seventy-five percent of the visitor's salary.

Available to: Japanese scholars, artists, and writers
Deadline: Inquire
Apply to: Above address

**JAPAN**
**Japan-U. S. Friendship Commission**
**1110 Vermont Avenue, NW, Suite 800**
**Washington, DC 20005**
**E-mail: artist@jusfc.gov**
**Web site: http://www.jusfc.gov**
**Fax: 202-418-9802**

The *United States/Japan Creative Artists' Program* provides six-month residences in Japan for individual creative artists in any discipline, to allow artists to enhance their creativity through exposure to Japanese culture and training in theater. When planning their stay abroad, prospective fellows should consider how proximity to Japan's contemporary or traditional cultures can influence their work. Each selected artist receives a monthly stipend of ¥400,000 for living expenses, ¥100,000 a month as a housing supplement, and up to ¥100,000 a month for professional support services. Artists also are provided with up to $6,000 for roundtrip transportation for themselves, domestic partners, and/or unmarried children (up to age eighteen); a baggage/storage allowance; and a stipend for pre-departure Japanese-language study in the U. S. Write, e-mail, or see the Web site for additional information and application.

Available to: U. S. citizens or permanent residents
Deadline: Inquire
Apply to: Above address

**Jentel Artist Residency Program**
**11 Lower Piney Creek Road**
**Banner, WY 82832**
**Phone: 307-737-2311**
**Web site: www.jentelarts.org**
**Fax: 307-737-2305**

® The *Jentel Artist Residency Program* offers artists and writers of nonfiction, fiction, poetry, and playwriting a one-month March residency at a picturesque thousand-acre cattle ranch east of Sheridan, Wyoming. The residence includes accommodation, workplace, and a $400 stipend. See the Web site for application and more information.

Available to: No restrictions
Deadline: Inquire
Apply to: Admissions Committee, above address

**The Jerome Foundation**
**125 Park Square Court**
**400 Sibley Street**
**St. Paul, MN 55101**
**E-mail: info@jeromefdn.org**
**Web site: http://www.jeromefdn.org**

The *Travel and Study Grant Program,* supported by the Jerome and General Mills foundations, annually offers up to $5,000 to Minnesota artists and art administrators in any discipline (including literary and dramatic arts), for foreign travel and a period of significant professional development.

Available to: Minnesota residents
Deadline: February (inquire for exact date)
Apply to: Above address

**Jewel Box Theatre**
**3700 North Walker**
**Oklahoma City, OK 73118**

Ⓓ The *Jewel Box Theatre Playwriting Award* offers $500 and possible production to an unproduced full-length play entailing a strong ensemble cast and an emphasis on character rather than spectacle. Send SASE in October for guidelines and entry form.

Available to: No restrictions
Deadline: January 15
Apply to: Playwriting Award, above address

**Jewish Book Council**
**15 East 26th Street**
**New York, NY 10010**
**E-mail: ericomic@aol.com**
**Web site: jewishbookcouncil.org**

Ⓜ The *National Jewish Book Awards* are given annually for published books, widely distributed in the U. S., that are of literary merit and of Jewish interest. Monetary prizes are given in the following categories: Jewish history, Jewish thought, Sephardic and Ashkenazic customs and culture, Israel, the Holocaust, Eastern European studies, other nonfiction, scholarship, reference, autobiography/memoir, fiction, children's literature, and illustrated children's books. Consult the Web site or write for submission guidelines.

Available to: No restrictions
Deadline: Inquire
Apply to: Above address

**Jewish Community Center of Cleveland**
**3505 Mayfield Road**
**Cleveland Heights, OH 44118**
**E-mail: Halletheatre@clevejcc.org**

Ⓓ The *Dorothy Silver Playwriting Competition* offers an award of $1,000 plus a staged reading of the winning play at the Halle Theatre in Cleveland; $500 is awarded on announcement, and $500 on or about the date of the reading, to help cover travel and in-residence expenses for the playwright. Submissions must be original, unproduced works, suitable for full-length presentation, that provide fresh, significant perspectives on the range of Jewish experience. The theater will have permission to perform the first fully staged production of the winning script after the staged reading, without payment of royalties. No submissions returned without SASE.

Available to: No restrictions
Deadline: End of May (inquire for exact date)
Apply to: Amy Kenerup, Administrative Director, Halle Theatre, above address

**The Lyndon Baines Johnson Foundation**
**2313 Red River Street**
**Austin, TX 78705**
**Phone: 512-478-7829**
**Web site: lbjlib.etexas.edu**
**Fax: 512-478-9104**

A limited number of *Grants-in-Aid of Research*, ranging from $500 to $2,000, are available semiannually for research at the Lyndon B. Johnson Library. The grant periods are September 1 through February 28, and March 1 through August 31. The funds are to be used to help defray living, travel, and related expenses incurred while conducting research at the Library. Before submitting a grant-in-aid proposal, applicants should write to the chief archivist of the library at the above address to obtain information about the availability of relevant materials.

Available to: Scholars and graduate students
Deadline: August 31 for fall-winter grant period; February 28 for spring-summer
Apply to: Executive Director, above address

**Johnson Publishing Company**
**820 South Michigan Avenue**
**Chicago, IL 60605**

(F)     The *Gertrude Johnson Williams Writing Contest* annually awards $5,000 for a short story of up
        to 2,500 words that best depicts the African-American spirit to confront adversity. The
        contest is open to all Americans of African descent who have not previously received
        money or other financial consideration for writing short stories, novels, plays, or television
        or movie scripts. The winning entry is announced in *Ebony*, which is issued by Johnson
        Publishing Company. Five runners-up will receive $1,000 each. Look for guidelines in
        *Ebony*, or send SASE to above address.

        Available to: African-American writers
        Deadline: Varies; consult *Ebony* for current deadline
        Apply to: Gertrude Johnson Williams Writing Contest, above address


**James Jones First Novel Fellowship**
**Wilkes University**
**Wilkes-Barre, PA 18766**
**E-mail: english@wilkes.edu**
**Web site: http://www.wilkes.edu/humanities/jones.html**

(F)     The *James Jones First Novel Fellowship* annually awards $5,000 for an unpublished novel, novella,
        or collection of related short stories by an American writer who has not published a book-
        length work of fiction. Writers should submit the first 50 pages of the manuscript, a two-
        page thematic outline, and a $15 application fee payable to Wilkes University. Send SASE
        or e-mail for guidelines.

        Available to: U. S. citizens
        Deadline: March 1
        Apply to: James Jones First Novel Fellowship, above address


**Journal of the History of Ideas**
**Rutgers University**
**88 College Avenue**
**New Brunswick, NJ 08901-8542**
**E-mail: dkelley@rci.rutgers.edu**
**Fax: 732-932-8708**

(N)     The *Morris D. Forkosch Prize* awards $2,000 for a first book on intellectual history published
        during the calendar year. Books must be in English (no translations) and must pertain to
        one or more of the major disciplines associated with "intellectual history": history
        (including the history of various arts and sciences), philosophy (including the philosophy
        of science, aesthetics, and other fields), political thought (including economics, social
        science, and anthropology), and literature (including literary criticism and theory).
        Publishers should limit nominations to two books. Write for additional information and
        submission procedures.

        Available to: First-book authors
        Deadline: December 31
        Apply to: Morris D. Forkosch Prize, above address


**The Henry J. Kaiser Family Foundation**
**2400 Sand Hill Road**
**Menlo Park, CA 94025**
**Web site: http://www.kff.org**
**Fax: 650-854-4800**

(J)     *Kaiser Media Fellowships in Health* fund up to six print, television, or radio journalists interested
        in health policy, health financing, and public health. The program aims to provide fellows
        with diverse opportunities to pursue individual projects combined with group briefings
        and site visits on a range of health and social policy matters. Fellows receive an annual
        stipend of $55,000 (prorated for the length of the fellowship); travel funds for research
        are also available. Applicants must be U. S. citizens working for an accredited U. S. media

organization, with at least five years' journalistic experience. Write, e-mail, or see the Web site for application procedures.

Available to: See above
Deadline: March (inquire for exact date)
Apply to: Penny Duckham, Executive Director, Kaiser Media Fellowship Program, above address

Ⓙ    *Kaiser Media Mini-Fellowships* offer up to fifteen print, television, or radio journalists the opportunity to research and report on a health policy, health financing, or public health topic of their choice. Typically, grants are $5,000 each (up to $10,000 for broadcast projects). Write, e-mail, or see the Web site for application procedures.

Available to: Working journalists
Deadline: October (inquire for exact date)
Apply to: Penny Duckham, Executive Director, Kaiser Media Fellowship Program above address

Ⓙ    *Kaiser Media Internships* are available to young minority journalists interested in reporting on urban public health. The program provides an initial weeklong briefing on urban public health and health reporting, held at the National Press Club in Washington, D.C., after which interns spend ten weeks at a host newspaper or television station under the direction of the health or metro editor/news director; there they report on health matters. The program ends with a three-day meeting and site visits in Boston. Interns receive a twelve-week stipend and paid travel expenses. Write, e-mail, or see the Web site for application procedures.

Available to: Young minority journalists
Deadline: Consult Web site
Apply to: Penny Duckham, Executive Director, Kaiser Media Fellowship Program, above address

**Kalamazoo Civic Theatre Holiday Competition**
**471 West South Street**
**Kalamazoo, MI 49007**
**Phone: 616-381-6316**
**Web site: www.kzoocivic.com**
**Fax: 616-343-0532**

Ⓓ    The *Kalamazoo Civic Theatre Holiday Competition* annually selects a play, suitable for the whole family, to be awarded $500 and a full production at the theater. Dramas, comedies, and musicals, either original works or adaptations, are eligible. Send script with bio and SASE for return.

Available to: No restrictions
Deadline: November 1
Apply to: Above address

**Kalliope**
**Florida Community College at Jacksonville**
**3939 Roosevelt Boulevard**
**Jacksonville, FL 32205**
**Web site: http://www.fccj.org/kalliope**

Ⓟ    The *Sue Saniel Elkind Poetry Contest* offers $1,000 plus publication in *Kalliope,* a journal of women's art, for the best unpublished poem of up to 50 lines written by a woman. The entry fee is $4 per poem, or $10 for three. Send SASE for guidelines.

Available to: Women
Deadline: November 1
Apply to: Sue Saniel Elkind Poetry Contest, above address

**Kansas Arts Commission**
**700 Southwest Jackson Street, Suite 1004**
**Topeka, KS 66603-3761**
**E-mail: KAC@arts.state.ks.us**
**Web site: http://arts.state.ks.us**
**Fax: 785-296-4989**

Ⓜ *Kansas Artist Fellowships* of $5,000 each are given annually to Kansas residents who have lived in the state for at least one year. Fellowships rotate in a two-year cycle, going to writers of fiction and poetry in even-numbered years and to playwrights in odd-numbered years. Up to twelve *Mini-Fellowships* of $500 each are available annually in any discipline. Write, e-mail, or consult the Web site for guidelines and application.

Available to: See above
Deadline: October (inquire for exact date)
Apply to: Kansas Artist Fellowships, above address

**Kappa Tau Alpha**
**University of Missouri**
**School of Journalism**
**120 Neff Hall**
**Columbia, MO 65211**
**E-mail: ktahq@showme.missouri.edu**
**Fax: 573-884-1720**

Ⓙ Ⓝ The *Frank Luther Mott-Kappa Tau Alpha Journalism and Mass Communications Research Award* of $1,000 is given annually for the best research-based book about journalism or mass communications published during the year. Applicants should submit six copies of the book. Edited volumes, textbooks, and revised editions of previously entered books are not eligible. Write or e-mail for additional information.

Available to: No restrictions
Deadline: Early December (inquire for exact date)
Apply to: Dr. Keith Sanders, Executive Director, above address

**Donald Keene Center of Japanese Culture**
**507 Kent Hall, MC 3920**
**Columbia University**
**New York, NY 10027**
**Phone: 212-854-5036**
**E-mail: donald-keene-center@columbia.edu**
**Web site: www.columbia.edu/cu/ealac/dkc/translation.htm**
**Fax: 212-854-4019**

Ⓣ The *Japan-U. S. Friendship Commission Prize for the Translation of Japanese Literature* of $5,000 is awarded annually to book-length translations of Japanese literature into English in the categories of modern and classical literature. The prize is intended for translators who are not widely recognized for their work, though they may have published. Submissions may include unpublished manuscripts, works in press, and translations published during the two years prior to the prize year. Send SASE for additional information and application.

Available to: No restrictions
Deadline: February 1
Apply to: Above address

**The Kennedy Center**
**American College Theater Festival**
**Washington, DC 20566-0001**
**E-mail: skshaffer@mail.kennedy-center.org**
**Fax: 202-416-8802**

The Kennedy Center American College Theater Festival (KCACTF) holds several regional festivals with workshops each year. All college and university theaters are eligible and encouraged to participate. Regional finalists are invited to Washington for an eight-day noncompetitive festival at the Kennedy Center, with transportation, lodging, and daily expenses provided. Eight of the following nine awards, which make up the *Michael Kanin Playwriting Awards Program*, are available to student playwrights whose plays are produced in the festival.

Ⓓ The *David Mark Cohen National Playwriting Award* is given to any working playwright whose play is produced by a college or university theater program and entered as an associate or participating entry within KCACTF. All rules regulating KCACTF entries apply except those related to the definition of student playwrights. The winner receives an award of $1,000, possible publication by Dramatic Publishing, and up to $500 toward travel and expenses to attend a script-in-hand reading at the annual meeting of the Association for Theatre in Higher Education.

Ⓓ The *Lorraine Hansberry Award* is given for the best student play on the black experience. First place wins a $2,500 prize, a fellowship at the National Playwrights Conference at the Eugene O'Neill Theatre Center, and possible publication by Dramatic Play Service. Second prize is $1,000. Grants of $750 and $500 are made to the theater departments of the institutions producing the first- and second-place plays, respectively.

Ⓓ The *KCACTF College Musical Theater Award* is given for outstanding achievement in the creation of a work for the musical theater by college/ university students. First prize is $1,000 in each of the categories lyrics, music, book, and producing institution. The musical must be produced by a college or university participating in KCACTF, and at least half of the creative team must be students.

Ⓓ The *KCACTF Sí TV Playwriting Award* is given for the best play by a Latino student playwright participating in KCACTF. The award consists of a cash prize of $2,500 and an internship at a prestigious playwriting retreat. The playwright also receives the possible offer of a contract with Dramatic Publishing, to publish, license, and market the script. A grant of $500 is made to the theater department of the college or university producing the winning play.

Ⓓ The *National AIDS Award for Playwriting* is given for the best new collegiate writing about the personal and social implications of HIV/AIDS. The winner receives a cash award of $2,500.

Ⓓ The *National Student Playwriting Award* is given for the best production of a play written by a full-time graduate or undergraduate student participating in regional festivals. The award consists of a cash prize of $2,500, membership in the Dramatists Guild of America, production at the Kennedy Center, a publication contract with royalties through Samuel French, and a nine-day fellowship at the Sundance Theatre Laboratory.

Ⓓ The *Short Play Awards Program* recognizes two or three outstanding productions of short plays at U. S. colleges or universities each year, with consideration for presentation at the Kennedy Center national festival. The award consists of a cash prize of $1,000, publication and catalogue listing by Samuel French, and membership in the Dramatists Guild of America. (A short play is defined as a one-act without intermission that does not constitute a full evening of theater.)

Ⓓ The *Jean Kennedy Smith Playwriting Award for the Best Play Written on the Theme of Disability* is given for the best student-written script that explores the human experience of living with a disability. The play must be produced and entered in KCACTF. The winning playwright receives an award of $2,500, active membership in the Dramatists Guild of America, and a fellowship to attend a prestigious playwriting program, with transportation, housing, and a per diem included.

Ⓓ The *Mark Twain Comedy Playwriting Award* is given for the best student-written full-length comedy play produced by a college or university and entered in KCACTF. The first-place award consists of a cash prize of $2,500, a fellowship to attend a prestigious playwriting retreat, and the offer of a contract with Dramatic Publishing, to publish, license, and market the play. The second-place award consists of $1,500. Grants of $750 and $500 are made to the producing institutions of the first- and second-place plays, respectively.

Available to: College and university students (except the David Mark Cohen Award)
Deadline: December 1
Apply to: Above address for application procedures

(D) The *Jane Chambers Playwriting Award*, co-sponsored by the Women and Theatre Program of the Association for Theatre in Higher Education, offers $1,000 for a full-length play or a performance-art text by a woman. The winner also receives free registration at the Women and Theatre Conference in late July, when the winning play receives a rehearsed reading. Submitted work should "reflect a feminist perspective and contain a majority of roles for women performers." Send SASE for guidelines and application form.

Available to: Women playwrights
Deadline: February 15
Apply to: Jane Chambers Playwriting Award, c/o Mary A. Donahoe, Department of Theatre Arts, Wright State University, Dayton, OH 45435-0001

(D) The Kennedy Center American College Theater Festival sponsors an annual *Ten-Minute Play Festival*. A first-place award of $1,000 is given to the playwright selected from the national festival finalists; another $1,000 award is given for the best comic monologue selected from the finalist 10-minute plays presented at the Center. Contact the regional chair for information and submission procedures.

Available to: College and university students
Deadline: Inquire
Apply to: Above address for list of regional chairs

**John F. Kennedy Library Foundation**
**John F. Kennedy Library**
**Columbia Point**
**Boston, MA 02125-3313**
**E-mail: kennedy.library@nara.gov**
**Web site: http://www.jfklibrary.org**
**Fax: 617-929-4599**

*Hemingway Research Grants*, ranging from $200 to $1,000, are offered to scholars and writers, five to ten in number, to help defray living, travel, and related costs incurred while doing research in the Hemingway Collection. Applications are evaluated on the basis of expected use of the Collection, the degree to which projects address research needs in Hemingway or related studies, and qualifications of applicants.

Available to: No restrictions; preference given to Ph.D. candidates doing dissertation research
Deadline: March 15
Apply to: Hemingway Research Grants, above address

*Kennedy Library Research Grants*, ranging from $500 to $1,500, are offered to scholars and students, fifteen to twenty in number, to help defray living, travel, and related costs incurred while doing research at the library. Applications are evaluated on the basis of expected use of available library holdings, the degree to which projects address research needs in Kennedy-related studies, and qualifications of applicants.

Available to: No restrictions; preference given to Ph.D. candidates doing dissertation research
Deadline: March 15 for spring grants; August 15 for fall
Apply to: William Johnson, Chief Archivist, above address

The *Marjorie Kovler Research Fellowship* of $2,500 is intended to support a scholar in the preparation of a substantial work in the area of foreign intelligence and the presidency, or a related topic.

Available to: No restrictions
Deadline: March 15
Apply to: William Johnson, Chief Archivist, above address

The *Arthur M. Schlesinger Jr. Research Fellowship,* carrying a stipend of up to $7,000, is intended to support scholars in the preparation of substantial works on the foreign policy of the Kennedy years, especially with regard to the Western Hemisphere, or on Kennedy domestic policy, especially with regard to racial justice and to the conservation of natural resources. The fellowship may be awarded to a single individual or divided between two recipients.

Available to: No restrictions
Deadline: August 15
Apply to: William Johnson, Chief Archivist, above address

The *Abba P. Schwartz Research Fellowship,* carrying a stipend of up to $3,100, is intended to support a scholar in preparing a substantial work on immigration, naturalization, or refugee policy.

Available to: No restrictions
Deadline: March 15
Apply to: William Johnson, Chief Archivist, above address

The *Theodore C. Sorensen Research Fellowship* of $3,600 is intended to support a scholar in preparing a substantial work on domestic policy, political journalism, polling, or press relations.

Available to: No restrictions
Deadline: March 15
Apply to: William Johnson, Chief Archivist, above address

**Robert F. Kennedy Memorial Book & Journalism Awards**
**1367 Connecticut Avenue, NW, Suite 300**
**Washington, DC 20036**
**E-mail: info@rfkmemorial.org**
**Web site: www.rfkmemorial.org**

Ⓕ Ⓝ The *Robert F. Kennedy Annual Book Award,* of $2,500, is given for the book that most faithfully and forcefully reflects Robert Kennedy's purpose: his concern for the poor and the powerless, his struggle for honest and even-handed justice, his conviction that a decent society must assure all young people a fair chance, and his faith that a free democracy can act to remedy disparities of power and opportunities. Books, which must have been published in the U. S. in the previous year, may be submitted by the publisher or the author. Multiple entries are allowed. There is a $25 handling fee per entry. Write or see the Web site for guidelines.

Available to: Published authors of fiction or nonfiction
Deadline: January (inquire for exact date)
Apply to: Director, RFK Book Awards, above address

Ⓙ Nine *Robert F. Kennedy Journalism Awards for Outstanding Coverage of the Problems of the Disadvantaged,* of $1,000 each, are presented annually for domestic or international work in the categories of print (newspaper, magazine), cartoon, television, radio, or photojournalism. At the discretion of the awards committee, an additional grand prize of $2,000 may be awarded. The competition is open to professional journalists in all categories and to college and high school student print and broadcast journalists. A $40 entry fee is required in the professional category. Write or see the Web site for guidelines.

Available to: See above
Deadline: Last Friday in January
Apply to: Director, RFK Journalism Awards, above address

Kent State University
Department of English
PO Box 5190
Kent, OH 44242-0001
Phone: 330-672-2067
E-mail: wickpoet@kent.edu
Web site: www.kent.edu/wick
Fax: 330-672-2567

(P) The *Stan and Tom Wick Poetry Prize* of $2,000 is given for a first book of poems in English by a writer who has not published a book of poetry. The winning collection will be published by Kent State University Press. Manuscripts should be between 48 and 68 pages; the poet's name must not appear within. Submissions should include a cover sheet with the applicant's name, address, and telephone number, and title of the manuscript. There is a $15 reading fee for each submission. Send SASE or see the Web site for additional information.

> Available to: No restrictions
> Deadline: May 1
> Apply to: Stan and Tom Wick Poetry Prize, above address

Kentucky Arts Council
Old Capital Annex
300 West Broadway
Frankfort, KY 40601-1950
E-mail: lori.meadows@mail.state.ky.us
Fax: 502-564-2839

(M) Artists' fellowships of $7,500 are available every other year in poetry, fiction, and playwriting. Write for application.

> Available to: Kentucky residents
> Deadline: September 15 in even-numbered years
> Apply to: Heather Lyons, Individual Artist Program Director, above address

Kentucky Foundation for Women
1215 Heyburn Building
332 West Broadway
Louisville, KY 40202
Phone: 502-562-0045
Web site: http://www.kfw.org
Fax: 502-561-0420

Grants are available to women writers in Kentucky whose work "focuses on a feminist, not feminine, consciousness." The Foundation seeks to support writers "who describe the realities of women's lives, who experiment in style and substance, analyze language, or who are working to enlarge the feminist literary and historical heritage." There are two grant programs: *Artist Enrichment*, supporting the development of individual artists, and *Art Meets Activism*, recognizing specific projects and activities that involve broader communities and have clear social goals. Grants range from $1,000 to $7,500. See the Web site for further information and guidelines.

> Available to: Feminist writers living or working in Kentucky or doing work that affects the lives of Kentucky women
> Deadline: September 21 for Artist Enrichment; March 1 for Art Meets Activism
> Apply to: Above address

Kentucky Writers' Coalition
851 South Fourth Street #207
Louisville, KY 40203
Phone: 502-585-9911, ext. 2767
Web site: http://kentuckywriters.org

(P) The *Jim Wayne Miller Prize in Poetry* awards $500 and publication in a regional journal, for a single poem. A reading in Louisville honors the winning poet. Poems may be of any length or style. Coalition members may enter one poem at no charge and additional poems at $3 each. The entry fee for nonmembers is $5 per poem. Write for guidelines.

Available to: U. S. citizens
Deadline: January 30
Apply to: Jim Wayne Miller Prize in Poetry, above address

Ⓕ Ⓟ The Coalition also sponsors an annual *Short Story Contest,* offering $300 and publication in the *Louisville Review,* and an annual *Poetry Chapbook Contest,* offering awards of $200 and 20 copies of the winning chapbook. Write for details.

**Kiplinger Reporting Program**
**Ohio State University**
**School of Journalism**
**242 West 18th Avenue**
**Columbus, OH 43210**
**Phone: 614-292-2607**
**Web site: http://communication.sbs.ohio-state.edu/sjc/gradprod/kip.html**

Ⓙ The Kiplinger Reporting Program annually offers fellowships for eight print and broadcast journalists to do aggressive reporting in the public interest. Each fellowship consists of a $20,000 stipend and a tuition waiver for a four-quarter master's degree at the Ohio State University School of Journalism. The application fee is $30. Write for additional information and application materials.

Available to: Journalists with at least five years' professional experience
Deadline: January 1
Apply to: James Neff, Director, above address

**Kiriyama Pacific Rim Institute**
**650 Delancey Street, Suite 101**
**San Francisco, CA 94107**
**Phone: 415-777-1628**
**E-mail: admin@kiriyamaprize.org**
**Web site: www.kiriyamaprize.org**
**Fax: 415-777-1646**

Ⓕ Ⓝ The *Kiriyama Pacific Rim Book Prize* annually awards $15,000 each for a book of fiction and one of nonfiction that promote "greater understanding among the nations and peoples of the Pacific Rim." Books must have been published in English, either originally or in translation, between October 1 of the preceding year and October 31 of the prize year. Six copies of each eligible book may be submitted as bound galleys or finished copies. Publishers may submit a maximum of three titles in each category. Write, e-mail, or see the Web site for guidelines and required entry form.

Available to: No restrictions
Deadline: July 2
Apply to: Kiriyama Pacific Rim Book Prize, above address

**Knight-Ridder Internships for Native American Journalists**
**c/o St. Paul Pioneer Press**
**345 Cedar Street**
**St. Paul, MN 55101-1057**
**Web site: www.freep.com/jobspage/interns/krintern.htm**

Ⓙ The *Knight-Ridder Internships for Native American Journalists* offer twelve-week summer apprenticeships for selected applicants. Interns receive paid positions at Knight-Ridder newspapers in the Midwest. Successful interns may be invited to return to a Knight-Ridder paper a second or third time. Internships vary by newspaper; consult the Web site for information on deadlines and stipends available.

Available to: Promising Native American journalists
Deadline: See Web site
Apply to: The newspaper of choice

**Knoxville Writers' Guild**
**PO Box 2565**
**Knoxville, TN 37901**
**Web site: http://www.korrnet.org/writers or http://www.sunsite.utk.edu/utpress**

(F)  The *Peter Taylor Prize for the Novel* offers $1,000 and publication with a standard royalty contract from the University of Tennessee Press, co-sponsor of the prize, for an unpublished novel. There is a $20 reading fee. Send SASE or consult either Web site for guidelines.

> Available to: U. S. residents
> Deadline: Submissions accepted February 1-April 30
> Apply to: Peter Taylor Prize, above address

**KOREA**
**Korea Literature Translation Institute**
**5th Floor, Seojin Building**
**149-1, Pyeong-dong, Jongno-gu**
**Seoul 110-102**
**Korea**
**Phone: 82-2-732-1442**
**E-mail: info@ltikorea.net**
**Web site: www.ltikorea.net**
**Fax: 82-2-732-1443**

(T)  The Institute offers *Korean Literature Translation Grants* of approximately 15 million won (based on the length of the work), to translators of classic and modern Korean literature. An additional grant is offered for the translation, into a specific target language, of a designated classic of Korean literature selected by the Institute. The *Korean Literature Translation Contest* offers a prize of 3 million won to recognize a young translator whose work contributes to the field of Korean literature in translation. Write, e-mail, or see the Web site for additional information.

> Available to: No restrictions
> Deadline: For Korean Literature Translation Grants, applications accepted July 1-August 15; for Korean Literature Translation Contest, October 21-November 15
> Apply to: Above address

**Kore Press**
**PO Box 3044**
**Tucson, AZ 85702**
**Phone: 520-882-7542**
**E-mail: kore@korepress.org**
**Web site: www.korepress.org**

(P)  The *Kore Press First Book Award* offers $1,000 and publication of a book-length manuscript of 48 to 70 pages by a woman who has not published a full-length collection of poetry. Writers who have published chapbooks of less and 42 pages, in editions of fewer than 400 copies, are eligible. There is a $15 reading fee. See the Web site for submission procedures.

> Available to: See above
> Deadline: June 24
> Apply to: Above address

**The Koret Foundation**
**33 New Montgomery, Suite 1090**
**San Francisco, CA 94105**
**Web site: http://www.koretfoundation.org**

[IN]  The *Koret Jewish Book Awards* are sponsored annually by the Koret Foundation in cooperation with the National Foundation for Jewish Culture. Prizes of $10,000 are given to the best books on aspects of Jewish life published in English during the calendar year, in four categories: biography/autobiography and literary studies; fiction; history; and philosophy and thought. *By Internal Nomination Only.*

**Kosciuszko Foundation**
**15 East 65th Street**
**New York, NY 10021-6595**
**Phone: 212-734-2130**
**E-mail: thekf@aol.com**
**Web site: http:www.kosciuszkofoundation.org**
**Fax: 212-628-4552**

In addition to the award listed below, the Kosciuszko Foundation offers tuition scholarships to graduate and undergraduate students, U. S. permanent residents and citizens, including those of Polish descent, pursuing research and education in Polish subjects, as well as in law, education, Slavic studies, literature, journalism, international relations, and other fields. Funds may be used at American colleges and universities or at academic institutions in Poland. Write, e-mail, or see the Web site for additional information.

The *Metchie J. E. Budka Award* of $1,000 is given for outstanding scholarly work in Polish literature from the fourteenth century to 1939, Polish history from 962 to 1939, and Polish-American relations. The award recognizes outstanding work in one of these fields by American graduate students or recent doctoral degree recipients. Write, e-mail, or consult the Web site for guidelines.

Available to: See above
Deadline: Inquire
Apply to: Metchie J. E. Budka Award, above address, or call the Foundation's Grants Department

**Lanesboro Residency Program**
**Box 152**
**Lanesboro, MN 55949**
**Phone: 507-467-2446**

Ⓡ    The *Lanesboro Residency Program* offers one-month residences for sculptors, artists, poets, and writers in a picturesque hamlet (population 858) with historic main street and nearby 200-foot bluffs, trout river, and bike trail. Stipends are $2,000 for the month. For more information and application, send SASE to above address.

Available to: No restrictions
Deadline: June 30
Apply to: Above address

**The Ledge**
**78-44 80th Street**
**Glendale, NY 11385**

Ⓟ    The *Ledge Poetry Award* offers $1,000 plus publication for an unpublished poem. Poems may be of any length; there is a $10 entry fee for up to three, and $3 for each additional. A second prize of $250 and a third of $100 are also offered. All poems submitted are considered for publication in *The Ledge*. Send SASE for guidelines.

Available to: No restrictions
Deadline: April 30
Apply to: Poetry Award, above address

Ⓟ    The *Ledge Poetry Chapbook Competition* annually awards $1,000 and 50 copies of a chapbook for a poetry manuscript of 16 to 28 pages. The $12 entry fee covers a copy of the winning chapbook. Send SASE for guidelines.

Available to: No restrictions
Deadline: October 31
Apply to: Poetry Chapbook Competition, above address

**Ledig House International Writers' Colony**
**59 Letter S Road**
**Ghent, NY 12075**
**Web site: www.artomi.org**

® Residences of one week to two months are available to writers in all fields during two sessions: April through June and mid-August through October. Applications should include a letter of recommendation, a brief biography, a copy of recently published work, or if unpublished, a ten-page sample (work will not be returned), and a one-page description of work to be undertaken. Write for further details.

Available to: Writers whose language of composition is English
Deadline: November 30
Apply to: Executive Director, Ledig House Applications, 55 Fifth Avenue, 15th floor, New York, NY 10003

**Lee & Low Books**
**95 Madison Avenue**
**New York, NY 10016**
**Web site: www.leeandlow.com**

© The *New Voices Award* recognizes the best children's picture books created by writers of color who are U. S. residents and who have not previously published such a book. Manuscripts should be no longer than 1,500 words and should address the needs of children of color; of special interest are stories with contemporary settings. The winner receives a $1,000 honorarium and a book contract, with an advance against royalties; second prize is $500.

Available to: See above
Deadline: Manuscripts accepted April 1-September 30
Apply to: New Voices Award, above address

**Leeway Foundation**
**123 South Broad Street, Suite 2040**
**Philadelphia, PA 19109**
**E-mail: info@leeway.org**
**Web site: http://www.leeway.org**
**Fax: 215-545-4021**

The Leeway Foundation supports women artists in the greater Philadelphia area and promotes their increased recognition and representation in the community. Grants of $2,500 to $50,000 are made in a selected visual or literary discipline each year. Write or e-mail for more information.

Available to: Philadelphia-area women artists
Deadline: Inquire
Apply to: Above address

**Levantine Cultural Center**
**8424A Santa Monica Boulevard, 789**
**West Hollywood, CA 90069**
**Phone: 323-650-7010**
**E-mail: info@levantinecenter.org**
**Web site: http://www.levantinecenter.org**

Ⓜ In 2003, the *Levantine Literary Contest* will offer more than $7,000 in stipends for fiction, poetry, and nonfiction by writers of Middle Eastern or Mediterranean heritage, or by authors of work that brings into focus a Levantine narrative. Writers may enter only one unpublished submission per category, up to 3,000 words. There are no restrictions on subject matter, but an affinity for Middle Eastern or Mediterranean cultures is encouraged. Send SASE, e-mail, or see the Web site for details and guidelines.

Available to: See above
Deadline: Inquire
Apply to: Levantine Literary Contest, above address

**Lifebridge Foundation**
**PO Box 793 Times Square Station**
**New York, NY 10108**
**E-mail: LB457@aol.com**
**Web site: http://www.lifebridge.org**
**Fax: 212-757-0246**

Project grants are offered to individuals who, "through cultural, educational, and/or scientific means, are dedicated to creating bridges of understanding among all people by bringing to realization the concepts of one humanity and the interconnectedness of all life." Although the Foundation generally considers its own nominations, it does accept introductory letters, of no more than three pages, specifying how a project reflects the Foundation's purposes and aims. Write, e-mail, or consult the Web site for additional information. (E-mail is for information requests only; e-mailed introductory letters or proposals will not be accepted.)

Available to: No restrictions
Deadline: Inquire
Apply to: Above address

**Lindbergh Foundation**
**2150 Third Avenue North, Suite 310**
**Anoka, MN 55303-2296**
**E-mail: info@lindberghfoundation.org**
**Web site: http://www.lindberghfoundation.org**
**Fax: 763-576-1664**

© The *Anne Spencer Lindbergh Prize in Children's Literature* awards $5,000 biennially to a children's fantasy novel published in English during the two years under consideration. Writers should submit four copies of each book and a $25 application fee for each title. Write, fax, or e-mail for further information.

Available to: No restrictions
Deadline: November 1
Apply to: Anne Spencer Lindbergh Prize, above address

**Literal Latte**
**61 East 8th Street, Suite 240**
**New York, NY 10003**
**E-mail: LitLatte@aol.com**
**Web site: http://www.literal-latte.com**

Ⓜ The *Literal Latte Fiction and Poetry Awards* and the *Literal Latte Roy T. Ames Essay Awards* annually offer a $1,000 first prize, a $300 second prize, and a $200 third prize in each genre for an unpublished short story, essay, and poem. Winning entries appear in *Literal Latte*, a journal of prose, poetry, and art. A $10 reading fee applies to each story, essay, or group of six or fewer poems; a $15 fee covers a one-year subscription. The journal also sponsors the *Literal Latte Food Verse Contest*, with a first prize of $500. Send SASE, e-mail, or see the Web site for guidelines.

Available to: No restrictions
Deadline: January for fiction; July for poetry; September for essay; December for food verse
Apply to: Above address

**Literary Arts, Inc.**
**219 NW 12th Avenue, Suite 201**
**Portland, OR 97209**
**Phone: 503-227-2583**
**E-mail: la@literary-arts.org**
**Web site: http://www.literary-arts.org**

Ⓜ The *Oregon Book Awards* are given to outstanding Oregon authors for works published during the twelve months ending March 31. Nominations are accepted for poetry, fiction, literary nonfiction, drama, and literature for young readers. The winner in each category receives a prize of $1,000. Publishers, authors, and colleagues may nominate books. Send SASE or see the Web site for guidelines.

Available to: Oregon residents
Deadline: Late May (inquire for exact date)
Apply to: Oregon Book Awards, above address

Ⓜ   *Oregon Literary Fellowships* and the *Women Writers Fellowship* help those in need of funds initiate, develop, or complete a literary project in poetry, fiction, literary nonfiction, drama, or literature for young readers. The Women Writers Fellowship gives special attention to work that explores experiences of race, class, physical disability, or sexual orientation. Fellowships range from $500 to $3,000. Send SASE or see the Web site for guidelines.

Available to: Oregon residents
Deadline: Late June (inquire for exact date)
Apply to: Oregon Literary Fellowships or Women Writers Fellowship, above address

**Gerald Loeb Awards**
**The Anderson School at UCLA**
**110 Westwood Plaza, B307**
**Box 951481**
**Los Angeles, CA 90095-1481**
**Phone: 310-206-1877**
**E-mail: loeb@anderson.ucla.edu**
**Web site: http://www.anderson.ucla.edu/media/loeb**
**Fax: 310-825-7977**

Ⓙ   The *Gerald Loeb Awards for Distinguished Business and Financial Journalism,* among the profession's highest honors, recognize journalists nationwide who have made significant contributions to the understanding of business, finance, and economic matters. The competition is open to business reporting over the calendar year in eight media categories: large, medium, and small newspapers; magazines; commentary; deadline/beat writing; television; radio. Prizes in each category are $2,000.

Available to: Writers for U. S. commercial publications
Deadline: Early February (inquire for exact date)
Apply to: Above address

**Loft Literary Center**
**1011 Washington Avenue, South**
**Minneapolis, MN 55415**
**E-mail: loft@loft.org**
**Web site: http://www.loft.org**

Ⓕ Ⓟ   The *Loft Mentor Series Contest* provides eight Minnesota poets and fiction writers the opportunity for intensive study with nationally known visiting writers, in addition to a small stipend. Winners participate in seminars, individual critiques, and public forums and readings with local and visiting mentors. The $10 application fee is waived for Loft members. Send SASE or see the Web site for additional information and guidelines.

Available to: Minnesota residents
Deadline: Mid-May (inquire for exact date)
Apply to: Loft Mentor Series, above address

Ⓜ   The *McKnight Artist Fellowships for Writers* offer $25,000 annually to five winners: one in children's literature, and four in poetry or creative prose (in alternating years). The awards provide Minnesota writers with an opportunity to work for a concentrated period of time on their writing. Send SASE or see the Web site for additional information and guidelines.

Available to: Minnesota residents
Deadline: Mid-November (inquire for exact date)
Apply to: McKnight Artist Fellowships for Writers, above address

*Minnesota Literature Live Grants* offer up to $800 to Minnesota groups of individuals or organizations outside the seven-county Minneapolis-St. Paul metropolitan area to present events that promote literature by Minnesota writers. Eligible events include readings, writing workshops, storytelling, oral history activities, and in-school residences.

Available to: See above
Deadline: Ongoing
Apply to: Minnesota Literature Live Grants, above address

Ⓜ The *Minnesota Writers' Career Initiative Program* provides financial support and professional assistance to advanced writers of poetry, fiction, creative nonfiction, or children's literature to develop and implement serious, multifaceted plans for the next phase of their career. This phase might involve, but is not limited to, greater recognition, increase in book sales, significant expansion of audience, or publication by a major press. As many as four winners receive grants of up to $8,000 and up to $1,500 in honoraria.

Available to: Minnesota residents
Deadline: Inquire
Apply to: Career Initiative Program, above address

**Longwood College Foundation**
**Department of English**
**201 High Street**
**Farmville, VA 23901**
**Phone: 434-395-2033**

ⓘⓝ The *John Dos Passos Prize for Literature*, consisting of $1,000 and a medal, is given annually to a writer with a substantial publication record. The award is intended primarily for American creative writers in mid-career, particularly those whose work shares with that of Dos Passos an intense and original exploration of American themes. *By Internal Nomination Only.*

**Los Angeles Public Library**
**630 West Fifth Street**
**Los Angeles, CA 90071**

ⓘⓝ The *Los Angeles Public Library Literary Award* of $10,000 is given annually for an outstanding body of work. There is no application process. *By Internal Nomination Only.*

**Los Angeles Times Book Prizes**
**Times Mirror Square**
**Los Angeles, CA 90053**

ⓘⓝ The *Los Angeles Times Book Prizes* are given in the following categories: fiction, first fiction (*Art Seidenbaum Award*), poetry, history, biography, current interest, science and technology, and body of work by a writer living in or writing on the American West (*Robert Kirsch Award*). Eligible books must have been published in English in the U. S. between January 1 and December 31 of the award year. The winner in each category receives $1,000 and a citation. *By Internal Nomination Only.*

**Lotus Press**
**PO Box 21607**
**Detroit, MI 48221**

Ⓟ The annual *Naomi Long Madgett Poetry Award* offers $500 and publication by Lotus Press for a volume of poems by an African-American author. Send SASE, to the attention of Constance Withers, for guidelines.

Available to: African-American poets
Deadline: Submissions accepted April 1-June 1
Apply to: Above address

**Louisiana Division of the Arts**
PO Box 44247
Baton Rouge, LA 70804
E-mail: arts@crt.state.la.us
Web site: http://www.crt.state.la.us/arts
Fax: 225-342-8173

Ⓜ Up to five fellowships of $5,000 are given annually to Louisiana writers of poetry, fiction, and creative nonfiction. Applicants must have been Louisiana residents for at least two years before the application date, and may not receive fellowships more than once in any ten-year period. Mini-grants of $500 are available twice a year for Louisiana writers of poetry, fiction, and creative nonfiction. Eligible writers may apply for fellowships and mini-grants in the same year. Write or see the Web site for guidelines and applications.

Available to: Louisiana residents
Deadline: Applications must be postmarked by March 1 for fellowships; by August 1 and/or December 1 for mini-grants
Apply to: Above address

**Love Creek Productions**
c/o Cynthia Granville
162 Nesbit Street
Weehawken, NJ 07086

Ⓓ The *Short Play Festival* selects more than a hundred finalists yearly to receive a mini-showcase production in New York City. The best in competition receives a cash prize. Plays should have at least two characters, should run less than forty minutes, and may not have been published or produced in New York City during the past year. Authors must enclose a permission letter for Love Creek to produce their play if it is chosen, and should state whether an Equity showcase is acceptable. Send SASE for application guidelines.

Available to: No restrictions
Deadline: Ongoing
Apply to: Consult application guidelines

**Amy Lowell Poetry Travelling Scholarship**
Choate, Hall & Stewart
Exchange Place
53 State Street
Boston, MA 02109-2891
Fax: 617-248-4000

Ⓟ The *Amy Lowell Poetry Travelling Scholarship* awards approximately $32,000 annually to an American-born poet to spend one year outside North America, in whatever place the recipient feels will most advance his or her work. Recipients in recent years have included published poets with professional standing. Write for application form and guidelines.

Available to: U. S. native citizens
Deadline: October 1 for application requests; October 15 for submissions
Apply to: Above address

**Lukas Prize Project**
**Columbia University**
**Graduate School of Journalism**
2950 Broadway
New York, NY 10027
Web site: http://www.jrn.columbia.edu/lukas

Ⓝ The *J. Anthony Lukas Prize* annually awards $10,000 for a published book-length work of narrative nonfiction on an American topic "that exemplifies the literary grace, the commitment to serious research, and the social concern that characterized the distinguished work of the award's namesake." See the Web site for guidelines and entry form.

Available to: No restrictions
Deadline: November 15 for books published January 1-September 30; January 5 for books published October 1-December 31
Apply to: J. Anthony Lukas Prize, above address

(N) The *J. Anthony Lukas Work-in-Progress Award* annually offers $45,000 to aid in the completion of a significant work of nonfiction. Applicants, who must already have a contract with a publisher to write the book, should send a copy of the original book proposal, a sample chapter, evidence of their contract, and an explanation of how the award will advance the book's progress. See the Web site for guidelines and entry form.

Available to: No restrictions
Deadline: January 25
Apply to: J. Anthony Lukas Work-in-Progress Award, above address

(N) The *Mark Lynton History Prize* annually awards $10,000 for the published book-length work of history, on any subject, that "best combines intellectual or scholarly distinction with felicity of expression." Send SASE, e-mail, or consult the Web site for guidelines and entry form.

Available to: No restrictions
Deadline: November 15 for books published January 1-September 30; January 5 for books published October 1-December 31
Apply to: Mark Lynton History Prize, above address

**Lullwater Review**
**Emory University**
**Box 22036**
**Atlanta, GA 30322**
**Phone: 404-727-6184**
**E-mail: ldecou@learnlink.emory.edu**

(P) The *Lullwater Prize for Poetry* awards $500 and publication in *Lullwater Review*. Poets may submit no more than six poems; all submissions are considered for publication. There is an $8 reading fee; sample issues of the review are available for $5 each. Send SASE for guidelines.

Available to: No restrictions
Deadline: November 1
Apply to: Lullwater Prize for Poetry, above address

**Lynchburg College**
**Department of English**
**Lynchburg, VA 24501**
**E-mail: allen@lynchburg.edu**

(M) Each semester, the *Richard H. Thornton Writer-in-Residence Program* selects a fiction writer, playwright, or poet to spend eight weeks at Lynchburg College. The resident receives a stipend of $8,000 and is provided with housing and meals. Although considerable time is reserved for personal work, the resident teaches a weekly seminar to advanced undergraduate writers, gives one public reading on campus, and visits classes as a guest speaker.

Available to: Writers with at least one published book and evidence of effective teaching
Deadlines: March 1 for fall term; September 1 for spring
Apply to: Send résumé and cover letter outlining qualifications to Tom Allen, Thornton Chair, Thornton Writer-in-Residence Program, above address

**Lynx House Press**
**c/o Creative Writing Program**
**Eastern Washington University**
**705 West First**
**Spokane, WA 99201**
**E-mail: cnhowell@mail.ewu.edu**

(P) The *Blue Lynx Poetry Prize* offers $1,500 and publication of a book-length manuscript of poems by a U. S. poet. Applicants should submit a manuscript of at least 48 pages, the $18 entry fee, and SASE for notification.

Available to: U. S. citizens and residents
Deadline: April 15
Apply to: Blue Lynx Poetry Prize, above address


**John D. and Catherine T. MacArthur Foundation**
**140 South Dearborn Street**
**Chicago, IL 60603**
**E-mail: 4answers@macfound.org**
**Web site: http://www.macfdn.org**

Research and writing grants are awarded annually through the Foundation's Program on Global Security and Sustainability. Grants are given to support research and writing projects that "promise to illuminate the dynamics of international security, sustainability and cooperation." Projects to be carried out by individuals or two-person teams are eligible; projects related to research or writing of doctoral dissertations are not. Grants are awarded for periods no longer than eighteen months. Applicants may request up to $75,000 for individual projects, and up to $100,000 for collaborations. Write for further information and guidelines.

Available to: No restrictions
Deadline: February 1
Apply to: Program on Global Security and Sustainability, above address


**John J. McCloy Fund**
**American Council on Germany**
**14 East 60th Street, Suite 606**
**New York, NY 10022**
**Phone: 212-826-3636**
**E-mail: info@acgusa.org**
**Web site: www.acgusa.org**
**Fax: 212-758-3445**

Ⓙ The *John J. McCloy Fund* offers fellowships for American journalists to spend approximately a month in Germany during the fall of the year while developing an individual project. Fellowships include a per diem of $150, the cost of transatlantic airfare and local ground transportation, and coverage of daily expenses.

Available to: U. S. citizens
Deadline: Ongoing; preference given to applications received by January 1
Apply to: Above address for information only; for applications, write to Professor Seymour Topping, Administrator of Pulitzer Prizes, Columbia University School of Journalism, Journalism 702; New York, NY 10027


**MacDowell Colony**
**100 High Street**
**Peterborough, NH 03458**
**Phone: 603-924-3886**
**E-mail: info@macdowellcolony.org**
**Web site: www.macdowellcolony.org**
**Fax: 603-924-9142**

Ⓡ *MacDowell Colony Fellowships* support residences of up to eight weeks for writers and other artists to concentrate on creative work without interruption. Studios and room and board are provided. Write to the admissions coordinator, e-mail, or see the Web site for further information and application.

Available to: Writers, visual artists, composers, filmmakers, architects, and interdisciplinary artists
Deadline: January 15 for May-August; April 15 for September-December; September 15 for January-April
Apply to: Above address

**The Madison Review**
Department of English
University of Wisconsin
600 North Park Street
Madison, WI 53706
Web site: http://mendota.english.wisc.edu/~MadRev/html/two/html

(F) (P) The *Madison Review/Phyllis Smart Young Prize in Poetry* and the *Madison Review/Chris O'Malley Fiction Award* are given annually for the best group of three poems and the best short story, respectively, submitted during the month of September. Each award carries a prize of $500 and publication in *The Madison Review*. Multiple or previously published submissions are ineligible. There is a $5 entry fee. Send SASE for guidelines.

Available to: No restrictions
Deadline: Submissions accepted in September only
Apply to: Phyllis Smart Young Prize in Poetry or Chris O'Malley Fiction Award, above address

**Maine Community Foundation**
245 Main Street
Ellsworth, ME 04605
E-mail: grants@mainecf.org
Web site: http//www.mainecf.org
Fax: 207-667-0447

(F) (P) The *Martin Dibner Memorial Fellowship for Maine Writers Fund* offers one or two grants, from $500 to $1,000, for the professional development of Maine writers, particularly those just becoming established. Grants may be used for writing workshops or for living expenses while a writer completes a manuscript. In even-numbered years the award goes to fiction writers, in odd-numbered years to poets. Write or e-mail for further information and guidelines.

Available to: Maine residents
Deadline: May 15
Apply to: Martin Dibner Memorial Fellowship, above address

**Manhattan Theatre Club**
311 West 43rd Street, 8th floor
New York, NY 10036
Phone: 212-399-3000
Web site: http://www.mtc-nyc.org
Fax: 212-399-4329

(D) Playwriting fellowships are offered annually to emerging New York City-based playwrights from all backgrounds who have completed their formal education and can demonstrate financial need. The fellowship includes a commission of $5,000 for a new play; a production assistantship, with a stipend of $1,500, during which the writer observes rehearsals for one of seven plays presented at MTC each season; and financial assistance of $3,500 for living and other expenses. Send SASE for deadlines and eligibility requirements before applying.

Available to: New York City-based playwrights, age thirty-five or younger
Deadline: Inquire
Apply to: Liz Frankel, Play Development Assistant, above address

**Marin Arts Council**
650 Las Gallinas Avenue, Suite C
San Rafael, CA 94903
Phone: 415-499-8350
Fax: 415-499-8537

(M) The *Individual Artist Grants Program* offers amounts ranging from $2,000 to $10,000 to Marin County artists at work in genres including poetry, fiction, and other creative prose. Send SASE for guidelines and application.

Available to: Marin County residents
Deadline: Inquire for next literature cycle
Apply to: Grants Coordinator, above address

**Marlboro Review**
PO Box 243
Marlboro, VT 05344
E-mail: marlboro@marlbororeview.com
Web site: http://www.marlbororeview.com

Ⓟ The *Marlboro Review Poetry Prize* annually offers $1,000 and publication in *Marlboro Review*, a biannual journal of poetry, fiction, essays, translations, and reviews, for the best poem or group of poems. Poets may submit up to five poems of any length or style; there is a $10 reading fee. All entries will be considered for publication. Send SASE or consult the Web site for guidelines.

Available to: No restrictions
Deadline: March 15
Apply to: Poetry Prize, above address

**Maryland Library Association**
1401 Hollins Street
Baltimore, MD 21223
Phone: 410-947-5090
Web site: www.mdlib.org
Fax: 410-625-9594

Ⓘ Ⓝ The *Maryland Author Award* of $2,000 is given annually for a body of work by a writer who was born or lives in, or has close ties to, Maryland. Awards are given on a rotating basis according to genre. There is no application process; nominations are made by the members of the Maryland Library Association. *By Internal Nomination Only.*

**Maryland State Arts Council**
175 West Ostend Street, Suite E
Baltimore, MD 21230
Phone: 410-767-6555
E-mail: pdunne@mdbusiness.state.md.us
Web site: http://www.msac.org
Fax: 410-333-1062

Ⓜ *Individual Artist Awards* are given to Maryland artists, through an anonymous, competitive process, to encourage and sustain their pursuit of artistic excellence. A limited number of awards of $1,000, $3,000, and $6,000 are offered each year in various disciplines on a rotating basis.

Available to: Maryland residents at least eighteen years old, excluding students
Deadline: Inquire for exact date and disciplines
Apply to: Above address

**Massachusetts Cultural Council**
10 St. James Avenue, 3rd floor
Boston, MA 02116-3803
Phone: 617-727-3668
Web site: http://www.massculturalcouncil.org
Fax: 617-727-0044

Ⓜ *Artist Grants Fellowships* of $12,500 are given to Massachusetts writers in fiction, poetry, and drama. Finalists in each category receive $1,000. Applicants must be at least eighteen years old, legal residents of Massachusetts for the last two years, and not enrolled in a related degree-granting program. Fellowship disciplines rotate on a two-year cycle, with fiction and poetry in even-numbered years and playwriting/new-theater work in odd-numbered years. Write, e-mail, or see the Web site for guidelines and application.

Available to: See above
Deadline: December (inquire for exact date)
Apply to: Artist Grants Fellowships, above address

Ⓜ *Professional Development Grants* promote the continuing professional education of Massachusetts artists and not-for-profit administrators in the arts, humanities, and interpretative sciences. Grants of up to $500 help cover costs associated with attending a professional conference, workshop, seminar, artist residency, or master class. Write, e-mail, or see the Web site for additional information and application.

Available to: Massachusetts residents at least eighteen years old
Deadline: 15th of every month except June
Apply to: Professional Development Grants, above address

**Massachusetts Institute of Technology**
**Knight Science Journalism Fellowships**
**E-32-300, 77 Massachusetts Avenue**
**Cambridge, MA 02139-4307**
**Phone: 617-253-3442**
**E-mail: www-ksjf@mit.edu**
**Web site: http://web.mit.edu/knight-science/**
**Fax: 617-258-8100**

Ⓙ Ten *Knight Science Journalism Fellowships* are awarded annually to U. S. and foreign print and broadcast journalists whose primary work is to inform broad audiences about recent developments in technology and science and their wider social effects. The fellowships, open to freelance journalists and employees of news-gathering organizations, involve full-time residence at MIT for the academic year; fellows receive a stipend of $45,000. Write for further information and application.

Available to: See above
Deadline: March 1
Apply to: Above address

**Maui Writers Conference**
**2118 Wilshire Boulevard, Suite 726**
**Santa Monica, CA 90403-5784**
**E-mail: mauiscript@aol.com**
**Web site: http://www.maui.net/~writers**

Ⓢ The Conference's *National Screenwriting Competition* offers a first prize of $3,000, and a fully paid admission to the Maui Writers Retreat and the Maui Writers Conference, for a feature-length screenplay. A second prize of $1,000 and a third of $500 are also offered; each includes admission to the Conference. There is a $45 entry fee. Write, e-mail, or see the Web site for guidelines and entry form.

Available to: No restrictions
Deadline: July 1
Apply to: National Screenwriting Competition, above address

**Medieval Academy of America**
**1430 Massachusetts Avenue**
**Cambridge, MA 02138**

Ⓝ The *John Nicholas Brown Prize* awards $1,000 annually for a first-published book in the field of medieval studies. Books published up to three years before the submission date are eligible. Three copies of the book should be sent to the Academy office, accompanied by copies of published reviews and by an author's statement that it is his or her first published book in the medieval field.

Available to: North American residents
Deadline: October 15
Apply to: John Nicholas Brown Prize, above address

Ⓝ The *Van Courtlandt Elliott Prize* awards $500 annually for a first-published article on a medieval topic, issued in any journal, of not less than five pages. Articles published up to one year before the submission date are eligible. Three copies of the article should be submitted, together with an author's statement that it is his or her first article published in the medieval field.

Available to: North American residents
Deadline: October 15
Apply to: Van Courtlandt Elliott Prize, above address

Ⓝ The *Haskins Medal* is presented annually to the author of a book in medieval studies judged to be of outstanding importance and distinction. Books published within five years before the submission date are eligible. Three copies of the book should be sent to the Academy office, accompanied by copies of published reviews.

Available to: North American residents
Deadline: October 15
Apply to: Haskins Medal, above address


**MEXICO**
**U. S.-Mexico Fund for Culture**
**Londres 16 P.B., 3rd floor**
**Col. Juarez 06600**
**Mexico, D.F.**
**Mexico**
**E-mail: usmexcult@fidemexusa.org.mx**
**Web site: http://www.fidemexusa.org.mx**
**Fax: 52-5-566-80-71**

The U. S.-Mexico Fund for Culture provides economic support, ranging from $2,000 to $25,000, for projects of excellence that reflect the artistic and cultural diversity of Mexico and the U. S. and that can lead to close, lasting collaboration and exchange among artists, researchers and scholars, independent groups, and related institutions of the two countries. In particular, the Fund seeks to promote editions of prose and poetry that help disseminate literature from one country in the other. Special consideration is given to translation and anthology projects that entail close work between author and translator or editor. Support is given also to residences, conferences, symposia, workshops, and other programs that unite authors, translators, editors, publishers, and interested audiences, in order to encourage dialogue about literature in both countries. Write, enclosing SASE with adequate return postage, to the above address, or consult the Web site for guidelines and application.

Available to: U. S. and Mexican citizens
Deadline: April (inquire for exact date)
Apply to: Above address


**Michener Center for Writers**
**University of Texas at Austin**
**J. Frank Dobie House**
**702 East Dean Keeton Street**
**Austin, TX 78705**
**Web site: www.utexas.edu/academic/mcw**

Ⓜ The *James A. Michener Fellowship* of $17,500 per year, plus remission of tuition, is offered to candidates accepted for the University of Texas MFA program designed for students who wish to work in at least two fields among fiction, poetry, screenwriting, and playwriting. Write for application procedures.

Available to: See above
Deadline: January 15
Apply to: Above address

ⁱ̄ⁿ̄ The *James A. Michener Memorial Prize* offers $10,000 a year to writers who have published a first book at age forty or later. A group of nominators submits names of deserving writers to a panel chosen by the Michener Center. There is no application process. *By Internal Nomination Only.*

**Michigan Council for Arts and Cultural Affairs.** *See* **ArtServe Michigan**

**Michigan Library Association**
**6810 South Cedar, Suite 6**
**Lansing, MI 48911**
**E-mail: mla@mlc.lib.mi.us**
**Web site: www.mla.lib.mi.us**

Ⓜ The *Michigan Author Award* of $1,000 is given for an outstanding body of work by a Michigan resident, a longtime Michigan resident who has recently relocated, or an author whose works are identified in subject with Michigan. The award is given in conjunction with the Library Association's annual conference, which the winner must attend. Writers are cited for a published body of fiction, nonfiction, and/or poetry, consisting of three or more titles, adult or juvenile. Nominations may be made by librarians, publishers, or individuals. Write for required application.

Available to: See above
Deadline: June 30
Apply to: Michigan Author Award, above address

**Michigan Quarterly Review**
**University of Michigan**
**3032 Rackham Building**
**Ann Arbor, MI 48109-1070**
**E-mail: mgr@umich.edu**
**Web site: http://www.umich.edu/~mqr/**

Ⓕ The *Lawrence Foundation Prize* annually awards $1,000 for the best short story published in *Michigan Quarterly Review* during the previous calendar year. The magazine's editorial board chooses the winner.

Available to: *Michigan Quarterly Review* contributors

**Middle East Report**
**1500 Massachusetts Avenue, Suite 119**
**Washington, DC 20005**
**E-mail: ctoensing@merip.org**
**Web site: http://www.merip.org**

Ⓙ The *Philip Shehadi New Writers Award*, established in memory of the *Middle East Report* contributing editor who was killed in Algiers in 1991, offers $500 and publication of an article (3,000 to 5,000 words) that focuses on the Middle East or contemporary relations of states and societies in the region. All entrants receive a one-year subscription to the *Report*. Send SASE, e-mail, or see the Web site for guidelines.

Available to: No restrictions
Deadline: Inquire
Apply to: Philip Shehadi New Writers Award, above address

**Midland Community Theatre**
**2000 West Wadley**
**Midland, TX 79705**
**Web site: http://www.mctmidland.org**

Ⓓ The *McLaren Memorial Comedy Playwriting Competition* is a nationwide contest for original, unproduced comedy scripts of any length. Three to five finalists receive a staged reading of their work at the McLaren Comedy Festival; a grand-prize winner is chosen for a cash stipend of $400. MCT may produce the winning script at a future date. The playwright retains all rights to work submitted. A $10 entry fee per script is required.

Available to: No restrictions
Deadline: Submissions accepted December 1-January 31
Apply to: McLaren Memorial Comedy Playwriting Competition, above address

**Mid-List Press**
4324 12th Avenue South
Minneapolis, MN 55407-3218
E-mail: guide@midlist.org
Web site: http://www.midlist.org
Fax: 612-823-8387

Ⓜ The *First Series Awards for the Novel, Poetry, Short Fiction, and Creative Nonfiction* offer publication and an advance against royalties to a writer who has never published a book in the particular genre (a chapbook is not considered a book of poetry). Novelists and authors of short fiction and creative nonfiction receive an advance of $1,000; poets receive $500. Manuscripts of novels, collections of short fiction, and creative nonfiction must be at least 50,000 words in length; poetry manuscripts at least 60 pages. There is a $20 reading fee in each category. Send #10 SASE for guidelines and entry form.

Available to: Unpublished writers
Deadline: Novel and poetry submissions accepted October 1-February 1; short fiction and creative nonfiction, April 1-July 1
Apply to: Above address

**Midwest Theatre Network**
5031 Tongen Avenue, NW
Rochester, MN 55901

Ⓓ The *Midwest Theatre Network Original Play Competition/Rochester Playwright Festival* biennially offers four to eight awards of $300 to $1,000 each (contingent on funding) and full production at cooperating theaters for unpublished works (full-length plays, collections of one-acts, musicals, experimental works) that have not received professional production. The winning playwrights also receive paid travel, and room and board, to attend the performance. Send SASE for guidelines and entry form. *(At press time, PEN was unable to confirm this information, but believes it is still current.)*

Available to: No restrictions
Deadline: November 30
Apply to: Joan Sween, Executive Director/Dramaturg, above address

**Milkweed Editions**
1011 Washington Avenue South, Suite 300
Minneapolis, MN 55415-1246
Web site: http://www.milkweed.org

Ⓕ The annual *Milkweed National Fiction Prize* offers a $7,500 cash advance on any royalties negotiated in a contract for the best work of fiction accepted for publication, of 150 to 400 pages, by a writer not previously published by Milkweed. Manuscript may be a novel, a collection of short stories, one or more novellas, or a combination of short stories and one or more novellas. All manuscripts submitted to Milkweed are considered for the prize. Send SASE or see the Web site for guidelines before submitting.

Available to: No restrictions
Deadline: Ongoing
Apply to: Fiction Prize, above address

Ⓒ The *Milkweed Prize for Children's Literature* offers a $10,000 cash advance on any royalties negotiated in a contract for the best manuscript for children ages eight to thirteen accepted for publication, by a writer not previously published by Milkweed. Only novels are eligible; collections of stories, picture books, or retellings of legends or folktales will not be considered. Texts should be of high literary quality and should "embody humane values that contribute to cultural understanding." Send SASE or see the Web site for guidelines.

Available to: No restrictions
Deadline: Ongoing
Apply to: Children's Literature Prize, above address

**Mill Mountain Theatre**
**One Market Square, SE**
**Roanoke, VA 24011-1437**
**Phone: 540-342-5749**
**E-mail: outreach@millmountain.org**
**Web site: http://www.millmountain.org**
**Fax: 540-342-5745**

Ⓓ The *Mill Mountain Theatre New Play Competition* annually awards $1,000, a staged reading (and possible production), and travel stipend and housing for an unproduced, unpublished play, preferably with a cast of no more than ten. One work per playwright must be submitted by an agent or accompanied by the professional recommendation of a director, literary manager, or dramaturg. Send SASE for guidelines.

Available to: U. S. residents
Deadline: October 1-January 1
Apply to: Maryke Huyding, Literary Coordinator, above address

**Millay Colony for the Arts**
**444 East Hill Road**
**PO Box 3**
**Austerlitz, NY 12017-0003**
**Web site: www.millaycolony.org**

Ⓡ The Millay Colony for the Arts provides work space, meals, and sleeping accommodations for qualified writers, composers, and visual artists for a period of one month. The Colony can accommodate six artists monthly; its main building is fully accessible and includes two work/living spaces. Samples of work must accompany applications. See the Web site for further information.

Available to: No restrictions
Deadline: February 1 for June-September residences; May 1 for October-January; September 1 for February-May
Apply to: Director of Admissions, above address

**Milton Center**
**Newman University**
**3100 McCormick Avenue**
**Wichita, KS 67213**
**E-mail: miltonc@newmanu.edu**
**Fax: 316-942-4483**

Ⓡ The Milton Center awards two postgraduate fellowships to "new writers of Christian commitment." Fellows are expected to complete their first book-length manuscript while in residence. Each fellow receives a stipend of $1,225 per month for a nine-month tenure. In addition, the Milton Center provides a supportive community in which to work. Write or e-mail for further information and application.

Available to: See above
Deadline: March 15
Apply to: Postgraduate Fellowships, above address

**Minnesota Monthly**
**Lumber Exchange Building**
**10 South Fifth Street, Suite 1000**
**Minneapolis, MN 55402**

Ⓕ The *Tamarack Award* offers $400 plus publication in *Minnesota Monthly*, the magazine of Minnesota Public Radio, for an unpublished work of short fiction (1,000 to 3,000 words) by a resident of the upper Midwest: Iowa, Michigan, Minnesota, North Dakota, South Dakota, or Wisconsin. Applicants may submit one unpublished story of up to 3,500 words. Minnesota Public Radio reserves the right to broadcast readings of the winning manuscript. Send SASE for guidelines.

Available to: See above

Deadline: May (inquire for exact date)
Apply to: Tamarack Award, above address

**Minnesota State Arts Board**
**400 Sibley Street, Suite 200**
**St. Paul, MN 55101-1928**
**E-mail: msab@artsstate.mn.us**
**Web site: http://www.artsstate.mn.us**
**Fax: 651-215-1602**

*Artist Assistance Fellowship Grants* of $8,000 are given annually for new works, advanced study, and works-in-progress. Short-term *Career Opportunity Grants*, which range from $500 to $1,500, are awarded three times a year.

Available to: Minnesota residents
Deadline: Early fall for fellowships; inquire for career grants
Apply to: Above address

**Mississippi Arts Commission**
**239 North Lamar Street, Suite 207**
**Jackson, MS 39201**
**Phone: 601-359-6546**
**E-mail: wilkins@arts.state.ms.us**
**Web site: http://www.arts.state.ms.us**
**Fax: 601-359-6008**

Ⓜ *Fellowships in Literary Arts* of $5,000 each are given to Mississippi writers each year. Write or e-mail for further information.

Available to: Mississippi residents
Deadline: Inquire
Apply to: Lynn Adams Wilkins, above address

**Mississippi Review**
**University of Southern Mississippi**
**Box 5144 USM**
**Hattiesburg, MS 39406-5144**
**E-mail: rief@netdoor.com**
**Web site: www.mississippireview.com**

Ⓕ Ⓟ The *Mississippi Review Prize in Fiction* and the *Prize in Poetry* award $1,000 for a winning story and $1,000 for a winning poem, plus publication in print and on-line editions of *Mississippi Review*. All runners-up are also published. There is a $15 fee per entry (one story or three poems); there is no limit to the number of entries. Send SASE or e-mail for guidelines.

Available to: U. S. citizen or resident
Deadline: August 31
Apply to: Prize in Fiction or Prize in Poetry, above address

**The Missouri Review**
**University of Missouri, Columbia**
**1507 Hillcrest Hall, UMC**
**Columbia, MO 65211**
**Web site: http://www.missourireview.org**

Ⓜ The *Larry Levis Prize in Poetry* offers $1,500 and publication for an unpublished poem. *Editors' Prize* awards of $1,000 and $1,500, plus publication in the *Review*, are offered for an essay and a short story, respectively. Finalists in all categories receive a minimum of $500, or consideration for publication at regular rates. All entries must be typed and double-spaced; poems must not exceed 10 pages, stories and essays must not exceed 25 pages. The $15 entry fee covers a one-year subscription to the *Review*.

Available to: No restrictions
Deadline: October 15
Apply to: Larry Levis Prize or Editors' Prize, above address

Ⓕ Ⓟ  The *William Peden Prize* offers $1,000 annually for the best fiction published in the *Review*. The *Tom McAfee Discovery Feature in Poetry* offers $125 to $250 once or twice a year for the best group of poems published in the journal by a poet who has not yet published a book. Write for submission guidelines.

Available to: Writers published in *The Missouri Review*


**The Mochila Review**
**Missouri Western State College**
**Department of English, Foreign Languages, and Journalism**
**St. Joseph, MO 64507**
**Web site: http://www.mwsc.edu/nmochila**

Ⓜ  The *John Gilgun Awards* in poetry and prose offer $250 and publication in *The Mochila Review* (formerly known as *Icarus*), an annual literary journal. Poets submit three to five poems, prose writers pieces of no more than 4,500 words. Send SASE or see the Web site for guidelines.

Available to: No restrictions
Deadline: December 1
Apply to: Ruth Ellen Kocher, Editor, John Gilgun Awards, above address


**Modern Language Association of America**
**26 Broadway, 3rd floor**
**New York, NY 10004-1789**
**E-mail: awards@mla.org**
**Web site: http://www.mla.org**
**Fax: 646-576-5141**

Ⓝ  The *Morton N. Cohen Award* offers $1,000 in odd-numbered years for an important collection of letters published in the two-year period preceding the award. The winning collection should have "a clear, accurate, and readable text; necessary background information; and succinct and eloquent introductory material and annotations. The edited collection should be in itself a work of literature." Editors may apply regardless of the fields they and the authors of the letters represent; MLA membership is not required. To enter, send four copies of each eligible volume.

Available to: No restrictions
Deadline: May 1
Apply to: Morton N. Cohen Award, above address

Ⓝ  The *Katherine Singer Kovacs Prize* offers $1,000 annually for the best book published in English in the field of Latin American and Spanish literatures and cultures.

Available to: No restrictions
Deadline: May 1
Apply to: Katherine Singer Kovacs Prize, above address

Ⓣ Ⓝ  The *Fenia and Yaakov Leviant Memorial Prize* awards $500 alternately in even-numbered years to an outstanding translation into English of a Yiddish literary work or an outstanding scholarly work in the field of Yiddish. In 2004, the prize will be awarded to a scholarly work. Books published in the five years preceding the award year are eligible. Translators and authors need not be MLA members. To enter, send four copies of the book and a letter of nomination.

Available to: No restrictions
Deadline: May 1
Apply to: Fenia and Yaakov Leviant Memorial Prize, above address

Ⓝ  The *James Russell Lowell Prize* of $1,000 is awarded annually to an MLA member who has published an outstanding literary or linguistic study, a critical edition of an important work, or a critical biography. Nominations may be made by publisher or author. To enter, send six copies of the work.

Available to: MLA members
Deadline: March 1
Apply to: James Russell Lowell Prize, above address

Ⓝ The *Howard R. Marraro Prize* offers $1,000 in even-numbered years to the author of a distinguished book- or essay-length scholarly study on any phase of Italian literature or comparative literature involving Italian. Nominations may be made by publisher or author. To enter, send four copies of the work.

> Available to: MLA members
> Deadline: May 1
> Apply to: Howard R. Marraro Prize, above address

Ⓝ The *Kenneth W. Mildenberger Prize* is given annually to the author of a research publication in the field of teaching foreign languages and literatures. Books compete in even-numbered years, for a prize of $1,000; articles compete in odd-numbered years, for $500. To enter, send four copies of the work.

> Available to: No restrictions
> Deadline: May 1
> Apply to: Kenneth W. Mildenberger Prize, above address

Ⓝ The *MLA Prize for a Distinguished Bibliography* awards $1,000 in even-numbered years for an enumerative and descriptive bibliography published in serial, monographic, book, or electronic format. A multivolume bibliography is eligible if at least one volume has been published during the specified two-year period. The prize is given without regard to the language of the compiler or of the text presented in the bibliography, as long as it falls within the subject scope of the MLA (e.g., modern languages and literatures, composition theory, folklore, linguistics). To enter, send four copies of the work.

> Available to: No restrictions
> Deadline: May 1
> Apply to: MLA Prize for a Distinguished Bibliography, above address

Ⓝ The *MLA Prize for a Distinguished Scholarly Edition* awards $1,000 in odd-numbered years. A multivolume edition is eligible if at least one volume has been published during the specified two year period. The edition should be based on an examination of all available relevant textual sources; source texts and edited text deviations should be fully described; the edition should employ and clearly articulate editorial principles appropriate to the materials edited; the text should be accompanied by appropriate textual and other historical contextual information; the edition should exhibit the highest standards of accuracy in text and apparatus, which should be presented as accessibly and elegantly as possible. To enter, send four copies of the work.

> Available to: No restrictions
> Deadline: May 1
> Apply to: MLA Prize for a Distinguished Scholarly Edition, above address

Ⓝ The *MLA Prize for a First Book* annually awards $1,000 for the first book-length scholarly publication by an MLA member. The book must be a literary or linguistic study, a critical edition of an important work, or a critical biography. To enter, send six copies of the book and a letter identifying the work and confirming the author's MLA membership.

> Available to: MLA members
> Deadline: April 1
> Apply to: MLA Prize for a First Book, above address

Ⓝ The *MLA Prize for Independent Scholars* for distinguished published research in modern languages and literatures, including English, is awarded annually to a person who at the time of publication is not enrolled in a program leading to an academic degree and does not hold a tenured, tenure-track, or tenure-accruing position in a postsecondary educational institution. (Tenure is understood as any comparable provision for job security in such an institution.) The award consists of a certificate, a check for $1,000, and a year's MLA membership. To enter, send six copies of the work and a completed application form.

> Available to: See above
> Deadline: May 1
> Apply to: MLA Prize for Independent Scholars, above address

(T) The *Lois Roth Award* offers $1,000 in odd-numbered years for an outstanding translation into English of a book-length literary work. Translators need not be MLA members. Books published during the preceding year are eligible. To enter, send six copies of the book and a letter of nomination.

Available: No restrictions
Deadline: April 1
Apply to: Lois Roth Award, above address

(N) The *Aldo and Jeanne Scaglione Prize for Comparative Literary Studies* awards $2,000 annually for an outstanding scholarly work in comparative literary studies, involving at least two literatures, by an MLA member. Works of literary history, literary criticism, philology, and literary theory are eligible, as are works dealing with literature and other arts and disciplines, including cinema. To enter, send four copies of the book and a letter confirming the author's MLA membership.

Available to: MLA members
Deadline: May 1
Apply to: Aldo and Jeanne Scaglione Prize for Comparative Literary Studies, above address

(N) The *Aldo and Jeanne Scaglione Prize for French and Francophone Studies* awards $2,000 annually for an outstanding scholarly work in French or Francophone linguistic or literary studies by an MLA member. Works of literary history, literary criticism, philology, and literary theory are eligible. To enter, send four copies of the book and a letter confirming the author's MLA membership.

Available to: MLA members
Deadline: May 1
Apply to: Aldo and Jeanne Scaglione Prize for French and Francophone Studies, above address

The *Aldo and Jeanne Scaglione Prize for Italian Studies* offers $2,000 in odd-numbered years for an outstanding scholarly book on any phase of Italian literature or culture or comparative literature involving Italian. Authors must be MLA members. Books published in the preceding two years are eligible. To enter, send four copies of the book and letter confirming author's MLA membership.

Available to: MLA members
Deadline: May 1
Apply to: Aldo and Jeanne Scaglione Prize for Italian Studies, above address

(N) The *Aldo and Jeanne Scaglione Prize for Studies in Germanic Languages and Literatures* offers $2,000 in even-numbered years for an outstanding scholarly work on the linguistics or literatures of the Germanic languages, including Danish, Dutch, German, Icelandic, Norwegian, Swedish, and Yiddish, by an MLA member. Works of literary history, literary criticism, philology, and literary theory are eligible. To enter, send four copies of the book and a letter confirming the author's MLA membership.

Available to: MLA members
Deadline: May 1
Apply to: Aldo and Jeanne Scaglione Prize for Studies in Germanic Languages and Literatures, above address

(N) The *Aldo and Jeanne Scaglione Prize for Studies in Slavic Languages and Literatures* offers $2,000 in odd-numbered years for an outstanding scholarly work on the linguistics or literatures of the Slavic languages. Works of literary history, literary criticism, philology, and literary theory are eligible; books that are primarily translations are not considered. To enter, send four copies of the book.

Available to: No restrictions
Deadline: May 1
Apply to: Aldo and Jeanne Scaglione Prize for Studies in Slavic Languages and Literatures, above address

(T) The *Aldo and Jeanne Scaglione Prize for Translation of a Literary Work* awards $2,000 in even-numbered years for an outstanding translation into English of a book-length literary work. Translators need not be MLA members. Books published during the preceding two years are eligible. To enter, send six copies of the book and a letter of nomination.

Available to: No restrictions
Deadline: April 1
Apply to: Aldo and Jeanne Scaglione Prize for Translation of a Literary Work, above
address

Ⓣ The *Aldo and Jeanne Scaglione Prize for Translation of a Scholarly Study of Literature* offers $2,000
in odd-numbered years for an outstanding translation into English of a book-length work
of literary history, literary criticism, philosophy, or literary theory. Translators need not
be MLA members. Books published in the preceding two years are eligible. To enter, send
four copies of the book and a letter of nomination.

Available to: No restrictions
Deadline: May 1
Apply to: Aldo and Jeanne Scaglione Prize for Translation of a Scholarly Study of
Literature, above address

Ⓝ The *William Sanders Scarborough Prize* awards $1,000 annually to an outstanding scholarly
study in the field of black American literature or culture. Authors need not be MLA
members. To enter, send four copies of the book and a letter of nomination.

Available to: No restrictions
Deadline: May 1
Apply to: William Sanders Scarborough Prize, above address

Ⓝ The *Mina P. Shaughnessy Prize* awards $1,000 annually to the author of a research publication in
the field of teaching English language and literature. To enter, send four copies of the work.

Available to: No restrictions
Deadline: May 1
Apply to: Mina P. Shaughnessy Prize, above address

**Money for Women/Barbara Deming Memorial Fund**
**PO Box 630125**
**Bronx, NY 10463**

Ⓜ The Fund provides grants of up to $1,500 to U. S. or Canadian women poets, fiction writers,
and nonfiction writers "whose work addresses women's concerns or speaks for peace
and justice from a feminist perspective." The *Gerty, Gerty, Gerty in the Arts, Arts, Arts
Award*, named for Gertrude Stein, honors "outstanding work by a lesbian [that] gives
voice to a lesbian sensibility or confronts homophobia." The *Fannie Lou Hamer Award* is
given to a woman "whose work combats racism and celebrates women of color." Send
SASE for application.

Available to: See above
Deadline: December 31 and June 30
Apply to: Above address

**Montana Artists Refuge**
**PO Box 8**
**Basin, MT 59631**
**Phone: 406-225-3500**
**Web site: www.montanaartistsrefuge.org**
**Fax: 406-225-9225**

Ⓡ The Montana Artists Refuge provides a place for artists of all types to find respite from the
rigors of modern life. Visiting artists may stay for three months to one year; three to five
artists are in residence at a time. Rents range from $395 to $550 per month, plus heat.
Financial assistance is available to a limited number of artists. Write or e-mail for additional
information and application procedures.

Available to: No restrictions
Deadline: January 15 for May-September residences; May 15 for September-December;
August 15 for January-April
Apply to: Above address

**Montana Arts Council**
PO Box 202201
Helena, MT 59620
E-mail: mac@state.mt.us
Fax: 406-444-6548

Ⓜ *Individual Artists Fellowships* of $5,000 are available in alternate years to non-degree-seeking
residents of Montana, ages twenty-one and over, in categories including fiction, nonfiction
and poetry. Write for guidelines and application.

Available to: See above
Deadline: Spring/summer 2003 (inquire for exact date)
Apply to: Above address


**Montclair State University**
1 Normal Avenue
Upper Montclair, NJ 07043
Phone: 973-655-7071
Web site: http://www.montclair.edu
Fax: 973-655-5335

Ⓓ The *TheatreFest Regional Playwriting Contest* annually offers $500, full production, and housing
to a Connecticut, New Jersey, or New York playwright for an unproduced, unpublished
full-length play exploring contemporary issues, with a maximum cast of eight. Send SASE
for guidelines.

Available to: Connecticut, New Jersey, or New York playwrights
Deadline: January 1
Apply to: TheatreFest, Regional Playwriting Contest, above address


**Monterey County Film Commission**
PO Box 111
Monterey, CA 93942
E-mail: mryfilm@aol.com
Web site: http://www.filmmonterey.org
Fax: 831-655-9244

Ⓢ The *Monterey County Film Commission Screenwriting Competition* offers a first prize of $2,002
for a full-length film or television movie script; a *Monterey County On Location Award* of
$1,000 is offered for an outstanding screenplay that includes at least fifty percent Monterey
County locations. Only writers who have not earned money writing for television or film
are eligible. Entries must not have been optioned for more than $1,000 or sold at the time
of submission. Submission fee is $35, $45, or $55, depending on the date of submission.
Send SASE or see the Web site for guidelines and application form.

Available to: See above
Deadline: October 31-January 31
Apply to: Screenwriting Competition or On Location Award, above address


**Jenny McKean Moore Writers Program.** *See* **George Washington University**


**William Morris Society in the United States**
PO Box 53263
Washington, DC 20009
E-mail: Biblio@aol.com
Web site: www.morrissociety.org

The William Morris Society offers fellowships of up to $1,000 for research and other expenses
incurred in individual projects related to the life and work of William Morris. Projects
may deal with any subject—biographical, historical, social, literary, political, artistic,
typographical—pertaining to Morris, and may be scholarly or creative.

Available to: U. S. citizens or permanent residents
Deadline: December 1
Apply to: Mark Samuels Lasner, President, above address

**Mountain West Center for Regional Studies**
**Utah State University-UMC 0735**
**Logan, UT 84322-0735**
**E-mail: mwc@cc.usu.edu**
**Web site: http://www.usu.edu/~pioneers/evans.html**
**Fax: 435-797-3899**

(N) The *Evans Biography Award* of $10,000 and the *Evans Handcart Prize* of $1,000 encourage fine writing about people who have shaped the growth and character of an important part of the U. S. The Biography Award recognizes outstanding scholarship and writing; the Handcart Prize recognizes a biography of merit, by an emerging author, that contributes to an understanding of any region characterized by Mormon settlement during the period of the biography. The biography, its subject, and the author need not be affiliated with the Church of Jesus Christ of Latter-Day Saints. Judges will consider book-length biographies, published during the given calendar year, of any person who lived a significant portion of his or her life in Mormon country. Authors or publishers should submit four copies of the book and the author's vita.

> Available to: No restrictions
> Deadline: December 1
> Apply to: Evans Biography Award or Evans Handcart Prize, above address

**Mountaineers Books**
**1001 SW Klickitat Way, Suite 201**
**Seattle, WA 98134**
**E-mail: mbooks@mountaineers.org**
**Fax: 206-223-6306**

(N) The *Barbara Savage "Miles from Nowhere" Memorial Award* is given in even-numbered years for an outstanding unpublished book-length manuscript (30,000 to 70,000 words) of personal-adventure nonfiction. Acceptable subjects include personal narratives involving hiking, mountain climbing, bicycling, snowshoeing, and so forth. The prize consists of a $3,000 cash award, publication, and a $12,000 guaranteed advance against royalties. Send SASE or see the Web site for details.

> Available to: No restrictions
> Deadline: Spring (inquire for exact date)
> Apply to: Barbara Savage "Miles from Nowhere" Memorial Award, above address

**Mountains and Plains Booksellers Association**
**19 Old Town Square, Suite 238**
**Fort Collins, CO 80524**
**E-mail: lknudsen@mountainsplains.org**
**Web site: http://www.mountainsplains.org**
**Fax: 970-407-1479**

(M) The *Regional Book Awards* honor outstanding books set in the Mountains and Plains region, which includes Arizona, Colorado, Idaho, Kansas, Montana, Nebraska, New Mexico, South Dakota, Texas, Utah, and Wyoming. The awards, of $500 each, are given in fiction, poetry, nonfiction, and children's literature, for books published between the November 1 and the October 31 preceding the submission deadline. Publishers and booksellers may nominate books throughout the year.

> Available to: No restrictions
> Deadline: November 1
> Apply to: Regional Book Awards, above address

**Municipal Art Society of New York**
**457 Madison Avenue**
**New York, NY 10022**
**Phone: 212-935-3960**
**Web site: www.mas.org**
**Fax: 212-753-1816**

(IN) The *Brendan Gill Prize*, consisting of a cash award and an engraved Steuben crystal vessel, is

159

given annually to the creator of "a single work of art which best captures the energy, vigor and verve of New York City." The award is open to all artistic disciplines, including writing. *By Internal Nomination Only.*

**Museum of Science**
**Science Park**
**Boston, MA 02114**

[IN] The *Bradford Washburn Award*, consisting of $10,000 and a gold medal, is presented annually to an individual who has made "outstanding contributions toward public understanding of science, its importance, its fascination, and the vital role it plays in all of our lives." The award honors a writer or lecturer of national or international influence, and is not meant to reward specific research, technical accomplishment, or teaching, although it may be given to an outstanding teacher or researcher who also is a highly effective writer or lecturer. There is no application process. *By Internal Nomination Only.*

**Mystery Writers of America**
**17 East 47th Street, 6th floor**
**New York, NY 10017**
**E-mail: mwa_org@earthlink.net**
**Web site: www.mysterywriters.org**
**Fax: 212-888-8107**

(F) The *Robert L. Fish Memorial Award* offers $500 for the best first mystery or suspense short story published during the calendar year. Eligible short stories should be sent to the judges of the short story committee by the editor of the magazine in which they first appeared, along with an entry form. Under special circumstances, writers may submit their own work. Write for additional information and guidelines.

Available to: No restrictions
Deadline: December 1
Apply to: Robert L. Fish Memorial Award, above address

**National Arts Journalism Program**
**Columbia University**
**2950 Broadway, Mail Code 7200**
**New York, NY 10027**
**E-mail: najp@columbia.edu**
**Web site: http://www.najp.org**
**Fax: 212-854-8129**

(J) Supported by a grant from the Pew Charitable Trusts, the National Arts Journalism Program offers fellowships to mid-career and senior journalists in the arts and culture. Ten mid-career fellows, supported by stipends of $40,000, spend an academic year at Columbia engaged in a blend of study and work with arts and cultural organizations. Working critics, reporters, or editors with at least five years' experience and demonstrated dedication to arts and cultural journalism are eligible. Several senior fellows spend shorter periods at Columbia, with a generous stipend and research assistance. Nominees for senior fellowships must have achieved singular and measurable distinction in arts and cultural journalism. Write or e-mail for additional information and application.

Available to: See above
Deadline: February (inquire for exact date)
Apply to: Above address

**National Association of Black Journalists**
**8701-A Adelphi Road**
**Adelphi, MD 20783-1716**
**Phone: 301-445-7100**
**Web site: http://www.nabj.org**
**Fax: 301-445-7101**

(J) Several *NABJ Scholarships* of $2,500 each, and one sustaining scholarship of $5,000, are awarded annually to African-American college students planning to pursue a career in journalism. Any student currently attending an accredited four-year U. S. college or university is eligible. Recipients, who also receive an all-expenses-paid trip to the NABJ convention, are required to participate in student convention projects. In addition, two four-year college scholarships are offered to African-American high school students. Write for additional information and application procedures.

Available to: See above
Deadline: Inquire
Apply to: Scholarship Program, above address

Ⓙ Fifteen *NABJ Summer Internships* are awarded annually to college sophomores, juniors, and seniors and graduate students committed to journalism careers. Candidates are offered a paid position in print, radio, or television at selected news organizations. Interns, who receive an all-expenses-paid trip to the NABJ convention, are required to participate in student convention projects. Write for additional information and application procedures.

Available to: See above
Deadline: Inquire
Apply to: Summer Internships, above address

Ⓙ Two *Ethel Payne Fellowships* are offered annually to African-American journalists interested in obtaining international reporting experience through assignments in Africa. The fellowships, designed for journalists who have a strong interest in Africa but limited opportunities to cover the continent for their news organizations, allow recipients to spend up to three weeks there and to produce news reports for the NABJ. Write for additional information and application procedures.

Available to: NABJ members with at least five years' experience as full-time or freelance journalists for a newspaper, magazine, or broadcast station
Deadline: Inquire
Apply to: Ethel Payne Fellowships, above address

**National Association of Hispanic Journalists**
**1000 National Press Building**
**Washington, DC 20045**
**Phone: 202-662-7145**
**E-mail: nahj@nahj.org**
**Web site: http://www.nahj.org**

Ⓙ Up to thirty scholarships, ranging from $1,000 to $5,000, are awarded each academic year to Hispanic students interested in pursuing careers in the media. Scholarships are open to high school seniors, college undergraduates, and graduate students. Applicants are judged according to financial need, scholastic achievement, journalistic ability, and commitment to the field. Write, e-mail, or consult the Web site for additional information and application.

Available to: See above
Deadline: Late February (inquire for exact date)
Apply to: Educational Programs, above address

**National Association of Science Writers**
**PO Box 294**
**Greenlawn, NY 11740**
**Web site: http://www.nasw.org**

Ⓙ The *Science in Society Journalism Awards* recognize "investigative and interpretive reporting about the sciences and their impact for good and bad." Three awards, of $1,000 each, are offered in the categories of newspapers, magazines, radio, television, books, and Web. Work must be written or spoken in English, intended for the layperson, and published or broadcast in North America between June 1 of the previous year and May 31 of the current application year. Applicants should submit five copies of books, or ten copies of videos, tapes, prints, etc. Write or consult the Web site for guidelines and entry form.

Available to: No restrictions
Deadline: Applications must be postmarked by July 1
Apply to: Above address

**National Book Awards**
**National Book Foundation**
**96 Madison Avenue, Suite 709**
**New York, NY 10016**
**Phone: 212-685-0261**
**E-mail: natbkfdn@mindspring.com**
**Web site: www.publishersweekly.com/nbf/docs/nbf.html**
**Fax: 212-213-6570**

Ⓜ The *National Book Awards* recognize literary excellence in four categories: fiction, nonfiction, poetry, and young people's literature. Full-length e-books of fiction and general nonfiction are eligible. E-book collections of short stories and e-book collections of poetry by one author are eligible. Each winner receives a cash prize of $10,000; sixteen runners-up receive $1,000 each. Eligible books must be published in the U. S. between the December 1 preceding the award year and November 30 of that year, and nominated by their publishers only. There is a $100 entry fee.

Available to: U. S. authors
Deadline: July 9 for publishers' nominations on books issued within the above-mentioned period; manuscripts or galleys submitted by August 13
Apply to: Above address

**National Book Critics Circle**
**245 West 17th Street**
**New York, NY 10016**
**E-mail: ReamyJ@aol.com**
**Web site: www.bookcritics.org**

Ⓜ The *National Book Critics Circle Awards* are given annually in five categories: fiction, general nonfiction, biography/autobiography, poetry, and criticism. Two special awards are also given: the *Nona Balakian Citation for Excellence in Reviewing,* and the *Ivan Sandrof Lifetime Achievement Award.* Write or see the Web site for more information and application guidelines.

Available to: Inquire
Deadline: Inquire
Apply to: Above address

**National Education Association**
**1201 Sixteenth Street, NW**
**Washington, DC 20036**
**E-mail: clehane@nea.org**
**Web site: http://www.nea.org/he**

The *Excellence in the Academy Awards,* consisting of the prizes listed below, are intended to advance the NEA's commitment in higher education. Winning entries are published in *Thought and Action,* the Association's journal of higher education. Prizewinners are asked to be guest presenters at the NEA Higher Education Conference. The competition is open to the entire academic community. Write, e-mail, or see the Web site for additional information and guidelines.

The *Art of Teaching Prize* offers $2,500 for an essay that "illuminates one professor's approach to the complex and intangible dynamic that inspires students with a love of learning" or an article that "offers practical approaches to improving teaching and learning at the college level."

The *Democracy in Higher Education Prize* offers $2,500 for an article that "contributes to the expansion of the welcoming and democratic culture of higher learning and the ideal of tolerance, justice, and the unfettered pursuit of truth traditional to the academy."

The *New Unionism in the Academy Prize* offers $2,500 for an article that "describes a higher education local union's collective approach to uniting the academic community in pursuit of quality higher education for all."

The *New Scholar Prize* offers $2,500 for an article by a scholar with less than seven years' full- or part-time employment in higher education. The submission can be made in any of the categories listed above.

Available to: Higher education faculty and staff
Deadline: September 30
Apply to: Con Lehane, Editor, Higher Education Publications (specify prize), above address

**National Endowment for the Arts**
**Literature Program**
**Nancy Hanks Center**
**1100 Pennsylvania Avenue, NW**
**Washington, DC 20506**
**Phone: 202-682-5428**
**E-mail: webmgr@arts.endow.gov**
**Web site: http://www.arts.endow.gov**

Ⓜ *Fellowships in Creative Writing* of $20,000 each are available, in alternating years, to published creative writers of exceptional talent in poetry and in prose (fiction and creative nonfiction). Fellowships are awarded to enable recipients to set aside time for writing, research, travel, and/or general career advancement. In 2003, fellowships are offered to poets. Applicants must meet specific prior-publication requirements. Write, e-mail, or consult the Web site for additional information and current guidelines.

Available to: U. S. citizens
Deadline: Consult the Web site
Apply to: Fellowships in Creative Writing, Information Management Division, Room 815, above address

Ⓣ *Translation Project Grants* of $20,000 each are available to published translators of literature for projects that involve the specific translation of prose (fiction, creative nonfiction, drama) or poetry (including verse drama) from other languages into English. Translations of writers and of work insufficiently represented in English are encouraged. All projects must be creative translations of published literary material into English; the work to be translated should be of interest for its literary excellence and value. Priority will be given to projects that involve work not yet translated into English. Applicants must meet specific prior-publication requirements. Write, e-mail, or consult the Web site for additional information and guidelines.

Available to: U. S. citizens
Deadlines: Consult the Web site
Apply to: Translation Project Grants, Information Management Division, Room 815, above address

**National Endowment for the Humanities**
**1100 Pennsylvania Avenue, NW**
**Washington, DC 20506**
**E-mail: for Fellowships for University Teachers, fellowsuniv@neh.gov; for Fellowships for College Teachers and Independent Scholars, fellowscollind@neh.gov; for Collaborative Research Grants, research@neh.gov**
**Web site: http://www.neh.gov**

*Fellowships for University Teachers, Fellowships for College Teachers and Independent Scholars,* and *Collaborative Research Grants* are offered through the NEH Division of Research for research, editing, and writing in the humanities. These grants are made for scholarly writing rather than fiction or poetry. The term "humanities" includes, but is not limited to, language, both modern and classical; linguistics; literature; history; jurisprudence; philosophy; archaeology; comparative religion; ethics; history, criticism, and theory of the arts; aspects of the social sciences that have humanistic content and employ humanistic methods; and the study and application of the humanities to the human environment, with particular attention to the diverse heritage, traditions, and history of Americans, and to the relevance of the humanities to conditions of national life. Write, e-mail, or see the Web site for further information on stipends, eligibility, and application procedures.

Available to: U. S. citizens and permanent residents
Deadline: May 1 for fellowships; September 1 for research grants
Apply to: Division of Research, above address

**National Foundation for Advancement in the Arts**
**800 Brickell Avenue, Suite 500**
**Miami, FL 33131**
**Phone: 305-377-1140**
**E-mail: info@nfaa.org**
**Web site: http://www.nfaa.org**
**Fax: 305-377-1149**

The *Arts Recognition and Talent Search Program* honors the achievements of high school seniors and other artists seventeen or eighteen years of age. Students demonstrating talent in writing, dance, jazz, theater, music, voice, photography, film and video, and other visual arts are eligible to apply. National finalists are invited to attend National ARTS Week in Miami, and have the opportunity to earn cash awards of up to $3,000 each and be named a Presidential Scholar in the Arts. ARTS Week in Miami includes master and technique classes, workshops, studio exercises, and interviews. NFAA pays all travel expenses. A $25 entry fee is required for applications postmarked by June 1, a $35 fee for those postmarked June 2-October 1. Write or see the Web site for additional information and the required registration form.

Available to: Seventeen- and eighteen-year-olds
Deadline: June 1; October 1, with late fee
Apply to: ARTS Program, above address, or contact high school teachers or counselors

**National Gallery of Art**
**Center for Advanced Study in the Visual Arts**
**Washington, DC 20565**
**E-mail: advstudy@nga.gov**
**Web site: http://www.nga.gov/resources/casva.htm**
**Fax: 202-842-6733**

*Senior Fellowships* and *Visiting Senior Fellowships* are available to scholars who have held a Ph.D. for five years or more or who possess an equivalent record of professional accomplishment, for study in the history, theory, and criticism of the visual arts of any area and any period. Senior Fellowships are normally awarded for an academic year, early fall to late spring; Visiting Senior Fellowships are available for up to sixty days. Fellowships are for full-time research, and scholars are expected to reside in the Washington area for the duration and to participate in the Center's activities. Grants are based on individual need. Senior Fellowships are normally limited to half of an applicant's salary, up to a maximum of $40,000, on the expectation that fellows bring sabbatical stipends or research grants from their home institution. Visiting senior fellows receive a stipend that covers roundtrip travel and local expenses, up to $7,000. Application materials are available online.

Available to: See above
Deadline: October 1 for Senior Fellowships; March 21 and September 21 for Visiting Senior
    Fellowships
Apply to: Senior Fellowship Program, above address

**National Humanities Center**
**PO Box 12256**
**Research Triangle Park, NC 27709-2256**
**E-mail: nhc@ga.unc.edu**
**Web site: http://www.nhc.rtp.nc.us**

The National Humanities Center offers thirty-five to forty residential fellowships for advanced study in all fields of the humanities. Applicants must hold a doctorate or equivalent credentials and have a record of publication. The Center provides an environment for individual research and fosters the exchange of ideas among scholars. Both senior and younger scholars are eligible; the latter should be engaged in research well beyond the subject of their doctoral dissertations. Fellowships are for the academic year (September through May). Individuals involved in the arts may apply. Fellowships are determined individually, the amount of a stipend depending on the needs of the fellow and on the Center's ability to meet them. The average stipend is $35,000, with a few available up to $50,000. Write, e-mail, or see the Web site for further information and application.

Available to: No restrictions
Deadline: October 15
Apply to: Fellowship Program, above address

**National Institute for Labor Relations Research**
**5211 Port Royal Road, Suite 510**
**Springfield, VA 22151**
**E-mail: research@nilrr.org**
**Web site: http://www.nilrr.org**

Ⓙ The *William B. Ruggles Journalism Scholarship* of $2,000 is available yearly to graduate or undergraduate students majoring in journalism or related mass media or mass communications studies who have demonstrated a financial need for tuition assistance. A 500-word essay on the right-to-work principle is required of applicants.

Available to: No restrictions
Deadline: Applications accepted January 1-March 31
Apply to: Mary-Kate Grover, Scholarship Coordinator, via e-mail

**National League of American Pen Women**
**1300 17th Street, NW**
**Washington, DC 20036**
**Phone: 202-785-1997**

Ⓜ The *NLAPW Scholarship for Mature Women in Letters*, in memory of Dr. Adeline Hoffman, offers $1,000 in even-numbered years to a woman over the age of thirty-five. Applicants may submit a published or unpublished article, short story, editorial, drama, teleplay, three poems, or first chapter of a novel. NLAPW members are ineligible. There is an $8 handling fee. Send SASE after August 1 of odd-numbered years for current guidelines.

Available to: See above
Deadline: January 1 of even-numbered years
Apply to: Scholarship for Mature Women in Letters, above address

**National Poetry Series**
**162 Nassau Street**
**Princeton, NJ 08542**
**Web site: www.nationalpoetryseries.org**

Ⓟ The National Poetry Series oversees an annual open competition in which several book-length manuscripts of poetry are selected by five well-known poets and published by participating publishers. Each of the five winning poets receives a $1,000 cash award. Entries must be previously unpublished; chapbooks, previously self-published works, or small clusters of poems are not eligible. Suggested length of manuscripts is 48 to 64 pages. There is a $25 entry fee. Send SASE for guidelines.

Available to: U. S. citizens
Deadline: Submissions accepted January 1-February 15
Apply to: Above address

**National Press Club**
**529 14th Street, NW, 13th floor**
**Washington, DC 20045**
**Web site: http://www.press.org**

Ⓙ The *Ellen Masin Persina/National Press Club Scholarship for Minorities in Journalism* annually awards a $20,000 scholarship to a minority high school senior planning a career in journalism (newspaper, magazine, trade paper, radio, television). The scholarship is awarded over four years of undergraduate studies, at $5,000 per year. See the Web site for more information.

Available to: Minority high school students with GPA 2.75 or higher, preparing to enter college in the upcoming year
Deadline: March 1
Apply to: Scholarship Committee, above address

**National Press Foundation**
**1211 Connecticut Avenue, NW, Suite 310**
**Washington, DC 20036**
**E-mail: npf@nationalpress.org**
**Web site: http://www.natpress.org**
**Fax: 202-530-2855**

Ⓙ The *Evert Clark Award* of $1,000 is given in recognition of outstanding reporting and writing in any field of science by young writers. The winner receives an all-expenses-paid trip to the annual meeting of the American Association for the Advancement of Science. The award is limited to nontechnical print journalism. Write, e-mail, or see the Web site for additional information and application.

Available to: No restrictions
Deadline: Early December (inquire for exact date)
Apply to: Evert Clark Award, above address

Ⓙ The *Everett McKinley Dirksen Award for Distinguished Reporting of Congress* annually offers $5,000 each to a print and a broadcast journalist whose work on the activities of Congress was published or broadcast during the calendar year. Write, e-mail, or consult the Web site for application procedure.

Available to: No restrictions
Deadline: October 1
Apply to: Everett Dirksen Award, above address

Ⓙ *Spanish Language Fellowships* are given to six working journalists, to cover three consecutive months of intensive Spanish language study during the academic year at the Cemanahuac Educational Community School in Cuernavaca, Mexico. The fellowships are given annually in recognition of the importance of Spanish in covering the growth of Hispanic communities in the U. S. as well as Latin American affairs. Write, e-mail, or see the Web site for information and application.

Available to: No restrictions
Deadline: Mid-June (inquire for exact date)
Apply to: Spanish Language Fellowships, above address

The National Press Foundation offers several other fellowships for working print and broadcast journalists to attend specific professional seminars. Write, e-mail, or consult the Web site for information on current offerings and application procedure.

**National Repertory Theatre Foundation**
**PO Box 286**
**Hollywood, CA 90078**
**Phone: 323-465-9517**
**E-mail: nrtf@nrtf.org**
**Web site: http://www.nrtf.org**
**Fax: 323-417-4722**

Ⓓ The *National Play Award*, consisting of $5,000 and production or a staged reading is given annually for an original unpublished full-length play that has not been produced with a paid Equity cast, and has not won a major award or been submitted previously. Four runners-up receive $500 each. There is a $25 submission fee. Send SASE for additional information.

Available to: No restrictions
Deadline: January 1-March 31
Apply to: National Play Award, above address

National Science Foundation
Office of Polar Programs
4201 Wilson Boulevard, Room 755
Arlington, VA 22230
Phone: 703-292-8030
E-mail: gguthrid@nsf.gov
Web site: http://www.nsf.gov/search97cgi/vtopic

The *Antarctic Artists & Writers Program* considers requests from particularly well qualified writers, historians, artists, or others in the liberal arts to work in Antarctica. Although the Foundation does not award funds, selected applicants are provided with polar clothing on loan, travel between New Zealand or southern South America and Antarctica, and room and board and logistics in Antarctica. The applicant pays for a medical examination, travel to a familiarization session in the United States, and any costs of completing and distributing the work. The Foundation may provide roundtrip economy air travel between a U. S. airport and New Zealand or South America. Applicants may seek supplemental funds from additional sources, including other federal agencies. Candidates must be well established and working full-time in their fields and have a means of presenting their work to the public.

Available to: No restrictions
Deadline: Applications accepted May 1-June 1
Apply to: Guy G. Guthridge, above e-mail address


National Screenwriting Competition
145 Broad Street
Matawan, NJ 07747
Phone: 732-566-1800
E-mail: director@skyweb.net
Web site: http://www.nationalscreenwriting.com

Ⓢ The *National Screenwriting Competition* offers a $2,500 first prize, a $500 second prize, and a $250 third prize for full-length film scripts, 90 to 130 pages long. All winning entries will be considered for possible production or development as feature films. There is a $45 entry fee. Send SASE, e-mail, or see the Web site for rules and guidelines.

Available to: No restrictions
Deadline: November 19
Apply to: Above address


National Society of Arts and Letters
4227 46th Street, NW
Washington, DC 20016
Phone: 202-363-5443
Web site: http://www.arts-nsal.org

Ⓜ The *National Society of Arts and Letters Literature Awards* offer cash prizes for creative work by artists ages twenty-six and younger in five categories—art, drama, dance, literature, and music—which rotate each year and include subcategories. The category in 2003 is literature (poetry); in 2005, drama. See the Web site for additional information.

Available to: See above
Deadline: Inquire
Apply to: Above address


National Space Club
2000 L Street NW, Suite 710
Washington, DC 20036
Phone: 202-973-8661

Ⓝ The *Robert H. Goddard Historical Essay Award Competition* offers $1,000 and a plaque for an essay, of no more than 5,000 words, that explores a significant aspect of the historical development of rocketry and astronautics. Entries will be judged on their originality and scholarship. Send SASE for guidelines.

Available to: U. S. citizens
Deadline: December 4
Apply to: Robert H. Goddard Historical Essay Competition, above address

**National Steinbeck Center**
**One Main Street**
**Salinas, CA 93901**
**Phone: 831-796-3833**
**E-mail: info@steinbeck.org**
**Web site: http://www.steinbeck.org**

Ⓕ   The *National Steinbeck Center Writing Competition* offers a first prize of $1,000 and a travel stipend to attend the Steinbeck Festival, for an unpublished short story of up to 5,000 words on a given theme. The winner is announced at the annual festival, held in Salinas in August. There is a $15 entry fee. Send SASE, e-mail, or consult the Web site for competition theme and guidelines.

Available to: No restrictions
Deadline: June 15
Apply to: Writing Competition, above address

**National Women's Studies Association**
**7100 Baltimore Avenue, Suite 500**
**College Park, MD 20740**
**E-mail: nwsa@umail.umd.edu**

The *Graduate Scholarship Award* of $1,000 is given to a student who is engaged in the research or writing stages of a master's thesis or Ph.D. dissertation in the interdisciplinary field of women's studies.

Available to: NWSA members
Deadline: Inquire
Apply to: Graduate Scholarship Award, above address

The *Graduate Scholarship in Lesbian Studies* awards $500 to a student who will be doing research or writing a master's thesis or Ph.D. dissertation in lesbian studies.

Available to: See above
Deadline: Inquire
Apply to: Graduate Scholarship in Lesbian Studies, above address

The *Jewish Caucus Prize* awards $500 to a graduate student enrolled for the fall semester whose area of research is Jewish women's studies.

Available to: See above
Deadline: Inquire
Apply to: Jewish Caucus Prize, above address

**National Writers Association**
**3140 South Peoria, #295**
**Aurora, CO 80014**
**E-mail: contests@nationalwriters.com**
**Web site: http://www.nationalwriters.com**

Ⓕ   The *Novel Writing Contest* offers a first prize of $500, a second of $250, and a third of $150 for unpublished novels of any genre. Manuscripts may be up to 90,000 words. There is a $35 entry fee; a critique of the submitted manuscript is available for an additional $1.25 per 1,000 words. Judging sheets are sent to applicants if SASE is enclosed with the submission. Send SASE or see the Web site for guidelines and application.

Available to: No restrictions
Deadline: April 1
Apply to: Novel Writing Contest, above address

In addition, the National Writers Association sponsors a *Screenplay Contest* and offers the *David Raffelock Award for Publishing Excellence*. Consult the Web site for more information.

**National Writers' United Service Organization**
**113 University Place, 6th floor**
**New York, NY 10003**
**Fax: 212-254-0673**
**Web site: www.bellwetherprize.org**

Ⓕ The *Bellwether Prize*, established and funded by Barbara Kingsolver, biennially offers $25,000 and publication by a major publisher (in 2000 it was HarperCollins) for a literary novel whose content addresses the subject of social justice and the impact of culture and politics on human relationships. Applicants for the prize must be U. S. citizens who have some publication history, but who have not published a book that sold more than 10,000 copies. The submission must be an original, previously unpublished novel of at least 80,000 words. All submissions must be accompanied by an application form and a $25 processing fee. Consult the Web site for complete guidelines, eligibility requirements, and application form before submission.

Available to: See above
Deadline: Submissions accepted during September 2003
Apply to: Bellwether Prize, above address

**Native American Journalists Association**
**3359 36th Avenue, South**
**Minneapolis, MN 55406**
**Phone: 612-729-9244**
**E-mail: info@naja.com**
**Web site: http://www.naja.com**
**Fax: 612-729-9373**

Ⓙ The Native American Journalists Association offers scholarships and internships. Scholarship recipients receive financial assistance for books and tuition costs. Interns have on-the-job learning opportunities with Native and mainstream organizations. See the Web site for additional information.

Available to: Native American journalism students
Deadline: Inquire
Apply to: Above address

**Native Writers' Circle of the Americas**
**English Department**
**University of Oklahoma**
**Norman, OK 73019-0240**

[IN] *Lifetime Achievement Awards for Literature* are given to Native American writers selected by fellow Native American writers. The awards carry a cash prize that varies yearly according to funding. There is no application process. *By Internal Nomination Only*.

Ⓜ The *North American Native Authors First Book Awards for Poetry and Prose* offer $500 in each genre and possible publication in book form. The awards are open to Native Americans of American Indian, Aleut, Inuit, or métis ancestry who have not yet published a book. Writers may be from North America, Mexico, or Central America; manuscripts must be in English or in bilingual format. Write for guidelines and further information.

Available to: See above
Deadline: Inquire
Apply to: North American Native Authors First Book Awards, above address

**Naval Historical Center**
**Washington Navy Yard**
**805 Kidder Breese, SE**
**Washington, DC 20374-5060**
**Web site: http://www.history.navy.mil**

Ⓝ The *Ernest M. Eller Prize in Naval History* annually offers $1,000 to the author of the best article on U. S. naval history published in a scholarly journal. Write or consult the Web site for further information.

Available to: No restrictions
Deadline: June 1
Apply to: Senior Historian, above address

Ⓝ The *Rear Admiral John D. Hayes Pre-Doctoral Fellowship* offers a stipend of $10,000 to support dissertation research and writing on any aspect of U. S. naval history. Write or consult the Web site for further information.

Available to: U. S. citizens enrolled in a recognized graduate school who will complete all requirements for a Ph.D. except the dissertation by June 30 of the application year and who have an approved dissertation topic in U. S. naval history
Deadline: February 28
Apply to: Senior Historian, above address

Ⓝ The *Vice-Admiral Edwin B. Hooper Research Grant* offers two awards, of up to $2,500 each, to scholars engaged in the research or writing of books or articles. Swards are to be used for travel, living, and document duplication costs related to the research project. Write or consult the Web site for further information.

Available to: U. S. citizens with a Ph.D. from an accredited university or equivalent attainment as published authors
Deadline: February 28
Apply to: Senior Historian, above address

**Nebraska Arts Council**
**3838 Davenport Street**
**Omaha, NE 68131-2329**
**Phone: 402-595-2122**
**Web site: http://www.nebraskaartscouncil.org**
**Fax: 402-595-2334**

Ⓜ *Individual Artist Fellowships* in literature are given every three years to Nebraska writers with demonstrated records of professional achievement. Three Distinguished Achievement Awards of $5,000 and several Merit Awards of $2,000 and $1,000 are available. In addition, *Artists in Schools/Communities Residency Sponsor Grants* support fees for artists' residences in school or community settings. Writers must be residents of Nebraska for at least two years before applying, and may not be students in an undergraduate or graduate degree program in the fellowship field. Applications are available on the Council's Web site.

Available to: Nebraska residents
Deadline: November 15 for Individual Artist Fellowships; March 1 and October for Artists in Schools/Communities Residency requesting more than $2,000; for all other applications, floating deadline of six weeks before project start date
Apply to: Above address

**The Nebraska Review**
**University of Nebraska at Omaha**
**College of Fine Arts**
**Omaha, NE 68182-0324**

Ⓜ The *Nebraska Review Fiction Prize, Creative Nonfiction Prize,* and *Poetry Prize* each offer $500 and publication for the best story or essay of 5,000 words or less, and for the best poem or group of poems, not to exceed five poems or six pages. There is a $15 entry fee. All entrants receive a one-year subscription to *The Nebraska Review*.

Available to: No restrictions
Deadline: November 30
Apply to: Fiction Prize, Creative Nonfiction, or Poetry Prize, above address

## Negative Capability Magazine
**62 Ridgelawn Drive East**
**Mobile, AL 36608**

Ⓕ Ⓟ The *Negative Capability Short Fiction Award* and the *Eve of St. Agnes Award in Poetry* each offer a cash prize of $500 and publication in *Negative Capability*. Fiction writers should submit unpublished short fiction of 1,500 to 4,500 words, with a $10 reading fee; poets may submit as many poems as they like, with $3 per poem. Send SASE for guidelines.

Available to: No restrictions
Deadline: January 15
Apply to: Short Fiction Award or Eve of St. Agnes Award in Poetry, above address

## Nevada Arts Council
**716 North Carson Street, Suite A**
**Carson City, NV 89701**
**Phone: 775-687-6680**
**E-mail: lvats@gov.mail.state.nv.us**
**Web site: www.nevadaculture.org**
**Fax: 775-687-6688**

Ⓜ *Jackpot Grants* of amounts up to $1,000 are available quarterly for arts projects and professional development opportunities. Fellowships of $5,000 each are offered annually to six professional Nevada artists in the literary, performing, and visual arts. Write or fax for additional information and guidelines.

Available to: Professional artists who are Nevada residents
Deadline: Inquire
Apply to: Call the Council or see its Web site

## New Century Writer Awards
**32 Alfred Street, Suite B**
**New Haven, CT 06512-3927**
**E-mail: newcenturywriter@yahoo.com**
**Web site: http://www.newcenturywriter.org**
**Fax: 203-468-0333**

Ⓜ The *New Century Writer Awards* are a suite of prizes intended to recognize and develop work by undiscovered writers, and to connect these new writers with publishers, producers, and agents. Awards are given as follows. Category I (short story): First- and second-place winners receive *Ray Bradbury Short Story Fellowships* to attend the Zoetrope Short Story Writers' Workshop, a weeklong program held at Francis Ford Coppola's Blancaneaux Lodge, in Belize. Each fellowship includes roundtrip air fare (for flights originating in the U. S. or Canada only), tuition, housing, meals (excluding alcoholic drinks), and a cash stipend. The third-place winner receives $500; fourth through tenth places, $100. Category II (novels/novella): First place, $2,000; second place, $1,000; third place, $500; fourth through tenth-places, $100. Category III (poetry): First place, $500; second place, $250; third place, $100. Category IV (screenplay): First place, $3,000; second place, $1,500; third place, $500; fourth through tenth-places, $200. Category V (stage play): First place, $2,000; second place, $1,000; third place, $500; fourth through tenth-places, $200. Write, e-mail, or see the Web site for additional information and application.

Available to: No restrictions
Deadline: January 31 (short story); March 30 (novel/novella); May 31 (poetry); July 31 (screenplay); July 31 (stage play)
Apply to: New Century Writer Awards, above address

**New Dramatists**
**424 West 44th Street**
**New York, NY 10036**
**E-mail: info@newdramatists.org**
**Web site: http://www.newdramatists.org**

ⅅ New Dramatists, a service organization, offers seven-year memberships to emerging playwrights of talent and ability. During this period, they are encouraged to use the organization's resources to develop and refine their artistry and vision. Primary among the services offered to members are play development workshops; playwright exchange programs with Australia, England, and Los Angeles; and ScriptShare, a national script distribution service. Additional services include musical theater workshops; writer work spaces; free-ticket program; script-copying facilities; and a summer playwriting residency in Lake Placid, New York. Write for additional information and guidelines.

Available to: Playwrights who live in the New York City area or who visit enough to take advantage of the programs and to participate in the community of playwrights
Deadline: Submissions accepted between July 15 and September 15
Apply to: Above address

**New England Poetry Club**
**2 Farrar Street**
**Cambridge, MA 02138**

ⓅThe *Daniel Varoujan Prize* annually awards $1,000 for a poem "worthy of the Armenian poet Daniel Varoujan, who was killed by the Turks in 1915." Translations are not eligible. For those who are not members of the New England Poetry Club, a reading fee of $10 must accompany each entry of three poems. Send SASE for complete guidelines to Virginia Thayer, 11 Puritan Road, Arlington, MA 02476.

Available to: No restrictions
Deadline: June 30
Apply to: Above address (Cambridge)

The Club offers several other awards, with lesser cash prizes, for individual poems. Inquire for further information.

**New England Theatre Conference**
**Northeastern University**
**360 Huntington Avenue**
**Boston, MA 02115**
**E-mail: netc@world.std.com**
**Web site: www.NETConline.org**
**Fax: 617-424-1057**

ⅅThe *John Gassner Memorial Playwriting Competition* offers cash awards for commercially unpublished, unproduced full-length plays. Send SASE for guidelines before submitting.

Available to: New England residents and NETC members
Deadline: April 15
Apply to: John Gassner Memorial Playwriting Competition, above address

©ⅅThe *Aurand Harris Memorial Playwriting Competition* offers cash awards for commercially unpublished, unproduced plays for young audiences. Send SASE for guidelines before submitting.

Available to: New England residents and NETC members
Deadline: May 1
Apply to: Aurand Harris Memorial Playwriting Competition, above address

172

**New Hampshire State Council on the Arts**
**40 North Main Street**
**Concord, NH 03301-4974**
**Web site: http://www.state.nh.us/nharts**
**Fax: 603-271-3584**

(M) *Individual Artist Fellowships* of up to $5,000 are available to New Hampshire writers in fiction, poetry, and playwriting. Write or consult the Web site for guidelines and application.

> Available to: New Hampshire residents of at least one year, over eighteen years of age, not enrolled as full-time students, and not recipients in the preceding year
> Deadline: Inquire
> Apply to: Above address

**New Hampshire Writers and Publishers Project**
**PO Box 2693**
**Concord, NH 03302-2693**
**Phone: 603-226-6649**
**E-mail: nhwp@nh.ultranet.com**
**Web site: http://www.nhwritersproject.org**

(M) The New Hampshire Writers and Publishers Project biennially offers the following awards: the *Jane Kenyon Award,* for an outstanding book of poetry published by a New Hampshire poet; the *Outstanding Emerging Writer Award,* given to a promising New Hampshire writer (published or unpublished) who has not yet been recognized widely; the *Outstanding Work of Fiction Award* and *Outstanding Work of Nonfiction Award* for published work by a New Hampshire writer; and the *Lifetime Achievement Award.* Each award carries a cash prize of $500 and is given in odd-numbered years. Write, call, or e-mail for guidelines and nomination form. There is a $25 submission fee.

> Available to: New Hampshire writers
> Deadline: Inquire
> Apply to: Above address

**The New Harmony Project**
**613 North East Street**
**Indianapolis, IN 46202**
**Web site: www.newharmonyproject.org**
**Fax: 317-635-4201**

(D) The New Harmony Project seeks writers and scripts that "explore the human journey by offering hope and showing respect for the positive values of life" for an annual development conference in historic New Harmony, Indiana. Writers and their work are offered a series of rehearsals and readings with actors, dramaturgs, and other media professionals, and are given time and freedom to explore their work in a setting removed from the pressures of production. Send SASE or see the Web site for complete guidelines.

> Available to: No restrictions
> Deadline: Mid-September (inquire for exact date)
> Apply to: Selection Committee, above address

**New Issues Press**
**Department of English**
**Western Michigan University**
**1201 Oliver Street**
**Kalamazoo, MI 49008-5092**
**Web site: http://www.wmich.edu/english/fac/nipps**

(P) The *Green Rose Prize in Poetry* annually awards $1,000 and publication for a book of poems by a poet who has published one or more full-length collections. Poets may submit manuscripts of 50 to 120 pages. Individual collections and volumes of new and selected poems are eligible. There is a $20 reading fee. New Issues may publish as many as three other manuscripts from the competition. Send SASE or see the Web site for guidelines.

Available to: Established poets writing in English
Deadline: September 30
Apply to: Green Rose Prize, above address

(P) The *New Issues First Book of Poetry Prize* annually awards $1,000 and publication for a first book of poems by a poet who has not published a full-length collection in an edition of 500 or more copies. Poets may submit manuscripts of 48 to 72 pages; there is a $12 reading fee. All entries are considered for publication. Send SASE or see the Web site for guidelines.

Available to: U. S. citizens or residents
Deadline: November 30
Apply to: New Issues First Book of Poetry Prize, above address

**New Jersey Council for the Humanities**
**28 West State Street, 6th floor**
**Trenton, NJ 08608-1602**
**E-mail: njch@njch.org**

(N) The *New Jersey Council for the Humanities Book Award* of $1,000 is given annually for the best nonfiction book in the humanities directed toward a general audience and written by an individual with a New Jersey connection (birth, current residence, place of work, subject matter, etc.). Write or e-mail for additional information.

Available to: See above
Deadline: May 1
Apply to: Above address

**New Jersey State Council on the Arts**
**225 West State Street**
**PO Box 306**
**Trenton, NJ 08625-0306**
**Phone: 609-292-6130**
**Web site: http://www.nj.artscouncil.org**
**Fax: 609-989-1440**

(M) The *New Jersey State Council on the Arts Fellowship Program* awards fellowships in poetry, prose, and playwriting in odd-numbered years. Fellowships are highly competitive and are given on the basis of artistic excellence. Applications are reviewed anonymously by a peer panel. Write or see the Web site for application.

Available to: New Jersey residents
Deadline: July 15
Apply to: NJSCA Fellowships, c/o MAAF, 22 Light Street, Baltimore, MD 21202

The *New Jersey Writers Project* places dozens of professional writers, playwrights, and poets in short-term residences in approximately two hundred New Jersey schools each year. Schools make the request for writer visits. Council funds pay for a portion of the writers' fees. Writers may apply to become certified to conduct residences.

Available to: Professional, practicing writers
Deadline: Mid-January
Apply to: Above address

**New Letters Magazine**
University of Missouri-Kansas City
University House
5101 Rockhill Road
Kansas City, MO 64110
E-mail: newletters@umkc.edu
Web site: http://www.umkc.edu/newletters
Fax: 816-235-2611

In addition to receiving the monetary prizes listed below, winners have their work published in the annual awards issue of *New Letters*, an international magazine of arts and letters. Each entry for each prize must be accompanied by a $10 reading fee. All entries must be previously unpublished. Send SASE for guidelines.

(N)     The *New Letters Creative Nonfiction Prize* awards $1,000 for the best creative nonfiction of 5,000 words or less. Applicants are strongly discouraged from submitting annotated, footnoted, or academic work.

(F)     The *New Letters Fiction Prize* awards $1,000 for the best short story of 5,000 words or less.

(P)     The *New Letters Poetry Prize* awards $1,000 for the best entry of three to six poems.

Available to: No restrictions
Deadline: May 15
Apply to: New Letters Literary Awards (specify genre), above address


**New Millennium Writings**
Room M2, PO Box 2463
Knoxville, TN 37901
E-mail: donwilliams7@att.net
Web site: http://www.newmillenniumwritings.com/awards.html

(M)     The *New Millennium Awards* offer $1,000 each for fiction, poetry, and nonfiction. All winning submissions are published in *New Millennium Writings*. There are no restrictions as to style or content; stories and essays should be no longer than 6,000 words, and poetry should be no more than three poems totaling no more than 5 pages. There is a $16 fee for each contest entry (one story; one essay; up to three poems). All contestants receive a copy of the issue in which the winning submissions appear. Send SASE or see the Web site for further information.

Available to: No restrictions
Deadline: July 31
Apply to: NMW Contest, above address


**New Orleans Literary Festival.** *See* **Tennessee Williams/New Orleans Literary Festival**


**New Professional Theatre**
424 West 42nd Street, 3rd floor
New York, NY 10036
E-mail: newprof@aol.com
Web site: www.newprofessionaltheatre.com
Fax: 212-398-2666

(D)     The *New Professional Theatre Writers Festival* annually offers three awards of $2,000 each for a full-length play by an African-American playwright, with special consideration given to work by women. Winning playwrights receive dramaturgical support and mentoring, as well as a stage reading, and are given the opportunity to attend business seminars. Excerpts of the winning plays are performed at the theater's October gala. There is a $15 administrative fee. Send SASE, fax, or e-mail for guidelines.

Available to: African-American playwrights
Deadline: June 1
Apply to: Writers Festival, above address

**New York Foundation for the Arts**
155 Avenue of the Americas, 14th floor
New York, NY 10013
Phone: 212-366-6900, ext. 217
E-mail: nyfaafp@nyfa.org
Web site: http://www.nyfa.org
Fax: 212-366-1778

*Artists' Fellowships* are granted to individual New York State creative artists, on the basis of the excellence of recent work, submitted as described below. The 2002-2003 cycle is for the following categories: computer arts, crafts, film, nonfiction literature, performance art/multidisciplinary work, poetry, printmaking/drawing/artists' books, sculpture. The $7,000 fellowship award may be used however the recipient sees fit. Recipients are required to perform a mutually agreed-upon public service during the grant period. See the Web site or e-mail for more details.

> Available to: New York State residents of at least two years, nonstudents, over eighteen years old
> Deadline: October (inquire for exact dates)
> Apply to: Artists' Fellowships, above address

**New York Mills Arts Retreat**
24 North Main Avenue
PO Box 246
New York Mills, MN 56567
Phone: 218-385-3339
E-mail: nymills@uslink.net
Web site: www.kulcher.org

® The New York Mills Regional Cultural Center offers residences of two or four weeks, in which artists live in a small, rural Minnesota community. Residents are given studio space and their own small house in town. In exchange, they work within the community for eight hours a week or more, depending on the length of the residence. Artists from Minnesota and New York are eligible for stipends from the Jerome Foundation, which provides fellowships above and beyond the accommodations.

> Available to: No restrictions
> Deadline: April 1 and October 1
> Apply to: Above address

**New York Public Library**
**Center for Scholars and Writers**
**Fifth Avenue & 42nd Street, Room 225**
New York, NY 10018-2788
Web site: http://www.nypl.org
Fax: 212-768-7439

The Center for Scholars and Writers annually awards up to fifteen resident fellowships to scholars, nonacademic research professionals, scientists engaged in the humanities, and creative writers of demonstrated achievement whose proposed work requires access to the rich and diverse collection of the Humanities and Social Sciences Library. Fellows are required to be in continuous residence for the academic year and to participate as much as possible in such Center activities as daily lunches, readings, lectures, colloquia, symposia, and conferences; they are also responsible for a public presentation of publishable quality. Fellows receive a stipend of $50,000. Write or see the Web site for additional information.

> Available to: See above
> Deadline: October 1
> Apply to: Center for Scholars and Writers, above address

**New York Public Library**
**Publications Office**
**8 West 40th Street, 6th floor**
**New York, NY 10018-2788**
**Web site: http://www.nypl.org**

Ⓙ Ⓝ  The *New York Public Library Helen Bernstein Book Award for Excellence in Journalism* annually offers $15,000 to an outstanding journalist "whose book has made an impact on public consciousness, events, or policy." Four finalists each receive $1,000. To be eligible, a book must be an outgrowth of the author's work as a journalist. Publishers, agents, or journalists may nominate books published within the calendar year by submitting five copies (or bound galleys), biographical information about the author, and available reviews. Authors may not nominate their own work. Write or see the Web site for further details and nomination form.

Available to: No restrictions
Deadline: October 1
Apply to: Above address

Ⓕ  The *Young Lions Fiction Award* of $10,000 annually honors a novel or a collection of short stories published within the calendar year by an American author age thirty-five or younger. Nominees are selected by a reading committee; the winner is announced at the award ceremony. Consult the Web site www.nypl.org/admin/pro/ylaward.htm for application and guidelines.

Available to: See above
Deadline: Inquire
Apply to: Above address

**New York State Archives Partnership Trust**
**9C49 Cultural Education Center**
**Albany, NY 12230**
**Phone: 518-473-7091**
**E-mail: aptrust@mail.nysed.gov**
**Web site: http://www.nysarchives.org**
**Fax: 518-473-7058**

The *Larry J. Hackman Research Residency Program* awards funds to pursue research using the holdings of the New York State Archives. The program supports advanced work in New York State history, government, or public policy, with preference given to projects that relate to enduring public policy, particularly in New York State, and that demonstrate a high probability of publication or other public dissemination. Although any proposal for advanced research will be considered, applicants working on doctoral dissertations and those at the postdoctoral level are especially encouraged to apply. Awards, intended to defray travel, living, and research expenses, range from $400 to $4,500, depending on need; they are greater for in-depth research over a substantial period of time. Write or see the Web site for guidelines and application.

Available to: No restrictions
Deadline: January 31
Apply to: Above address

**New York State Historical Association**
**PO Box 800**
**Cooperstown, NY 13326**
**Phone: 607-547-1491**
**Web site: http://www.nysha.org**
**Fax: 607-547-1405**

Ⓝ  The *Dixon Ryan Fox Manuscript Prize of the New York State Historical Association*, consisting of $3,000 and assistance in publication, is awarded annually to the best unpublished book-length monograph on an aspect of New York State history, as judged by a special editorial committee.

Available to: No restrictions
Deadline: January 20
Apply to: Daniel Goodwin, Director of Publications, above address

**New York State Writers Institute**
**State University at Albany**
**Humanities 355**
**Albany, NY 12222**
**E-mail: writers@uamail.albany.edu**
**Web site: http://www.albany.edu/writers-inst/**

[IN]   The *New York State Edith Wharton Citation of Merit* (State Author) and the *New York State Walt Whitman Citation of Merit* (State Poet) are awarded biennially to a New York state fiction writer and a New York state poet, respectively, for a lifetime of works of distinction. Winners receive an honorarium of $10,000 and must give two public readings a year. There is no application process. *By Internal Nomination Only.*


**New York Stories**
**La Guardia Community College**
**English Department, E-103**
**31-10 Thomson Avenue**
**Long Island City, NY 11101**
**E-mail: ventry@aol.com**
**Web site: www.newyorkstories.org**

(F)   The *New York Stories Fiction Prize* offers $750 and publication for an unpublished short story not longer than 6,500 words. There is a $15 entry fee. Consult the Web site for guidelines.

Available to: No restrictions
Deadline: Inquire
Apply to: New York Stories Fiction Prize, above address


**Newberry Library**
**60 West Walton**
**Chicago, IL 60610**
**E-mail: research@newberry.org**
**Web site: http://www.newberry.org**

The Newberry Library offers a number of long-term fellowships to postdoctoral scholars and, in some cases, Ph.D. candidates, for periods of six to eleven months. These include the *National Endowment for the Humanities Fellowship*; the *Lloyd Lewis Fellowship in American History*; the *Monticello College Foundation Fellowship for Women*, designed for a woman early in her academic career whose work gives clear promise of scholarly productivity; the *Mellon Postdoctoral Research Fellowship*; and the *Spencer Foundation Fellowship in the History of Education*. Stipends and application procedures vary. Write, e-mail, or consult the Web site for further information and application.

Available to: See above
Deadline: Mid-January (inquire for exact date)
Apply to: Committee on Awards, above address

Short-term residential fellowships are available to scholars in the humanities, including those at the dissertation stage, who desire a residency to use particular Newberry collections. These include the *Newberry Library/American Antiquarian Society Short-Term Fellowship*; the *American Society for Eighteenth-Century Studies Fellowships*, for scholars wishing to use the Newberry's collections to study the period 1660-1815; the *Frances C. Allen Fellowship* for women of Native American heritage; and the *Arthur Weinberg Fellowship for Independent Scholars* for people outside the academy who have demonstrated excellence through publishing and who are working in a field appropriate to the Newberry's collections. Stipends and application procedures vary. Write, e-mail, or see the Web site for further information and application.

Available to: No restrictions
Deadline: Mid-February (inquire for exact date)
Apply to: Committee on Awards, above address

The Center for Renaissance Studies at the Newberry Library offers three types of awards:

*Consortium Funds*, for faculty members and graduate students of the Center's member institutions, to participate in a broad range of interdisciplinary and archival programs at the Library or the Folger Institute; the *Audrey Lumsden-Kouvel Fellowship*, carrying a stipend of up to $3,000 for postdoctoral scholars in late medieval or Renaissance studies who wish to carry on research in residence at the Library for three months; and the *Rockefeller Foundation Fellowship in Gender Studies in Early Modern Europe*, for postdoctoral scholars in literature, history, and other humanities fields who will spend ten months in full-time residence at the Library.

Available to: See above
Deadline: March 1
Apply to: Center for Renaissance Studies, above address

The *Newberry-British Academy Fellowship for Study in Great Britain* offers a three-month exchange fellowship for study in Great Britain to scholars in any field in which the Newberry holdings are strong. This postdoctoral award pays £40 per day in Great Britain. Preference is given to readers and staff of the Newberry and to scholars who have used the Library. Write for further information and application.

Available to: Ph.D. scholars
Deadline: Mid-January (inquire for exact date)
Apply to: Newberry-British Academy Fellowship, above address

**Newcomen Society in the United States**
**412 Newcomen Road**
**Exton, PA 19341**
**Phone: 610-363-6600**
**Web site: www.newcomen.org**

Ⓝ The *Thomas Newcomen Book Award in Business History* is given in cooperation with *Business History Review* to the author of an outstanding book dealing with the history of business in the U. S. or Canada. One award of $4,000 is granted triennially; it will be awarded next in 2004.

Available to: No restrictions
Deadline: Inquire
Apply to: Book Review Editor, Business History Review, Harvard Business School Publishing, 60 Harvard Way, Boston, MA 02163

**Newspaper Guild—CWA**
**501 Third Street, NW, 2nd floor**
**Washington, DC 20001**
**Phone: 202-434-7177**
**Web site: http://www.newsguild.org**

Ⓙ The *Heywood Broun Award* is given annually for work published or broadcast during the preceding calendar year that embodies "the spirit of Heywood Broun," the newspaper columnist who was the Guild's founder. Eligible are nonmanagerial employees of newspapers, news services, newsmagazines, and radio and television stations in the United States, Canada, and Puerto Rico, whether members of the Guild or not. One $5,000 award is given annually, and two awards of $1,000 are given for entries of substantial distinction (one for a broadcast entry). Write or see the Web site for guidelines.

Available to: See above
Deadline: January (inquire for exact date)
Apply to: Broun Award Committee, above address

Nieman Foundation
Harvard University
Walter Lippmann House
One Francis Avenue
Cambridge, MA 02138
E-mail: sgoldstein@harvard.edu
Web site: http://www.nieman.harvard.edu
Fax: 617-495-8976

Ⓙ    The *Christopher J. Georges Journalism Scholarship* awards $10,000 to a journalist age thirty or under, to support an independent investigative reporting project. In addition to a written proposal for the project, candidates are asked to submit a résumé, a brief biographical essay, and a selection of published work. The journalist chosen receives a portion of the award at the beginning of the project and the remainder upon publication of the story or stories. See the Web site for guidelines and application.

Available to: See above
Deadline: December 31
Apply to: Christopher J. Georges Scholarship, above address

Ⓙ Ⓡ  The *Lucius W. Nieman Fellowships for Journalists* offer working journalists a mid-career opportunity to study and broaden their intellectual horizons in residence at Harvard. Applicants must have at least three years' media experience and must obtain employer consent for a leave of absence for the academic year. Fellows agree to refrain from professional work during that period; to complete all work in at least two academic courses, one each semester; to remain in residence during term time; and to return at the end of the sabbatical year to the employer who granted the leave of absence. Each year fellowships are awarded to some twelve U. S. and ten to twelve international journalists. U. S. journalists receive tuition and a $40,000 stipend for living expenses. Funding arrangements vary for international journalists, who must obtain funding by competing successfully for restricted grants available to the Nieman Foundation, or securing their own financial backing.

Available to: Working journalists
Deadlines: January 31 for U. S. journalists; March 1 for international
Apply to: Program Officer, above address


Nimrod International Journal of Fiction & Poetry
University of Tulsa
600 South College
Tulsa, OK 74104
E-mail: nimrod@utulsa.edu
Web site: http://www.utulsa.edu/nimrod
Fax: 918-631-3033

Ⓕ Ⓟ  *Nimrod* sponsors the *Pablo Neruda Prize for Poetry* and the *Katherine Anne Porter Prize for Fiction*, each offering a first prize of $2,000 and a second prize of $1,000. Winners are flown to Tulsa for readings and an awards dinner with the judges. The $20 entry fee covers a subscription to *Nimrod*. Send SASE for guidelines.

Available to: Authors of previously unpublished works
Deadline: Submissions accepted January 1-April 20
Apply to: Nimrod Prize Competition, above address


96 Inc.
PO Box 15559
Boston, MA 02215

The *Bruce Rossley Literary Award* of $1,000, named for Boston's first commissioner of the arts and humanities, is presented in even-numbered years to a writer of merit by 96 Inc., an artists' collaborative and literary magazine. There are no specific publication requirements for eligibility; anyone may nominate a writer by sending a letter of recommendation and support materials. The writer's accomplishments in teaching and community service will be considered. Send SASE to above address for guidelines.

Available to: No restrictions
Deadline: Inquire
Apply to: Above address

**Norcroft**
**PO Box 218**
**Lutson, MN 55612**
**E-mail: info@norcroft.org**
**Web site: www.norcroft.org**

® Residences of one to four weeks from May through October at a remote lodge on the shores of Lake Superior are available to feminist women writers whose work demonstrates an understanding of and commitment to feminist change. Each resident has her own private bedroom and individual "writing shed." Housing is free; groceries are provided for residents to do their own cooking. Send SASE for application.

Available to: Women writers age twenty-one or over
Deadline: October 1
Apply to: Above address

**North American Conference on British Studies**
**Department of History**
**University of Texas**
**Austin, TX 78712**
**E-mail: levack@mail.utexas.edu**
**Web site: www.nacbs.org**

Ⓝ The *John Ben Snow Foundation Prize* awards $1,000 for the best book published annually on any topic in British studies before 1800. The *British Council Prize* awards $1,000 for the best book published annually on any topic in British studies after 1800. Consult the Web site for submission procedures.

Available to: Citizens or permanent residents of U. S. and Canada
Deadline: Submissions accepted January 1-April 1
Apply to: Brian Levack, above address

**North Carolina Arts Council**
**Department of Cultural Resources**
**Raleigh, NC 27699-4632**
**Web site: http://www.ncarts.org**
**Fax: 919-733-4834**

Ⓜ® Fellowships of up to $10,000 are available to North Carolina artists in various disciplines including performance, literary and visual arts. The applicants should, through their artistic work, provide programs or services to the state's arts community, or promote awareness about the arts in the state; advance public discussion and understanding of an artist or art form; support an innovative arts program for public radio or public television. The Council also supports residence opportunities for writers at Headlands Center for the Arts in California, the La Napoule Foundation in France, and the Vermont Studio Center. Write, e-mail, or see the Web site for additional information and guidelines.

Available to: North Carolina residents
Deadline: Inquire
Apply to: Literature Director, above address

**North Carolina Writers' Network**
**Box 954**
**Carrboro, NC 27510**
**E-mail: mail@ncwriters.org**
**Web site: http://www.ncwriters.org**
**Fax: 919-929-0535**

Ⓓ The *Paul Green Playwrights Prize* of $500 is given annually for an unpublished, unproduced play on any theme (no musicals). Playwrights should submit two copies and a synopsis. There is a $12 entry fee.

Available to: No restrictions
Deadline: September 30
Apply to: Paul Green Playwrights Prize, North Carolina Writers' Network, 3501 Highway 54 West, Studio C, Chapel Hill, NC 27516

(P)    The *Randall Jarrell Poetry Prize* of $1,000 is given annually for an unpublished poem composed in any form or genre. The winner will be published in *Parnassus: Poetry in Review*. Two copies of up to three poems should be submitted, not exceeding a total of 10 single-spaced pages. There is a $10 entry fee.

Available to: No restrictions
Deadline: November 1
Apply to: Randall Jarrell Poetry Prize, North Carolina Writers' Network, 3501 Highway 54 West, Studio C, Chapel Hill, NC 27516

**Northeastern University**
**English Department**
**406 Holmes Hall**
**Boston, MA 02115**
**Web site: http://www.casdn.neu.edu/~english/morse.htm**

(P)    The *Samuel French Morse Poetry Prize*, awarded annually for the manuscript of a first or second book of poems by a U. S. poet, consists of publication of the work by Northeastern University Press and a cash award of $1,000. A $15 reading fee must accompany the manuscript. Send SASE or see the Web site for guidelines.

Available to: U. S. citizens and residents
Deadline: September 15
Apply to: Professor Guy Rotella, Editor, Morse Poetry Prize, above address

**Northern Kentucky University**
**Department of Theatre**
**Highland Heights, KY 41099-1007**
**E-mail: forman@nku.edu**
**Fax: 606-572-6057**

(D)    The *Year-End-Series New Play Festival* biennially awards four prizes of $500 each, plus production and travel expenses to attend late rehearsals and performance, for unproduced musicals, adaptations, and plays. Preference is given to plays with roles that can be handled by actors eighteen to twenty-five years old. Write for application.

Available to: No restrictions
Deadline: October 31
Apply to: YES Project Director, above address

**Northern Michigan University**
**Forest Roberts Theatre**
**1401 Presque Isle Avenue**
**Marquette, MI 49855-5364**
**E-mail: theater@nmu.edu**
**Web site: http://www.nmu.edu/theatre**

(D)    The *Mildred and Albert Panowski Playwriting Award* of $2,000 is given to the author of the best original full-length play, unproduced and unpublished, submitted to the competition. A full production of the winning play will be included in the Forest Roberts Theatre season. The playwright will act as artist-in-residence at the university during the run of the show, with transportation and room and board provided. Send SASE or see the Web site for guidelines.

Available to: No restrictions
Deadline: Friday before Thanksgiving
Apply to: Panowski Playwriting Contest, above address

Northwood University
Alden B. Dow Creativity Center
4000 Whiting Drive
Midland, MI 48640
Phone: 989-837-4478
E-mail: creativity@northwood.edu
Web site: www.northwood.edu/abd
Fax: 989-837-4468

®    The *Summer Residency Fellowship Program* is open to individuals in all professions who wish
to pursue innovative and creative ideas. Awards for the ten-week residency include travel
to/from Midland, room and board, and a $750 stipend. Fellows should be able to work
independently and live cooperatively. Project ideas should be submitted with specific
goals attainable during the residency. Accommodations for spouses/families are not
available. There is a $10 application fee. Write for additional information and guidelines
or see the Web site.

Available to: U. S. citizens
Deadline: Submissions must be postmarked by December 31
Apply to: Above address


NORWAY
Nordmanns-Forbundet (The Norse Federation)
Rådhusgaten 23b
0158 Oslo
Norway
E-mail: norseman@norseman.no
Web site: www.norseman.no

The *Emigration Fund of 1975* awards grants to U. S. citizens and residents for advanced or
specialized studies in Norway of subjects dealing with emigration history and other
relations between the U. S. and Norway. The *HM King Olav V Travel Grant* in the amount
of 10,000 kroner supports education abroad for people between the ages of eighteen and
twenty-three. It is available only to those who are members of the Norse Federation or
whose parents are members. Applicants from abroad must pursue their studies in Norway.
The *America-Norway Heritage Fund*, established in 1985 through an endowment from the
Lutheran Brotherhood Insurance Society, awards grants to Americans of Norwegian
descent who have made significant contributions to American culture, enabling them to
visit Norway to share their contributions.

Available to: See above
Deadline: April 1 for HM King Olav V Travel Grant; inquire for others
Apply to: The Norse Federation, above address


NORWAY
NORLA—Norwegian Literature Abroad
Bygdoy alle 21
N-0262 Oslo
Norway
E-mail: firmapost@norla.no
Web site: http://www.norla.no
Fax: 47-2-212-25-44

ⓣ    NORLA offers grants for the translation of Norwegian fiction, poetry, and children's books
into any language. Translators must apply for grants through their publisher, and grants
will be assessed on the basis of the quality of the book and its translation, and the
publisher's ability to market the translation satisfactorily. Contact NORLA for additional
information and application.

Available to: No restrictions
Deadline: See Web site
Apply to: Kristin Brudevoll, above address

Nuclear Age Peace Foundation
PMB 121
1187 Coast Village Road, Suite 1
Santa Barbara, CA 93108-2794
E-mail: wagingpeace@napf.org
Web site: http://www.wagingpeace.org
Fax: 805-568-0466

(P)   The *Barbara Mandigo Kelly Peace Poetry Awards* offer $1,000, publication in *Waging Peace,* the
      Nuclear Age Peace Foundation newsletter, and posting on the Foundation Web site for a
      poem that explores and illuminates an aspect of peace and the human spirit. Two copies
      of up to three unpublished poems, maximum 40 lines each, may be submitted. There is a
      $10 entry fee. Awards of $200 are offered for a poem by a young adult (age thirteen to
      eighteen) and by a child (twelve and under); there is no entry fee for these age groups.
      Send SASE for guidelines.

      Available to: No restrictions
      Deadline: July 1
      Apply to: Peace Poetry Awards, above address


Oberlin College Press
Oberlin College
10 North Professor Street
Oberlin, OH 44074
E-mail: ocpress@oberlin.edu
Web site: http://www.oberlin.edu/~ocpress/

(P)   The *Field Poetry Prize* awards a $1,000 honorarium and publication by Oberlin College Press
      as part of its Field Poetry Series for a manuscript of poems 50 to 80 pages long. A reading
      fee of $22 includes a year's subscription to *Field,* a biannual journal of contemporary
      poetry and poetics. Send SASE or see the Web site for guidelines.

      Available to: No restrictions
      Deadline: Submissions accepted in May only
      Apply to: Field Poetry Prize, above address


Scott O'Dell Award for Historical Fiction
c/o Zena Sutherland
1700 East 56th Street #3906
Chicago, IL 60637
Fax: 773-702-0775

(C)   The *Scott O'Dell Award for Historical Fiction* offers $5,000 for a distinguished work of historical
      fiction for children or young adults published in the U. S. during the calendar year under
      consideration. The book must be set in the New World (North, Central, or South America).

      Available to: U. S. citizens
      Deadline: December 31
      Apply to: Above address


Oglebay Institute
c/o Stifel Fine Arts Center
1330 National Road
Wheeling, WV 26003

(D)   The *Towngate Theatre Playwriting Competition* annually offers a cash prize of $300, production,
      and partial payment of travel expenses. Authors may submit more than one unproduced
      nonmusical play; coauthored plays are accepted. Scripts of a serious and thoughtful nature
      are encouraged.

      Available to: No restrictions
      Deadline: January 1
      Apply to: Towngate Theatre Playwriting Competition, above address

**Ohio Arts Council**
**727 East Main Street**
**Columbus, OH 43205-1796**
**Phone: 614-466-2613**
**E-mail: kemerick@oac.state.oh.us**
**Web site: http://www.oac.state.oh.us**
**Fax: 614-466-4494**

Ⓜ Fellowships of $5,000 and $10,000 are given annually to Ohio poets, fiction writers, nonfiction writers, playwrights, and critics. Write for guidelines and application.

Available to: Ohio residents at least eighteen years old who are not students
Deadline: September 1
Apply to: Ken Emerick, Coordinator, Individual Artists Fellowship Program, above address

**Ohio State University Press**
**1070 Carmack Road**
**Columbus, OH 43210**
**E-mail: ohiostatepress@osu.edu**
**Web site: http://www.ohiostatepress.org**

Ⓟ The *Ohio State University Press/Journal Award in Poetry* selects one full-length manuscript each year for a $1,000 prize and publication by the Press. Entries must be at least 48 pages long; a $20 reading fee is required. Those submitting a manuscript and the fee receive a one-year subscription to the *Journal,* the literary magazine of Ohio State University.

Available to: No restrictions
Deadline: Submissions accepted in September only
Apply to: David Citino, Poetry Editor, above address

Ⓕ The *Sandstone Prize in Short Fiction* annually awards $1,500 and publication by the Press under a standard book contract for a collection of short fiction. The winner is invited to direct a workshop and to give a paid reading at OSU. Writers should submit a book-length collection (150 to 300 manuscript pages) of short stories, a novella (not exceeding 125 pages), or a combination. There is a $20 entry fee. Send SASE or see the Web site for guidelines.

Available to: No restrictions
Deadline: Submissions accepted in January only
Apply to: Bill Roorbach, Fiction Editor, above address

**Ohio University Press**
**Scott Quadrangle**
**Athens, OH 45701**
**Web site: http://www.ohiou.edu/oupress/**
**Fax: 740-593-4536**

Ⓟ The *Hollis Summers Poetry Prize,* named after a poet who taught at Ohio University, annually awards $500 and publication by the Press for an unpublished poetry manuscript. The contest is open to all poets, regardless of previous publication. Poetry manuscripts may be 60 to 95 pages long. There is a $15 entry fee. Write for complete guidelines.

Available to: No restrictions
Deadline: October 31
Apply to: Hollis Summers Poetry Prize, above address

**Ohioana Library Association**
**274 East First Avenue, Suite 300**
**Columbus, OH 43201**
**E-mail: ohioana@sloma.state.oh.us**
**Web site: http://www.oplin.lib.oh.us/OHIOANA**
**Fax: 614-728-6974**

The *Walter Rumsey Marvin Grant* of $1,000 is given annually to an unpublished writer under age thirty. Up to six pieces of prose may be submitted.

Available to: Ohio natives or residents for at least five years
Deadline: January 31
Apply to: Walter Rumsey Marvin Grant, above address

©  The *Ohioana Award for Children's Literature/Alice Wood Memorial Award* of $1,000 is given to an author whose body of published work has made a significant contribution to literature for children or young adults.

Available to: Ohio natives or residents for at least five years
Deadline: December 31
Apply to: Alice Wood Memorial Award, above address

℗  The *Ohioana Poetry Award/Helen and Laura Krout Memorial Award* of $1,000 is given to a poet whose body of published work has contributed significantly to poetry, and through whose writing, teaching, administrating, or community service other people's interest in poetry has developed.

Available to: Ohio natives or residents for at least five years
Deadline: December 31
Apply to: Ohioana Poetry Award, above address

**Omohundro Institute of Early American History and Culture**
**Box 8781**
**Williamsburg, VA 23185-8781**
**E-mail: pmschw@wm.edu**
**Fax: 757-221-1047**

Ⓝ  The *Jamestown Prize* of $3,000 plus publication is offered annually for the best book-length scholarly manuscript on early American history or culture before 1815, or on the related history of the British Isles, Europe, West Africa, or the Caribbean during the same period. The competition is open only to writers who have not published a book.

Available to: See above
Deadline: None
Apply to: Editor of Publications, above address

**Eugene O'Neill Playwrights Conference**
**534 West 42nd Street**
**New York, NY 10036**
**Phone: 212-244-7008**
**Fax: 212-967-2957**

Ⓓ  The Conference offers staged readings at the Eugene O'Neill Theatre Center in Waterford, Connecticut, in the summer of twelve to fifteen stage plays. Authors of the selected plays receive a four-day workshop and two script-in-hand readings with professional actors and directors, as well as a stipend, room and board, and transportation. Attendance is required for the duration of the Conference, held in June/July. Full scripts should not be submitted. Send SASE for guidelines.

Available to: U. S. citizens or permanent residents
Deadline: Submissions accepted September 15-November 1
Apply to: O'Neill Playwrights Conference, James Houghton, Artistic Director, above address

**Open Society Institute**
**The Soros Foundation**
**400 West 59th Street**
**New York, NY 10019**
**Phone: 212-548-0600**
**Web site: www.soros.org**
**Fax: 212-548-4679**

Ⓙ The *Soros Crime and Communities Media Fellowships* are awarded to outstanding individuals at the outset of their careers in journalism in any media. Four to five fellowships of up to $45,000 are given annually for one- or two-year projects. One fellowship of up to $30,000 is given to a local television reporter to devote up to a year on a series of stories about local or regional issues related to topics suggested in the fellowship guidelines. For more information consult the Web site www.soros.org/crime.

Available to: Professional journalists with at least three years' experience
Deadline: September 21
Apply to: Above address

Ⓜ The *Soros Supplementary Grants Program* assists citizens of the countries of Central and Eastern Europe, and the former Soviet Union, and Mongolia who are pursuing advanced study within this region but outside their home countries. Awards are offered for one academic year, in amounts ranging from $1,000 to $5,000. They are available to undergraduates and postgraduates in the social sciences, humanities, writing, and fine and performing arts, enrolled at recognized institutes of higher education outside their home country or permanent residence and in any of the following countries: Albania, Armenia, Azerbaijan, Belarus, Bosnia and Herzegovina, Bulgaria, Croatia, Czech Republic, Estonia, Georgia, Hungary, Kazakhstan, Kirghizstan, Latvia, Lithuania, Macedonia, Moldova, Mongolia, Poland, Romania, Russia, Slovakia, Slovenia, Tajikistan, Turkmenistan, Ukraine, Uzbekistan, and Yugoslavia. For application guidelines, consult the Web site www.osi.hu/nsp/.

Available to: See above
Deadline: April 15
Apply to: Scholarship program coordinator at national foundation in applicant's home country (see Web site for addresses).

**Oregon Arts Commission**
**775 Summer Street NE**
**Salem, OR 97310**
**Phone: 503-986-0082**
**E-mail: oregon.artscomm@state.or.us**
**Web site: http://art.econ.state.or.us**
**Fax: 503-986-0260**

Ⓜ *Individual Artists Fellowships* of $3,000 are available in even-numbered years to Oregon residents in creative fiction, nonfiction, poetry, and playwriting. Write for application.

Available to: Oregon residents
Deadline: September 1
Apply to: Individual Artists Fellowship Program, above address

**Organization of American Historians**
**112 North Bryan Street**
**Bloomington, IN 47408-4199**
**Web site: http://www.oah.org**

The organization sponsors or co-sponsors the following awards and prizes recognizing of scholarly and professional achievements in American history:

Ⓝ  The *ABC-Clio America: History and Life Award* of $750, given biennially to recognize and encourage scholarship in American history in journal literature that advances new perspectives on accepted interpretations or previously unconsidered topics.

> Available to: No restrictions
> Deadline: December 1 of even-numbered years
> Apply to: ABC-Clio America: History and Life Award, above address

Ⓝ  The *Ray Allen Billington Prize* of $1,000, given biennially to the author of a book on American frontier history, defined broadly so as to include the pioneer periods of all geographical areas and comparisons between American frontiers and others.

> Available to: No restrictions
> Deadline: October 1 of even-numbered years
> Apply to: Ray Allen Billington Prize, above address

Ⓝ  The *Binkley-Stephenson Award* of $500, given for the best scholarly article published in *Journal of American History* during the preceding calendar year.

> Available to: Contributors to *Journal of American History*
> Deadline: December 31
> Apply to: Journal of American History, above address

Ⓝ  The *Avery O. Craven Award* of $500, given annually for the most original book on the coming of the Civil War, the Civil War years, or the era of Reconstruction, except works of purely military history. The exception reflects the Quaker convictions of Craven.

> Available to: No restrictions
> Deadline: October 1
> Apply to: Avery O. Craven Award, above address

Ⓝ  The *Merle Curti Award* of $1,000, given in odd-numbered years to a book on American intellectual history and in even-numbered years to one on American social history; books must have been published during the preceding two years.

> Available to: No restrictions
> Deadline: October 1
> Apply to: Merle Curti Award, above address

Ⓝ  The *Ellis W. Hawley Prize* of $500, given annually for the best book-length historical study of the political economy, politics, or institutions of the United States, in domestic or international affairs, from the Civil War to the present.

> Available to: No restrictions
> Deadline: October 1
> Apply to: Ellis W. Hawley Prize, above address

The *Huggins-Quarles Awards*, given annually to minority graduate students in American history at the dissertation research stage of their Ph.D. programs. Amounts vary but do not exceed $1,000.

> Available to: Minority doctorate students
> Deadline: December 1
> Apply to: Huggins-Quarles Awards, above address

Ⓝ  The *Richard W. Leopold Prize* of $1,500, given biennially for the best book written by a historian connected with federal, state, or municipal government, in the areas of foreign policy, military affairs broadly construed, or the historical activities of the federal government, or in biography in one of these areas. Candidates must have been employed in a government position for at least five years, and the publisher should include verification of this fact when a book is submitted.

Available to: See above
Deadline: October 1 of odd-numbered years
Apply to: Richard W. Leopold Prize, above address

The *Lerner-Scott Prize* of $1,000 and a certificate, given annually for the best doctoral dissertation in U. S. women's history completed during the previous academic year (July 1-June 30).

Available to: Doctoral candidates
Deadline: December 1
Apply to: Lerner-Scott Prize, above address

(N) The *Horace Samuel & Marion Galbraith Merrill Travel Grants in Twentieth-Century American Political History*, which promote access of younger scholars to the Washington, D.C., region's rich primary-source collections in late-nineteenth- and twentieth-century American political history. The program offers stipends to underwrite travel and lodging expenses for members of the Organization of American Historians who are working toward completion of a dissertation or first book. Grants range from $500 to $3,000.

Available to: See above
Deadline: December 1
Apply to: Horace Samuel & Marion Galbraith Merrill Travel Grants, above address

(N) The *Louis Pelzer Memorial Award*, given annually for the best essay (up to 7,000 words) about any topic or period of U. S. history written by a graduate student in any field. The award includes publication of the essay in *Journal of American History*, a medal, and a prize of $500.

Available to: Graduate students
Deadline: December 1
Apply to: Louis Pelzer Memorial Award, Journal of American History, 1125 East Atwater, Indiana University, Bloomington, IN 47401

(N) The *James A. Rawley Prize* of $750, given annually for a book dealing with the history of race relations in the United States.

Available to: No restrictions
Deadline: October 1
Apply to: James A. Rawley Prize, above address

(N) The *Frederick Jackson Turner Award* of $1,000, given annually for an author's first book on a significant phase of American history. Write for specific rules.

Available to: No restrictions
Deadline: October 1
Apply to: Frederick Jackson Turner Award, above address

**Orion Society**
**195 Main Street**
**Great Barrington, MA 01230**
**Phone: 413-528-4422**
**E-mail: orion@orionsociety.org**
**Web site: www.oriononline.org**

[IN] The *John Hay Award* annually offers $3,000 to a person whose writing has succeeded in addressing two of the three following categories: "the relationship between people and nature, environmental education, and conservation." There is no application process. *By Internal Nomination Only.*

189

**Overseas Press Club of America**
**40 West 45th Street**
**New York, NY 10036**

The Overseas Press Club annually offers nineteen awards for newspaper, magazine, wire service, radio, television, cartoon, book, and photographic reporting from abroad. Work must be published or broadcast by a U. S.-based publication during the calendar year. Each award offers a $1,000 cash prize; each submission must be accompanied by a $125 entry fee. The following are for print journalists:

ⓙ The *Whitman Bassow Award*, sponsored by AT&T, for the best reporting, in any medium, on international environmental issues.

ⓙ The *Robert Spiers Benjamin Award*, sponsored by the Robert S. Benjamin Fund, for the best reporting, in any medium, on Latin America.

ⓙ The *Hal Boyle Award*, sponsored by AT&T, for the best newspaper or wire service reporting from abroad.

ⓙ The *Bob Considine Award*, sponsored by King Features Syndicate, for the best newspaper or wire service interpretation of foreign affairs.

ⓙ The *Ed Cunningham Memorial Award*, sponsored by Ford Motor Company, for the best magazine reporting from abroad.

ⓙ The *Joe and Laurie Dine Award*, for the best print medium reporting dealing with human rights.

ⓙ The *Malcolm Forbes Award*, sponsored by *Forbes* magazine, for the best business reporting from abroad in a newspaper or wire service.

ⓙ The *Morton Frank Award*, for the best business magazine reporting from abroad.

ⓙ The *Madeline Dane Ross Award*, for international reporting, in any medium, showing a concern for the human condition.

ⓙ The *Cornelius Ryan Award*, for the best nonfiction book on international affairs.

> Available to: No restrictions
> Deadline: January 31
> Apply to: Sonya Fry, Executive Director, above address

**The Paris Review**
**541 East 72nd Street**
**New York, NY 10021**
**Web site: www.parisreview.com/guidelines.htm**

ⓕ The *Aga Khan Prize for Fiction* is awarded annually by the editors of *The Paris Review* for the best previously unpublished short story (1,000 to 10,000 words). Translations are acceptable and should be accompanied by a copy of the original text. The winner receives $1,000 in addition to publication in the *Review*. One submission per envelope; SASE is required for a response or the return of a manuscript. Online submissions are not accepted.

> Available to: No restrictions
> Deadline: Ongoing
> Apply to: Aga Khan Prize for Fiction, above address

ⓟ The *Bernard F. Conners Prize for Poetry* is awarded annually for the best previously unpublished long poem (more than 200 lines). The winner receives $1,000 plus publication. One submission per envelope; SASE is required for a response or the return of a manuscript. Online submissions are not accepted.

> Available to: No restrictions
> Deadline: Ongoing
> Apply to: Bernard F. Conners Prize for Poetry, above address

**Passager**
**University of Baltimore**
**1420 North Charles Street**
**Baltimore, MD 21201-5779**
**E-mail: kkopelke@ubmail.ubalt.edu**
**Web site: http://raven.ubalt.edu/features/passager/guidelines.htm**

(P)   The *Passager Poetry Contest* awards a cash prize ($500 in 2002, but may be reduced in future years) and publication in *Passager: A Journal of Remembrance and Discovery* for an original poem or group of poems by a writer over age fifty. *Passager* is a quarterly journal of poetry, fiction, essays, and interviews that promotes the writing of older writers. Poets may submit up to five poems of not more than 30 lines each, along with a $10 reading fee. Write or consult the Web site for guidelines.

   Available to: Writers over age fifty
   Deadline: February 15
   Apply to: Poetry Contest, above address

**Passages North**
**Department of English**
**Northern Michigan University**
**1401 Presque Isle Avenue**
**Marquette, MI 49855**

(P)   The *Elinor Benedict Poetry Prize*, offered in even-numbered years, awards $500 for an unpublished poem. Two poems may be submitted, with an entry fee of $4 each; for additional poems, $3 each. All entries will be considered for publication. Send SASE for guidelines.

   Available to: No restrictions
   Deadline: Inquire
   Apply to: Elinor Benedict Poetry Prize, above address

(F)   The *Waasmode Short Fiction Prize*, offered in odd-numbered years, awards a first prize of $1,000 and publication of a short story. There is a reading fee of $8. Send SASE for the announcement of winners in the spring.

   Available: No restrictions
   Deadline: Inquire
   Apply to: Waasmode Fiction Contest, above address

**Passaic County Community College**
**Poetry Center**
**One College Boulevard**
**Paterson, NJ 07505-1179**
**E-mail: mgillan@pccc.cc.nj.us**
**Web site: http://www.pccc.cc.nj.us/poetry**
**Fax: 973-523-6085**

(P)   The *Allen Ginsberg Poetry Awards* offer a first prize of $1,000 for an original unpublished poem. Applicants may submit up to five poems, not exceeding two pages. Send SASE for guidelines.

   Available to: No restrictions
   Deadline: April 1
   Apply to: Allen Ginsberg Poetry Awards, above address

(F)   The *Paterson Fiction Prize* awards $500 for the novel or collection of short fiction that, in the opinion of the judges, is the strongest work published in the preceding year. Publishers should submit three copies of each book, along with an application form. Send SASE for application.

   Available to: No restrictions
   Deadline: April 1
   Apply to: Maria Mazziotti Gillan, Director, above address

(P)   The *Paterson Poetry Prize* offers $1,000 for a book of poetry published in the preceding year. The poet is asked to participate in an awards ceremony and to give a reading at the Poetry Center. Books must be at least 48 pages long, with a minimum press run of 500 copies. Publishers should submit three copies of each book, along with an application form. Send SASE for application.

Available to: No restrictions
Deadline: February 1
Apply to: Paterson Poetry Prize, above address

(C)   The *Paterson Prize for Books for Young People* offers a $500 award in each of three categories: pre-K through grade 3, grades 4 to 6, and grades 7 to 12. For each category, one book will be selected that, in the opinion of the judges, is the most outstanding book for young people published in the preceding year. Publishers should submit three copies of each book, along with an application form. Send SASE for application.

Available to: No restrictions
Deadline: March 15
Apply to: Maria Mazziotti Gillan, Director, above address

**Alicia Patterson Foundation**
**1730 Pennsylvania Avenue, NW, Suite 850**
**Washington, DC 20006**
**E-mail: execdirector@aliciapatterson.org**
**Web site: http://www.aliciapatterson.org**

(J)   Six to eight *APF Fellowships* are given yearly to working print journalists who wish to pursue independent projects of significant interest and write articles based on their investigation for *The APF Reporter*. Each fellowship is for one year and carries a stipend of $35,000. Applicants must be U. S. citizens who are full-time print journalists, or, if not U. S. citizens, must work full-time for U. S. print publications, either in this country or abroad. Write, e-mail, or consult the Web site for additional information and application.

Available to: See above
Deadline: October 1
Apply to: APF Fellowship Program, above address

**Pavement Saw Press**
**PO Box 6291**
**Columbus, OH 43206**
**E-mail: editor@pavementsaw.org**

(P)   The *Pavement Saw Press Transcontinental Poetry Award* offers $1,000 and publication by the Press for a full-length book of poetry. There is a $15 entry fee. Send SASE or e-mail for guidelines.

Available to: No restrictions
Deadline: Inquire
Apply to: Transcontinental Poetry Award, above address

(P)   The *Pavement Saw Chapbook Contest* awards $500 and 25 copies of the winning chapbook for the finest collection of poetry received. Submit up to 32 pages of poetry and an entry fee of $7. See the Web site for entry requirements.

Available to: No restrictions
Deadline: December 15
Apply to: Chapbook Contest, above address

**PeaceWriting**
**2582 Jimmie**
**Fayetteville, AR 72703-3420**
**E-mail: jbennet@uark.edu**

(M)   The *PeaceWriting International Writing Awards* are given for unpublished book-length manuscripts about the causes, consequences, and solutions to violence and war, and about the ideas and practices of nonviolent peacemaking and the lives of nonviolent peacemakers. A prize of $500 is given in each of three categories: nonfiction (history, biography, political science, international law, etc.), imaginative work (novel, short story, poem, play), and work for young people (nonfiction or imaginative). Send SASE or e-mail for guidelines.

Available to: No restrictions
Deadline: December 1
Apply to: International Writing Awards, above address

**Pearl Editions**
**3030 East Second Street**
**Long Beach, CA 90803**
**Web site: www.pearlmag.com**

(P) The *Pearl Poetry Prize* annually awards $1,000 and book publication for an original poetry manuscript, 48 to 64 pages in length. A $20 entry fee covers a copy of the winning book. The winning author will receive 25 copies. Send SASE for guidelines, or see the Web site.

Available to: No restrictions
Deadline: Submissions accepted May 1-July 15.
Apply to: Above address

(F) The *Pearl Short Story Prize* annually awards $250 and publication in *Pearl*'s annual fiction issue to a previously unpublished story of up to 4,000 words (about 15 or 16 manuscript pages). In addition to the cash prize, the winner receives 10 copies of the issue where the story appears. A $10 entry fee covers a copy of the magazine.

Available to: No restrictions
Deadline: Submissions accepted May 1-July 15.
Apply to: Above address

**PEN American Center**
**568 Broadway**
**New York, NY 10012-3225**
**E-mail: jm@pen.org**
**Web site: www.pen.org**
**Fax: 212-334-2181**

(T) The *Gregory Kolovakos Award* of $2,000 is given triennially (next award: 2004) to an American literary translator, editor, or critic whose work honors the richness of Hispanic literature and expands its English-language audience. The award's primary purpose is to recognize work from Spanish, but contributions from other languages of the Hispanic world are accepted. Candidates are considered for individual works as well as for collections of criticism or distinguished careers as translators or editors. Candidates may not nominate themselves. A letter of nomination must be received from the candidate's editor or a colleague, with the candidate's vita. As the award honors a sustained contribution over time to Latin American literatures in English translation, nominating letters should not focus exclusively on a single work, but rather document the candidate's qualifications with particular attention to the depth and vision of the work.

Available to: No restrictions
Deadline: January 5
Apply to: Gregory Kolovakos Award, above address

(N) The *PEN/Martha Albrand Award for the Art of the Memoir* of $1,000 is given to an American author for a first published memoir, distinguished by qualities of literary and stylistic excellence. Eligible books must have been published in the calendar year under consideration. Authors may have published books in another literary genre, but the work submitted for this prize must be their first published memoir. Books submitted for this award may not be submitted for the PEN/Martha Albrand Award for First Nonfiction. There is no application form; three copies of the book should be submitted.

Available to: U. S. citizens or permanent residents
Deadline: December 15
Apply to: PEN/Martha Albrand Award for the Art of the Memoir, above address

(N) The *PEN/Martha Albrand Award for First Nonfiction* of $1,000 is given annually for a U. S. writer's first published book of general nonfiction, distinguished by literary and stylistic excellence. Eligible books must have been published in the calendar year under consideration. There is no restriction on content, but nonliterary texts (how-to guides, inspirational tracts, craft and exercise manuals) are not considered. Memoirs should be submitted for the PEN/Martha Albrand Award for the Art of the Memoir. There is no application form; three copies of each title should be submitted.

Available to: U. S. citizens or permanent residents
Deadline: December 15
Apply to: PEN/Martha Albrand Award for First Nonfiction, above address

(T) The *PEN Award for Poetry in Translation* of $3,000 is given for a book-length translation of poetry from any language into English published in the U. S. during the current calendar year. Translators may be of any nationality. Submission of a book for this award does not preclude simultaneous submission for the PEN/Book-of-the-Month Club Translation Prize. There is no application form; two copies of the eligible book should be submitted.

Available to: No restrictions
Deadline: December 15
Apply to: PEN Award for Poetry in Translation, above address

(F) Three *PEN/Robert Bingham Fellowships for Writers*, of $35,000 a year for two consecutive years each, are given to exceptionally talented fiction writers whose debut work (a first novel or a collection of short stories), published by a U. S. trade publisher in the two years preceding the award, represents distinguished literary achievement, and suggests great promise. Nominations are welcome from writers, editors, literary agents, and members of the literary community. The next cycle of fellowships is in 2004. See the Web site for more information.

Available to: U. S. residents
Deadline: January 15
Apply to: PEN/Robert Bingham Fellowships, above address

(T) The *PEN/Book-of-the-Month Club Translation Prize*, sponsored by Book-of-the-Month Club, is awarded for the best book-length translation into English from any language published in the U. S. during the current calendar year. Technical, scientific, and reference works are not eligible. One prize of $3,000 is awarded annually. There is no application form; three copies of the eligible book should be submitted.

Available to: No restrictions
Deadline: December 15
Apply to: PEN/Book-of-the-Month Club Translation Prize, above address

(N) The *PEN/Jerard Fund Award* of $5,500 is awarded in odd-numbered years for a book-length work-in-progress of general nonfiction, marked by high literary quality, by a woman writer early in her career. There are no restrictions on the content; emphasis is on the quality of the writing and the literary character of the subject. How-to manuals, cookery or craft books, vocational guides, and the like are not considered. Applicants should submit two copies of no more than 50 pages of the work-in-progress, accompanied by a list of publications.

Available to: Women U. S. residents who have published at least one article in a national magazine or major literary magazine, and who have published no more than one book of any kind
Deadline: January 2, 2003 (manuscripts not accepted before September 1, 2002)
Apply to: PEN/Jerard Fund Award, above address

(IN) The *PEN/Nabokov Award* of $20,000 recognizes a living author whose body of work, either written in or translated into English, represents achievement in a variety of literary genres and is of enduring originality and consummate craftsmanship. Honorees will be writers, principally novelists, whose works evoke Nabokov's brilliant versatility and commitment to literature. Only authors who have published a book in the U. S. within the past two years will be considered. In light of the importance of translation in international letters, translators will also receive due recognition if the award is given to an author writing in a language other than English. There is no application process. *By Internal Nomination Only.*

Ⓒ The *PEN/Phyllis Naylor Working Writer Fellowship* of $5,000 is offered annually to a North American writer of children's fiction in financial need who has published at least two, but no more than three, novels during the past ten years that were well received by literary critics but not widely recognized by the reading public. Candidates must be nominated by an editor or a fellow writer, who should submit a list of the candidate's published work (accompanied by copies of reviews, where possible), a description of the candidate's financial resources and needs, and three copies of up to 75 pages of the candidate's current work-in-progress.

Available to: See above
Deadline: January 2
Apply to: PEN/Phyllis Naylor Working Writer Fellowship, above address

Ⓟ The *PEN/Joyce Osterweil Award for Poetry* of $5,000 is given in odd-numbered years to an emerging American poet of any age whose published work to date is marked by a high literary character and the promise of further literary achievement. Candidates must be nominated by a PEN member, and must have published no more than one book of poetry. Letters of nomination should describe the literary character of the candidate's work, articulate the degree of promise it shows, and summarize the candidate's publications to date.

Available to: See above
Deadline: January 2
Apply to: PEN/Joyce Osterweil Award for Poetry, above address

Ⓓ The *PEN/Laura Pels Foundation Awards for Drama* are given to playwrights working indisputably at the highest level of achievement. Two U. S. playwrights are selected annually: the Master American Dramatist award is a specially commissioned art object, given in recognition of the writer's body of work; the award to an American playwright in mid-career is a cash prize of $5,000, given to a writer whose literary achievements are apparent in the rich and striking language of his or her work. Candidates for the mid-career award must write in English and must have had a professional production of two or more full-length works mounted in a theater of at least 299 seats and contracted specifically for either limited or open runs. Nominations are not accepted for the Master American Dramatist award, while nominations for the mid-career award may be made by producers, agents, critics, or other playwrights, who should write a letter of support, describing the literary character of the candidate's work, and submit a list of the candidate's produced plays. Do not send scripts.

Available to: U. S. playwrights
Deadline: January 15
Apply to: PEN/Laura Pels Foundation Awards for Drama, above address

Ⓝ The *PEN/Spielvogel-Diamonstein Award for the Art of the Essay* of $5,000 is given for a distinguished book of previously uncollected essays on any subject by an American writer, published in the calendar year under consideration. Individual essays included in books submitted may have appeared previously in magazines, journals, or anthologies, but must not have been published collectively in book form. There are no restrictions on subject matter; books are judged solely on the basis of literary character and distinction of writing, and equal consideration is given to the work of renowned essayists and more recently established writers. Essays may deal with a range of subjects or may explore one theme; the book should be a series of individual essays, not a single book-length work of nonfiction. There is no application form; four copies of each title should be submitted.

Available to: U. S. citizens or permanent residents
Deadline: December 15
Apply to: PEN/Spielvogel-Diamonstein Award, above address

Ⓟ The *PEN/Voelcker Award for Poetry* of $5,000 is given in even-numbered years to an American poet whose distinguished and growing body of work to date represents a notable and accomplished presence in American literature. Candidates must be nominated by PEN members. Letters of nomination should describe the scope and literary caliber of the candidate's work, summarize the candidate's publications, and articulate the degree of accomplishment the candidate has attained and the esteem in which his or her work is held within the American literary community.

Available to: U. S. poets
Deadline: January 2
Apply to: PEN/Voelcker Award for Poetry, above address

The *PEN Writers Fund* helps established writers in financial emergencies. Grants and loans—maximum $1,000—are given periodically. The *PEN Fund for Writers and Editors with AIDS* is administered under the Writers Fund and gives grants ranging from $500 to $1,000. Applications are reviewed every six to eight weeks.

Available to: U. S. residents
Deadline: None
Apply to: Writers Fund, above address

**PEN Center USA West**
**672 South Lafayette Park Place, Suite 42**
**Los Angeles, CA 90057**
**E-mail: pen@pen-usa-west.org**
**Web site: http://www.pen-usa-west.org**
**Fax: 213-365-9616**

Ⓜ *PEN Center USA West Literary Awards* recognize outstanding works published or produced by writers who live in the western United States. Cash prizes of $1,000 are given in the categories of fiction, creative nonfiction, research nonfiction, poetry, children's literature, translation, journalism, drama, screenplay, and teleplay. Winners are honored at an annual literary festival in Los Angeles. Submit four copies of each title, completed entry form, and $25 entry fee. Send SASE or see the Web site for entry form.

Available to: Writers living west of the Mississippi River
Deadline: December 28 for book awards; January 31 for script awards
Apply to: Literary Awards, above address

Ⓜ Several *"Emerging Voices" Rosenthal Fellowships*, with cash prize of $1,000 each, are available to emerging writers from minority, immigrant, and underserved communities. The program includes a one-on-one mentoring relationship with an established writer, master classes with established novelists, classes in the Writers' Program at UCLA Extension, informal visits with writers, and literary readings. For application procedure see the Web site.

Available to: No restrictions
Deadline: October 15
Apply to: Terri Clark, Program Coordinator, above address

**PEN New England**
**PO Box 400725**
**North Cambridge, MA 02140**
**Web site: www.pen-ne.org**

Ⓕ The *Hemingway Foundation/PEN Award* of $7,500 is given annually to recognize distinguished first books of fiction by American writers. Only works published in the U. S. by an established house during the current calendar year will be considered. Genre fiction will not be considered unless the commercial character of the work is deemed secondary to its overall literary purpose and quality. Eligible titles may be submitted by publishers, agents, or the authors themselves. Authors are not disqualified by the previous publication of nonfiction, poetry, drama, or books for children. One copy of the book should be mailed directly to each of the judges. Write for list of judges' names and addresses, and required form.

Available to: U. S. citizens or permanent residents
Deadline: December 15
Apply to: Above address

Ⓕ Ⓝ The *L. L. Winship/PEN New England Award*, of $3,000, sponsored by PEN New England and *The Boston Globe*, is given annually for the best book published in the calendar year preceding the deadline, with a New England topic or setting, and/or by an author whose principal residence is New England. Children's books and anthologies are not eligible. Publishers should submit one copy of each eligible title to each of the five judges. Write for list of judges' names and addresses, and required form.

Available to: See above
Deadline: December 15
Apply to: Above address

**PEN Northwest: See Boyden Residency**

**PEN/Faulkner Foundation**
**c/o Folger Shakespeare Library**
**201 East Capitol Street, SE**
**Washington, DC 20003**
**E-mail: delaney@folger.edu**
**Web site: http://www.penfaulkner.org**

(F) The *PEN/Faulkner Award for Fiction* of $15,000 is given annually to the most distinguished work of fiction by an American writer published in the U. S. in the calendar year preceding that of the award. Four nominees each receive $5,000. Publishers of book-length works of fiction (novels or short story collections; no juvenile titles), as well as authors and agents, are invited to submit four copies of each eligible title. No forms are needed.

Available to: U. S. citizens
Deadline: October 31
Apply to: PEN/Faulkner Award for Fiction, above address

[IN] The *PEN/Malamud Award for Excellence in Short Fiction* annually awards $2,000 to an author who has demonstrated long-term excellence in short fiction. Winners are chosen by a committee of PEN/Faulkner board members and Malamud's literary executors. There is no application process. *By Internal Nomination Only.*

**Peninsula Community Foundation**
**1700 South El Camino Real, Suite 300**
**San Mateo, CA 94402-3042**
**E-mail: f.lalle@pcf.org**
**Web site: http://www.pcf.org**
**Fax: 650-358-9817**

(M) The *Peninsula Artists Fund* offers support to artists and arts groups living and working in San Mateo and northern Santa Clara counties in California. Grants of up to $5,000 are awarded twice annually, in winter and summer. Grantees are required to match the grant dollar for dollar. All media are eligible, including visual, performing, literary, and horticultural arts. Write, e-mail, or see the Web site for additional information and application.

Available to: Residents of San Mateo and northern Santa Clara counties for the last two years, at least nineteen years of age
Deadline: Inquire
Apply to: Peninsula Artists Fund, above address

**Pennsylvania Council on the Arts**
**Room 216, Finance Building**
**Harrisburg, PA 17120**
**E-mail: csavage@state.pa.us**
**Web site: http://www.artsnet.org/pca**
**Fax: 717-783-2538**

(M) The Pennsylvania Council on the Arts supports outstanding Pennsylvania artists by annually awarding fellowships of $5,000 to $10,000. Fellowships are awarded in prose (fiction and creative nonfiction) and poetry in alternate years. Applicants must have established careers as writers. Write, e-mail, or see the Web site for guidelines and application. The Pennsylvania Council on the Arts has other grants for public programs aimed at bringing interpretation and discussion to the experiences of the arts in various communities.

Available to: Pennsylvania residents; no students
Deadline: Inquire
Apply to: Fellowship Partner, above address

**Penumbra Theatre Company**
**270 North Kent Street**
**St. Paul, MN 55102-1794**
**Web site: www.penumbratheatre.org**
**Fax: 651-224-7074**

Ⓓ The *Cornerstone Dramaturgy and Development Project* is intended to nurture emerging playwrights who address the African-American and/or Pan-African experience. On the basis of artistic merit of submissions, one playwright a year is offered a main-stage production with a possible three-to-four-week residence, and one playwright is offered a four-week workshop-residence culminating in a staged reading. Financial assistance varies according to the need of playwright and project. Write for additional information.

Available to: No restrictions
Deadline: Ongoing
Apply to: Cornerstone Dramaturgy and Development Project, above address

**Pew Center for Civic Journalism**
**1101 Connecticut Avenue, NW, Suite 420**
**Washington, DC 20036-4303**
**E-mail: news@pccj.org**
**Web site: http://www.pewcenter.org**
**Fax: 202-347-6440**

Ⓙ The *James K. Batten Award for Excellence in Civic Journalism* of $25,000 is given for print, broadcast, or electronic news reports, series, or accumulated bodies of work published or aired during the calendar year that support public involvement in the life of the community. Print submissions must be accompanied by a nominating letter from an editor or reporter describing the projects and the techniques used. Write, e-mail, or see the Web site for guidelines and application form.

Available to: No restrictions
Deadline: February (inquire for exact date)
Apply to: Batten Award, above address

**Pew Fellowships in the Arts**
**230 South Broad Street, Suite 1003**
**Philadelphia, PA 19102**
**Phone: 215-875-2285**
**E-mail: pewarts@mindspring.com**
**Web site: www.pewarts.org**
**Fax: 215-875-2276**

Ⓜ The *Pew Fellowships in the Arts* provide financial support to artists so that they may dedicate themselves wholly to their artwork for up to two years. Applicants must be residents of Bucks, Chester, Delaware, Montgomery, or Philadelphia counties in Pennsylvania, and at least twenty-five years old; students are not eligible. Up to twelve fellowships of $50,000 each are awarded annually in three fields, which vary yearly. Write or see the Web site for additional information and guidelines.

Available to: See above
Deadline: December (inquire for exact date)
Apply to: Above address

**Phi Beta Kappa**
17 Massachusetts Avenue, NW, 4th floor
Washington, DC 20036
Phone: 202-265-3808
E-mail: ccurtis@pbk.org
Web site: www.pbk.org
Fax: 202-986-1601

Ⓝ The *Ralph Waldo Emerson Award* of $2,500 is given annually for an outstanding interpretation of the intellectual and cultural condition of man, published in the U. S. during the year preceding the submission deadline. Studies in history, religion, philosophy, sociology, anthropology, political science, and related fields are eligible. Submissions must be made by publishers for books published between May 1 of the year preceding the award year and April 30 of the award year.

Available to: U. S. citizens or residents
Deadline: See above
Apply to: Ralph Waldo Emerson Award, above address

Ⓝ The *Christian Gauss Award* of $2,500 is given annually for an outstanding book of literary scholarship or criticism published in the United States during the year preceding the submission deadline. Submissions must be made by publishers for books published between May 1 of the year preceding the award year and April 30 of the award year.

Available to: U. S. citizens or residents
Deadline: See above
Apply to: Christian Gauss Award, above address

Ⓟ The *Phi Beta Kappa Poetry Award* offers $10,000 for a book of poetry in English by an American writer. Four finalists receive $2,500 each. To be eligible, books must be published between June 1 of the year preceding the award and May 31 of the award year. Write or see the Web site for more information.

Available to: U. S. citizens or residents
Deadline: Submissions must be postmarked by July 1
Apply to: Phi Beta Kappa Poetry Award, above address

Ⓝ The *Phi Beta Kappa Award in Science* of $2,500 is given annually for an outstanding book on science or interpretation of science written by a scientist and published in the U. S. during the year preceding the submission deadline. Submissions must be made by publishers for books published between May 1 of the year preceding the award year and April 30 of the award year.

Available to: U. S. citizens or residents
Deadline: See above
Apply to: Science Award, above address

The *Mary Isabel Sibley Fellowship* is given annually for advanced study, research, or writing projects; in odd-numbered years for endeavors dealing with Greek language, literature, history, or archaeology; and in even-numbered years for those dealing with any aspect of French language or literature. The fellowship carries a stipend of $20,000 for a period of one year.

Available to: Unmarried women between ages twenty-five and thirty-five who hold a doctorate or have fulfilled all the requirements except for the dissertation
Deadline: January 15
Apply to: Mary Isabel Sibley Fellowship Committee, above address

**Phillips Exeter Academy**
Exeter, NH 03833
Web site: http://www.exeter.edu

The *George Bennett Fellowship* is awarded annually to a person contemplating or embarking on a career as a writer who has under way a manuscript requiring time and freedom from material considerations to complete. The fellow must remain in residence while the Academy is in session and write, and should be available to students interested in writing. The primary criterion for selection is the manuscript submitted (preferably one in progress). Writers who have not issued a book-length work with a major publisher are favored. The grant consists of a $6,000 stipend plus room and board for the writer and the writer's family during the academic year. Send SASE or see the Web site for information and application.

Available to: See above
Deadline: December 1
Apply to: Chair, Selection Committee, George Bennett Fellowship, above address

**The Phillips Foundation**
**7811 Montrose Road, Suite 100**
**Potomac, MD 20854**
**E-mail: jfarley@phillips.com**
**Web site: www.thephillipsfoundation.org**
**Fax: 301-424-0245**

Ⓙ    The *Phillips Foundation Journalism Fellowships* are offered to advance the cause of objective journalism. Full-time ($50,000) and part-time ($25,000) fellowships are given to complete a one-year project of the applicant's choosing. The project should be original, and focused on journalism supportive of American culture and a free society, and should be deliverable in four installments that might be published sequentially in a periodical or together as a book. Working print journalists with less than five years' experience are eligible. Write or see the Web site for additional information and application.

Available to: U. S. citizens; see above
Deadline: March 1; fellowships start September 1
Apply to: John Farley, Journalism Fellowship Program, above address

**Phoebe: A Journal of Literary Arts**
**MSN 2D6**
**George Mason University**
**4400 University Drive**
**Fairfax, VA 22030-4444**
**E-mail: phoebe@gmu.edu**

Ⓕ Ⓟ    The *Phoebe Winter Fiction Prize* and the *Greg Grummer Poetry Award* each offer $1,000 and publication in *Phoebe* for an unpublished short story and poem, respectively. Fiction writers may submit one story, not to exceed 25 pages; poets may submit up to four poems, not to exceed 10 pages. There is a $10 reading fee for each contest. Send SASE or e-mail for guidelines.

Available to: No restrictions
Deadline: December 1
Apply to: Fiction Contest or Poetry Contest, above address

**Pilgrim Project**
**Religion and Public Life**
**156 Fifth Avenue, Suite 400**
**New York, NY 10010**
**E-mail: davida@firstthings.com**

Ⓓ    The Pilgrim Project offers grants to playwrights ranging from $1,000 to $7,000, with an average award of $3,350. Grants are intended to defray the cost of readings, workshop productions, or full productions of plays dealing with "questions of moral significance." Applications are reviewed year-round, on an ongoing basis. Write for further information.

Available to: No restrictions
Deadline: Ongoing
Apply to: Above address

**Pioneer Drama Service**
**PO Box 4267**
**Englewood, CO 80155-4267**
**E-mail: piodrama@aol.com**
**Web site: http://www.pioneerdrama.com**
**Fax: 303-779-4315**

Ⓓ The *Shubert Fendrich Memorial Playwriting Contest* offers publication with a $1,000 advance on royalties (10 percent for books, 50 percent for performances) for produced, unpublished work not longer than 90 minutes. Full-length plays, one-acts, translations, adaptations, musicals, and plays for young audiences are eligible; subject matter and language should be appropriate for schools and community theaters. Work with a preponderance of female roles and minimal set requirements is preferred, but all entries will be considered for publication. Send SASE for guidelines.

Available to: Anyone not already published by Pioneer Drama
Deadline: March 1
Apply to: Shubert Fendrich Memorial Playwriting Contest, above address

**Pirate's Alley Faulkner Society**
**624 Pirate's Alley**
**New Orleans, LA 70116**
**Web site: http://www.wordsandmusic.org**
**Fax: 504-522-9725**

Ⓜ The *William Faulkner Creative Writing Competition* offers $7,500 for a novel ($2,500 of which is designated as an advance against royalties to encourage a publisher to issue the winning book); $2,500 for a novella ($1,000 as an advance against royalties); $1,500 for an individual short story ($250 as an advance against royalties or writer's fees as an incentive for publication); $1,000 for a personal essay; and $750 for a single poem of up to 750 words. Novels should be up to 100,000 words; novellas up to 50,000; short stories up to 15,000. Entry fees are $35 for novel, $30 for novella, and $25 for short story, essay, or poem. The Society also sponsors a $1,000 award for a short story by a high school student ($750 for the winning student and $250 for the sponsoring teacher). The entry fee for this competition is $10. Winners of the competitions should expect to make a presentation at the Society's annual meeting in September. Send SASE for further information, guidelines, and application, or see the Web site.

Available to: U. S. citizens and residents
Deadline: April 15
Apply to: William Faulkner Creative Writing Competition, above address

**Playboy Enterprises**
**730 Fifth Avenue**
**New York, NY 10019**
**Phone: 212-261-5000**
**Web site: www.playboyenterprises.com**

Ⓕ The *Playboy College Fiction Contest* awards a first prize of $3,000 and publication in *Playboy* to a work of fiction, 25 pages or less, by a college or MFA graduate student. Second prize is $500 and a one-year subscription to *Playboy*. Enclose a 3-by-5-inch card listing name, age, college/university affiliation, permanent home address, and telephone number with manuscript submission. Send SASE for further information.

Available to: See above
Deadline: Submissions accepted September 1-January 1
Apply to: Playboy College Fiction Contest, above address

**Playboy Foundation**
**680 North Lake Shore Drive**
**Chicago, IL 60611**
**Web site: playboyenterprises.com/foundation_awards.html**

The *Hugh M. Hefner First Amendment Awards*, of $5,000 each, recognize the efforts of individuals working to protect and enhance First Amendment freedoms. Awards are given in the following categories: publishing, education, individual conscience, law, lifetime achievement, and arts and entertainment.

Available to: No restrictions
Deadline: Inquire
Apply to: Hugh M. Hefner First Amendment Awards, above address

**Playhouse on the Square**
**51 South Cooper Street**
**Memphis, TN 38104**

Ⓓ  The *Playhouse on the Square New Play Competition* annually awards $500 and production to an unproduced work with a small cast. Full-length plays and musicals are eligible.

Available to: No restrictions; southern playwrights preferred
Deadline: April 1
Apply to: New Play Competition, above address

**Plays on Tape**
**Box 5789**
**Bend, OR 97708-5789**
**E-mail: theatre@playsontape.com**
**Web site: http://www.playsontape.com**
**Fax: 541-923-9679**

Ⓓ  The *Auricle Award* annually offers up to $500 for full-length plays and long one-acts suitable for audio production (there is a $100 prize for possible audio-production consideration). Any play with a running time of approximately 74 minutes that has not been audio-produced is eligible. Scripts with two to five characters are preferred; minority playwrights are encouraged to apply. There is a $3 entry fee. Send SASE, e-mail, or see the Web site for guidelines.

Available to: No restrictions
Deadline: December 31
Apply to: Auricle Award, above address

**The Playwrights' Center**
**2301 Franklin Avenue, East**
**Minneapolis, MN 55406**
**E-mail: info@pwcenter.org**
**Web site: http://www.pwcenter.org**
**Fax: 612-332-6037**

Ⓓ  Three *McKnight Advancement Grants*, of $25,000 each, are awarded annually to recognize playwrights whose work demonstrates exceptional artistic merit and potential and whose primary residence is in the state of Minnesota. The grants, intended to advance recipients' art and careers, can be used to support a variety of expenses, including writing time, artistic costs of residency at a theater or arts organization, travel/study, production, or presentation. Additional funds of up to $1,500 per grant recipient are available for workshops and readings using the Center's developmental program or may be designated to a partner organization for joint development and/or production worldwide. These grants are funded by the Minneapolis-based McKnight Foundation as part of its Arts Program. Recipients are selected on the basis of artistic excellence, professional achievement, and proposed residency plans. Consult the Web site for more details.

Available to: Residents of Minnesota
Deadline: Inquire
Apply to: See Web site for application process

Ⓓ   Five *Jerome Fellowships*, in the amount of $7,500 each, are awarded annually, providing emerging American playwrights with funds and services to aid them in the development of their craft. Fellows spend a twelve-month residency in Minnesota using Center services, including readings and workshops with professional directors, dramaturgs and actors, and special projects and symposia. Applications are screened for eligibility by the Center's lab director, and evaluated by a panel of Minnesota theater artists; finalists are evaluated by a panel of national theater artists. Selection is based on artistic excellence, potential, and commitment. See the Web site for application.

      Available to: No restrictions
      Deadline: Inquire
      Apply to: Above address

Ⓓ   *PlayLabs* is a nationally recognized developmental workshop for new American plays, open by script submission to playwrights around the country. Playwrights choose distinguished national directors and dramaturges, and Twin Cities professional actors to work on their scripts. PlayLabs gives four or more writers 30 to 40 hours of intensive workshop time to explore, refine and test their scripts. At the end of the conference, each play receives a public reading followed by an optional audience discussion of the work. Playwrights receive honoraria, paid travel expenses, room and board. Consult the Web site for guidelines and application.

      Available to: U. S. playwrights
      Deadline: Inquire
      Apply to: Above address

Ⓓ   Many Voices is a program that supports opportunities for African-American, American Indian, Asian-American, and Latino/Chicano writers, and provides cash grants, education, and opportunities for them to develop new work with theater professionals. Designed to increase cultural diversity in the contemporary theater, both locally and nationally, the program includes two components: *Many Voices Residencies* and *Many Voices Multicultural Collaboration Grants*. Eight nine-month residencies are awarded to artists of color who are interested in developing playwriting skills and creating theater in a supportive artists' community. Residency artists receive a $750 stipend; a one-on-one mentorship with an established playwright or theater artist of their choosing; a full scholarship to a Center class; a private script workshop with a professional director, dramaturg, and actors; a public reading with professional actors and an audience discussion; and a one-year Playwrights' Center membership. Two to four grants of between $200 and $2000 each are awarded to culturally diverse teams of two or more artists for collaboration in developing new theater pieces. The grants are intended to support early project collaborations, artistic research and development, and/or first productions. See the Web site for application.

      Available to: Minority writers
      Deadline: Inquire
      Apply to: Above address

**Playwrights' Center of San Francisco**
**Box 460466**
**San Francisco, CA 94146-0466**
**Phone: 415-626-4603**
**E-mail: playctrsf@aol.com**
**Web site: http://www.playwrights.org**

Ⓓ   *DramaRama*, an annual playwriting competition, offers a staged reading of up to eight scripts (four long plays and four short) at the Center's fall festival. A $500 prize is awarded to the best long and the best short (under one hour) play on the basis of the readings. Musicals, screenplays, translations, and children's plays are not eligible. There is a $25 submission fee. Send SASE, e-mail, or see the Web site for guidelines.

      Available to: No restrictions
      Deadline: March 15
      Apply to: DramaRama, above address

**Playwrights First**
c/o National Arts Club
15 Gramercy Park South
New York, NY 10003

Ⓓ The *Playwrights First Award* of $1,000 is given annually for the best unproduced full-length play written within the last two years. Adaptations and translations are not accepted. Playwrights should submit script and résumé. Scripts are not returned. Write for further information.

Available to: No restrictions
Deadline: October 15
Apply to: Above address


**Playwrights Theater**
Box 803305
Dallas, TX 75380
E-mail: jackmarsh@earthlink.net
Web site: www.playwrighttheatertexas.org

Ⓓ *Plays for the 21st Century* awards $1,500 and a public reading with possible production for a full-length play written in or translated into English. There is a $15 application fee. Send SASE for guidelines and application, or download from the Web site.

Available to: No restrictions
Deadline: January 31
Apply to: Plays for the 21st Century, above address


**Pleiades Press**
**Department of English and Philosophy**
**Central Missouri State University**
**Warrensburg, MO 64093**
Phone: 660-593-8106
E-mail: kdp8106@cmsu2.cmsu.edu

Ⓟ The *Lena-Miles Wever Todd Poetry Series,* formerly the Winthrop Poetry Series, offers a $1,000 honorarium and publication by Pleiades Press and distribution by Louisiana State University Press for a poetry manuscript of more than 48 pages. There is a $15 reading fee, which covers a copy of the winning book. Send SASE for guidelines.

Available to: U. S. and Canadian residents
Deadline: September 15
Apply to: Lena-Miles Wever Todd Poetry Series, above address


**Ploughshares**
**Emerson College**
**100 Beacon Street**
**Boston, MA 02116**
Web site: http://www.pshares.org
Fax: 617-824-8991

[IN] The *Cohen Award in Poetry and Fiction* offers $600 each to the best short story and poem published in *Ploughshares* in the year. There is no application process. *By Internal Nomination Only.*

[IN] The *John C. Zacharis First Book Award* offers $1,500 for the best debut book of poetry or short fiction published by a *Ploughshares* writer. Writers are nominated by the advisory editors of *Ploughshares*. There is no application process or deadline. *By Internal Nomination Only.*

**Pockets Magazine**
**The Upper Room**
**1908 Grand Avenue**
**PO Box 340004**
**Nashville, TN 37203-0004**
**E-mail: pockets@upperroom.org (for queries only)**
**Web site: http://www.upperroom.org/pockets**
**Fax: 615-340-7267**

©    The *Pockets Fiction Writing Contest* awards $1,000 and publication in *Pockets*, a devotional magazine for children, for an unpublished short story of 1,000 to 1,600 words written for children grades 1 through 6. Send SASE for additional information and guidelines.

Available to: No restrictions
Deadline: Submissions must be postmarked between March 1 and August 15
Apply to: Fiction Writing Contest, above address

**The Poetry Center & American Poetry Archives**
**San Francisco State University**
**1600 Holloway Avenue**
**San Francisco, CA 94132**
**E-mail: newlit@sfsu.edu**
**Web site: http://www.sfsu.edu/~newlit**
**Fax: 415-338-0966**

Ⓟ    The Poetry Center's *Book Award* offers a $500 cash prize and an invitation to read in the Poetry Center reading series, to the author of an outstanding book of poems published in the current year. The award is for a volume by an individual poet; anthologies and translations are not accepted. A $10 reading fee must accompany the submitted book.

Available to: No restrictions
Deadline: January 31
Apply to: Book Award, above address

**Poetry Magazine**
**60 West Walton Street**
**Chicago, IL 60610**
**Web site: http://www.poetrymagazine.org**

Ⓟ    Two *Ruth Lilly Poetry Fellowships* of $15,000 each are given annually to undergraduate or graduate students enrolled in English or creative writing programs who will not have received an M. A. or MFA degree as of December 31 of the year of the award. Program directors and department chairs in the U. S. should submit nominations on an official application form from *Poetry*. Send SASE after February 1 for application form and guidelines.

Available to: See above
Deadline: April 15
Apply to: Ruth Lilly Poetry Fellowships, above address

[IN]    The *Ruth Lilly Poetry Prize* of $100,000 is given annually to a U. S. citizen in recognition of outstanding poetic achievement. Applications and nominations are not accepted. *By Internal Nomination Only*.

Ⓟ    Eight *Poetry Magazine Awards*, ranging from $200 to $3,000, are given annually for poetry published in the magazine. Applications are not accepted. All verse published in the magazine during the preceding year is automatically considered.

Available to: Poets whose work has appeared in *Poetry* during the previous year

**Poetry Society of America**
**15 Gramercy Park**
**New York, NY 10003**

In addition to those listed below, other awards, some of which are open only to PSA members, are given annually. For guidelines, entry forms, and details of all awards, send SASE to the above address.

(P)   The *George Bogin Memorial Award* of $500 is given for a selection of four or five poems that reflect "the encounter of the ordinary and [the] extraordinary," use language in an original way, and take a stand "against oppression in any of its forms." There is a $15 entry fee for nonmembers.

Available to: U. S. citizens
Deadline: December 21
Apply to: George Bogin Memorial Award, above address

(P)   The *Alice Fay Di Castagnola Award* of $1,000 is given for a manuscript-in-progress of poetry, prose, or verse drama by a PSA member.

Available to: PSA members
Deadline: December 21
Apply to: Alice Fay Di Castagnola Award, above address

(P)   The *Norma Farber First Book Award* of $500 is given annually for a first book (not a chapbook) of original poetry by an American published during the calendar year. Submissions must be made by publishers. There is a $20 entry fee per book.

Available to: U. S. citizens
Deadline: December 21
Apply to: Norma Farber First Book Award, above address

(P)   The *Lyric Poetry Award* of $500 is given for a lyric poem of no more than 50 lines by a PSA member.

Available to: PSA members
Deadline: December 21
Apply to: Lyric Poetry Award, above address

(P)   The *Lucille Medwick Memorial Award* of $500 is given for an original poem in any form on freedom or a humanitarian theme by a PSA member.

Available to: PSA members
Deadline: December 21
Apply to: Lucille Medwick Memorial Award, above address

(P)   The *William Carlos Williams Award* is a purchase prize between $500 and $1,000 for a book of poetry published by a small, nonprofit, or university press. Submissions must made by publishers and must be original works by one author who is a permanent U. S. resident. Translations are not eligible. There is a $20 entry fee per book.

Available to: See above
Deadline: December 21
Apply to: William Carlos Williams Award, above address

(P)   The *Robert H. Winner Memorial Award* of $2,500 is given to a poet more than forty years old who has published no book or only one. Poets may submit a brief but cohesive manuscript of up to ten poems or 20 pages. There is a $15 entry fee for nonmembers.

Available to: Poets over age forty
Deadline: December 21
Apply to: Robert H. Winner Award, above address

**Poets Out Loud**
**Fordham University at Lincoln Center**
**113 West 60th Street, Room 924**
**New York, NY 10023**
**Phone: 212-636-6792**
**E-mail: pol@fordham.edu**
**Web site: http://www.fordham.edu/english/pol**

Ⓟ    The *Poets Out Loud Prize* offers $1,000 and publication by Fordham University Press for a previously unpublished poetry manuscript, 50 to 80 pages long. There is a $25 entry fee. Send SASE or visit the Web site for guidelines and application form.

Available to: No restrictions
Deadline: Submissions accepted September 1-October 15
Apply to: Poets Out Loud Prize, above address


**Poets & Writers**
**72 Spring Street**
**New York, NY 10012**
**Web site: http://www.pw.org**
**Fax: 212-226-3963**

Ⓜ    The *Poets & Writers Readings/Workshops Program* in California and New York State and in Chicago and Detroit provides matching fee money to pay poets, fiction writers, and literary performance poets for giving readings and writing workshops in various public settings. Eligible to apply for writers' matching funds are libraries, Y's, community centers, small presses, colleges and universities, correctional facilities, bookstores, religious organizations, and community groups interested in presenting literary events. Applications must be submitted by organizations; writers may contact them to initiate the application. Write or visit the Web site for additional information and application procedures.

Available to: Organizations in New York State, California, Chicago, and Detroit
Deadline: Ongoing; applications must be submitted eight weeks before the event
Apply to: Readings/Workshops Program, above address; or Poets & Writers, 580 Washington Street, Suite 308, San Francisco, CA 94111

Ⓕ Ⓟ    The *Writers Exchange Program* is designed to encourage a sharing of works and resources among emerging writers nationwide. A poet and a fiction writer from a designated state are chosen annually. Each receives a $500 honorarium and gives readings and meets with the literary community in New York City during October. All related travel and lodging expenses and a daily stipend are covered. The designated state for 2002 is Louisiana; inquire for 2003. Guidelines and applications available on-line at the above New York address.

Available to: Emerging writers from states designated by Poets & Writers
Deadline: December 1
Apply to: Writers Exchange Program, above address


**Pope Foundation**
**700 White Plains Road**
**Scarsdale, New York 10583**

Ⓙ    The *Pope Foundation Journalism Awards* offer honorariums of $15,000 to each of three mid-career journalists and social commentators to be used as working fellowships. Special consideration is given to entrants whose work displays investigative initiative for a greater social cause. Applicants should have a minimum of ten years' journalistic background. Send SASE for application and guidelines.

Available to: See above
Deadline: November 15
Apply to: Catherine Pope, Journalism Awards Program Director, above address

**Prairie Schooner**
201 Andrews Hall
University of Nebraska
Lincoln, NE 68588-0334
Web site: http://www.unl.edu/schooner/psmain.htm

Writers whose work has been published in *Prairie Schooner* during the preceding calendar year are eligible for the following annual awards:

The *Virginia Faulkner Award for Excellence in Writing* of $1,000 for the best writing of any kind.

Ⓕ     The *Lawrence Foundation Award* of $1,000 for the best short story.

Ⓟ     The *Larry Levis Poetry Prize* of $1,000.

The *Hugh J. Luke Award* of $250 for writing in any genre.

The *Bernice Slote Award* of $500 for the best work by a beginning writer.

Ⓟ     The *Edward Stanley Award for Poetry* of $1,000.

Ⓟ     The *Strousse Award* of $500 for the best poem or group of poems.

    Available to: *Prairie Schooner* contributors


**Prince William Sound Community College**
PO Box 97
Valdez, AK 99686
E-mail: vntc@uaa.alaska.edu
Web site: http://www.uaa.alaska.edu/pwscc
Fax: 907-834-1611

Ⓓ     The Last Frontier Theatre Conference sponsors a Play Lab for the staged readings of new works. Of approximately fifty new works selected for the Lab, three will receive the *Last Frontier New Play Award*. Top plays may also be selected for readings in New York, and the highest-rated play will receive full production at the University of Alaska in Anchorage, and at the following year's conference in Valdez. Send SASE, e-mail, or see the Web site for guidelines.

    Available to: No restrictions
    Deadline: March 1
    Apply to: Above address


**Princess Grace Foundation—USA**
150 East 58th Street
New York, NY 10155
E-mail: pgfusa@pgfusa.com
Web site: http://www.pgfusa.com
Fax: 212-317-1473

Ⓓ     The *Princess Grace Awards Playwright Fellowship,* given annually to a young American playwright, consists of a $7,500 grant and a ten-week residence, including paid travel, at New Dramatists, a playwright service organization, in New York City. The award is based primarily on the artistic quality of a submitted play and the potential of the fellowship to assist in the writer's growth. Write for guidelines.

    Available to: U. S. citizens or permanent residents
    Deadline: March 31
    Apply to: Playwright Fellowship, above address

Film grants are available for writing and production of new student films by young filmmakers who have already completed one film. Nominations are submitted by deans and department chairmen, in conjunction with faculty, of established colleges and universities by invitation only. Film grants are made as scholarships for undergraduate and graduate thesis film productions. Candidates must apply in their second-to-last year of study. See the Web site for more information.

Available to: See above
Deadline: June 1
Apply to: Film Grants, above address


**Princeton University**
**The Council of the Humanities**
**Joseph Henry House**
**Princeton, NJ 08544-5264**
**E-mail: dsteidl@princeton.edu**
**Web site: http://www.princeton.edu/~humcounc**
**Fax: 609-258-2783**

Two *Alfred Hodder Fellowships,* of $49,000 each, are given annually to writers and/or scholars with "much more than ordinary intellectual and literary gifts," for the pursuit of independent work in the humanities. The selected fellows are usually from outside academia, and in the early stages of their careers. Fellows spend an academic year in residence at Princeton. Ph.D. candidates are not eligible. For further information, consult the Web site.

Available to: No restrictions
Deadline: Applications must be postmarked by November 1
Apply to: Alfred Hodder Fellowship, above address


**Providence Athenaeum**
**251 Benefit Street**
**Providence, RI 02903**
**Web site: www.providenceathenaeum.org**
**Fax: 401-421-2860**

(P)  The *Philbrick Poetry Award* offers $500 and publication for a chapbook by a New England poet who has not yet had a poetry book published. Applicants must reside in Connecticut, Maine, Massachusetts, New Hampshire, Rhode Island, or Vermont. The winner will be invited to read at the Athenaeum. There is a $5 entry fee. Send SASE or consult the Web site for submission guidelines.

Available to: See above
Deadline: Submissions accepted June 15-October 15
Apply to: Philbrick Poetry Award, above address


**PublishingOnline.com**
**1200 South 192nd Street, Suite 300**
**Seattle, WA 98148**
**Phone: 888-730-7266**
**E-mail: pubinfo@publishingonline.com**
**Web site: http://www.publishingonline.com**

(F)  The *North American Authors and Fiction Writers Contest* offers a first prize of $10,000, four second prizes of $5,000 each, ten third prizes of $1,000 each, and twenty-five fourth prizes of $500 each for works of fiction more than 100 pages long. Submissions must be in electronic format. The contest is limited to the first 500 qualified manuscripts received before the deadline. Romance, mystery, adventure, science fiction, fantasy, and horror writers are encouraged to enter. There is a $25 reading fee. Write, e-mail, or consult the Web site for guidelines.

Available to: North American authors
Deadline: September 1
Apply to: North American Authors and Fiction Writers Contest, above address


(P)  The *Annual Poetry Contest* recognizes the best poems with $1,500 for first, $1,000 for second, and $750 for third place. Winners are published in the PublishingOnline anthology of poetry, as are up to thirty finalists. See the Web site for more details.

Available to: No restrictions
Deadline: Inquire
Apply to: Above address

**Publishing Triangle**
**17 East 47th Street, 3rd floor**
**New York, NY 10017**
**E-mail: info@publishingtriangle.org**
**Web site: http://www.publishingtriangle.org**

Ⓓ The *Robert Chesley Award for Lesbian and Gay Playwriting* recognizes a body of work or an emerging talent. The award alternates yearly between men and women; winners receive an honorarium of $1,000. Write to the address below for more information.

Available to: Lesbian or gay playwrights
Deadline: Inquire
Apply to: Victor Bumbalo, 828 North Laurel Avenue, Los Angeles, CA 90046

Ⓕ The *Ferro-Grumley Award*s of $1,000 each are given annually to two writers for literary excellence in lesbian and gay fiction. Publishers should submit six copies of nominated books (or bound galleys if books are not available). Members of the Publishing Triangle may nominate books for free; the nominating fee for nonmembers is $25. Write for additional information and nomination form.

Available to: No restrictions
Deadline: January 1
Apply to: Ferro-Grumley Awards, above address

Ⓝ The *Judy Grahn Award* for literary excellence in lesbian nonfiction and the *Randy Shilts Award* for literary excellence in gay nonfiction each annually offer an honorarium of $1,000. Publishers should submit four copies of nominated books (or bound galleys if books are not available). Members of the Publishing Triangle may nominate books for free; the nominating fee for nonmembers is $25. Write, e-mail, or see the Web site for additional information and nomination form.

Available to: No restrictions
Deadline: January 1
Apply to: Judy Grahn Award or Randy Shilts Award, above address

[IN] The *Bill Whitehead Award for Lifetime Achievement* of $3,000 recognizes a body of work with significant gay content. The award is given in even-numbered years to a woman; in odd-numbered years to a man. There is no application process. *By Internal Nomination Only.*

**Puffin Foundation Ltd.**
**20 East Oakdene Avenue**
**Teaneck, NJ 07666**

The Puffin Foundation offers grants to artists and performers, including writers, committed to "continuing the dialogue between art and the lives of ordinary people." The Foundation seeks to foster and encourage new artists and projects that might find funding difficult because of genre and/or social philosophy. Average grants range from $1,000 to $2,500. Write for further information and application.

Available to: No restrictions
Deadline: Applications accepted October 1-December 31
Apply to: Above address

**The Pulitzer Prizes**
**Columbia University**
**709 Journalism**
**2950 Broadway**
**New York, NY 10027**
**Web site: www.pulitzer.org**

Ⓜ *Pulitzer Prizes* are given to U. S. authors for the most distinguished volume of original verse, book of fiction, produced play, biography or autobiography, and book of nonfiction, and to authors of all nationalities for the most distinguished book on American history. Prizes are also given for journalism published in U. S. daily or weekly newspapers. Several prizes of $7,500 each are awarded annually.

Available to: See above
Deadlines: July 1 and November 1 for books; February 1 for journalism; March 1 for plays
Apply to: Above address

**Pulliam Journalism Fellowships**
**The Indianapolis Star**
**PO Box 145**
**Indianapolis, IN 46206-0145**
**E-mail: russell.pulliam@indystar.com**
**Web site: http://www.mdystar.com/pjf**
**Fax: 317-444-6750**

Ⓙ The *Pulliam Journalism Fellowships* are awarded to twenty college journalism or liberal arts students serious about a career in newspaper journalism. Fellows participate in a ten-week summer internship and receive a stipend of $6,000. Write, e-mail, or see the Web site for further information and application packet.

Available to: See above
Deadline: November 15 for early admission; March 1 for others
Apply to: Russell B. Pulliam, Fellowships Director, above address

**Pushcart Press**
**Box 380**
**Wainscott, NY 11975**

Ⓕ Ⓝ The *Editors' Book Award* offers $1,000 and hardcover publication for any book-length manuscript, fiction or nonfiction, submitted to but not yet accepted by a commercial publisher. Manuscripts must be nominated by an editor at a U. S. or Canadian publishing company.

Available to: No restrictions
Deadline: October 15
Apply to: Above address

Ⓜ The *Pushcart Prize* offers publication in *The Pushcart Prize: Best of the Small Presses* for the best literary works published by small presses in the current calendar year. Works of poetry, short fiction, essays, or self-contained portions of books or chapbooks are eligible. Submissions, in the form of tear sheets or photocopies, are accepted from editors only, who may nominate up to six works. Work to be published between the deadline and December 31 may be submitted in manuscript form. Write for complete guidelines.

Available to: No restrictions
Deadline: December 1
Apply to: Pushcart Prize, above address

**Quarterly Review of Literature**
Princeton University
26 Haslet Avenue
Princeton, NJ 08540
Web site: www.princeton.edu/~qrl/poetryseries.html
Fax: 609-258-2230

(P) The *Quarterly Review of Literature Poetry Book Awards* are presented annually to four to six winners for an unpublished manuscript of poetry. The award consists of $1,000, publication in the *QRL* poetry series, and 100 copies of the published book. Applicants should submit a collection of miscellaneous poems, a poetic play, a long poem, or a poetry translation of 40 to 100 pages. Manuscripts in English from outside the U. S. are also invited. A $20 subscription to *QRL* is required with submission. Send SASE for complete information.

Available to: No restrictions
Deadlines: Submissions accepted in May and November
Apply to: QRL Awards, above address

**Quarterly West**
University of Utah
200 South Central Campus Drive, Room 317
Salt Lake City, UT 84112-9109
Web site: www.utah.edu/quarterlywest/

(F) The *Quarterly West Novella Competition* biennially awards two prizes of $500 and publication in *Quarterly West* for novellas between 50 and 125 pages long. There is a $20 reading fee. Send SASE for guidelines before submitting. *(As this edition goes to press, PEN was unable to confirm this information, but believes it is accurate.)*

Available to: No restrictions
Deadline: Submissions accepted October 1-December 31
Apply to: Novella Competition, above address

**Radcliffe College**
Institute for Advanced Study
34 Concord Avenue
Cambridge, MA 02138
Phone: 617-496-1324
E-mail: fellowships@radcliffe.edu
Web site: www.radcliffe.edu
Fax: 617-495-8135

(M) The *Radcliffe Institute for Advanced Study Fellowships*, of up to $50,000 for one year with the possibility of additional funds for project expenses, support women scholars and writers of exceptional promise and demonstrated accomplishment who wish to pursue independent work in academic and professional fields and the creative arts. Appointments are full-time, from September 15 to August 15 of the following year, and require residence in the Boston area during that time. Applicants should have received their doctorate at least two years before applying; applicants without doctorates but with equivalent professional experience will be considered. Applicants in fiction and nonfiction must have a contract for the publication of a book-length manuscript, or must have had at least three short works published, preferably in the past five years. Applicants in poetry must have had at least twenty poems or a book of poetry published in the past five years, and be in the process of completing a book-length manuscript. Playwrights must have produced a significant body of work, usually a play produced or under option by a professional theater. Write, e-mail, or consult the Web site for more information.

Available to: See above
Deadline: October 1
Apply to: Radcliffe Institute Fellowships Office, above address

**Ragdale Foundation**
**1260 North Green Bay Road**
**Lake Forest, IL 60045**
**E-mail: ragdale1@aol.com**
**Web site: www.ragdale.org**

® Ragdale offers writers, artists, and composers an opportunity to work undisturbed on their own projects. Comfortable living and working space is provided in historic buildings adjoining a large nature preserve. Studios are available for visual artists and composers. Maximum stay is two months. Those accepted for residence are asked to pay $15 per day; some waivers are available on the basis of financial need.

Available to: No restrictions
Deadline: January 15 and June 1
Apply to: Above address

® The *Frances Shaw Fellowship for Older Women Writers* offers a six week residency to an as yet unpublished woman whose serious writing career began after age fifty-five. Send SASE for information.

Available to: See above
Deadline: February 1
Apply to: Above address

**Ayn Rand Institute**
**4640 Admiralty Way #406**
**Marina del Rey, CA 90292**
**E-mail: essay@aynrand.org**
**Web site: http://www.aynrand.org**

Ⓝ The *Anthem Essay Contest* annually offers 251 prizes in total, the first prize $2,000, for an essay by a ninth- or tenth-grader about one of three topics related to Ayn Rand's novelette *Anthem*. Essays should be between 600 and 1,200 words. Send SASE, e-mail, or consult the Web site for guidelines.

Available to: See above
Deadline: March 18
Apply to: Anthem Essay Contest, Dept. W, Ayn Rand Institute, PO Box 6099, Inglewood, CA 90312

Ⓝ The *Atlas Shrugged Essay Contest* annually offers nine prizes in total, the first prize $5,000 for an essay by an undergraduate or graduate business student about one of two topics related to Ayn Rand's novel *Atlas Shrugged*. Essays should be between 1,000 and 1,200 words. Send SASE, e-mail, or consult the Web site for guidelines.

Available to: See above
Deadline: September 16
Apply to: Atlas Shrugged Essay Contest, above address

Ⓝ *The Fountainhead Essay Contest* annually offers a total of 251 prizes, with the first prize of $10,000 for an essay by an eleventh- or twelfth-grader about one of three topics related to Ayn Rand's novel *The Fountainhead*. Essays should be between 800 and 1,600 words. Send SASE, e-mail, or consult the Web site for guidelines.

Available to: Eleventh- or twelfth-grade students
Deadline: April 15
Apply to: The Fountainhead Essay Contest, Dept. W, Ayn Rand Institute, PO Box 6004, Inglewood, CA 90312

**Red Hen Press**
**PO Box 3537**
**Granada Hills, CA 91394**
**Phone: 818-831-0649**
**E-mail: editors@redhen.org**
**Web site: www.redhen.org**
**Fax: 818-831-6659**

(P)  The *Benjamin Saltman Poetry Award* offers $1,000 and publication by Red Hen Press for an original, full-length poetry manuscript. Poets may submit 64 to 96 pages of poetry with SASE. There is a $15 reading fee. Send SASE, e-mail, or see the Web site for submission guidelines.

   Available to: No restrictions
   Deadline: October 21
   Apply to: Poetry Editor, above address


**Red Rock Review**
**English Department, J2A**
**Community College of Southern Nevada**
**3200 East Cheyenne Avenue**
**North Las Vegas, NV 89030**
**Phone: 702-651-4094**
**E-mail: rich_logsdon@ccsn.nevada.edu**
**Web site: ccsn.nevada.edu/enflish/redrockreview/mdev.htm**
**Fax: 702-651-4639**

(P)  The *Red Rock Poetry Award* offers $500 and publication in *Red Rock Review* for a poem of no more than 20 lines. Poets may submit up to three poems, with a $6 reading fee. Send SASE for guidelines.

   Available to: No restrictions
   Deadline: Inquire
   Apply to: Red Rock Poetry Award, above address

(F)  The *Mark Twain Award for Short Fiction* offers $1,000 and publication in *Red Rock Review*, a biannual journal of fiction, poetry, and creative nonfiction, for a short story of no more than 3,500 words. There is a $10 reading fee. Send SASE for guidelines.

   Available to: No restrictions
   Deadline: Inquire
   Apply to: Mark Twain Award for Short Fiction


**The Refined Savage**
**28 Kanawha View Road**
**Red House, WV 25168**
**E-mail: therefinedsavage@peoplepc.com**
**Web site: http://members.tripod.com/trswv/index.htm**

(P)  *The Refined Savage Poetry Competition* offers $500 and publication in *The Refined Savage*, a bilingual poetry review, for a poem in English or Spanish. The top ten finalists will also be published and translated. There is a $7 reading fee for three poems; $2 each for additional poems. Send SASE or e-mail for guidelines. *(As this edition goes to press, PEN was unable to confirm this information, but believes it is accurate.)*

   Available to: No restrictions
   Deadline: November 15
   Apply to: Poetry Competition, above address

**Rhode Island State Council on the Arts**
**83 Park Street, 6th floor**
**Providence, RI 02903-1037**
**E-mail: randy@risca.state.ri.us**
**Web site: http://www.risca.state.ri.us**
**Fax: 401-521-1351**

Ⓜ Literature fellowships are given annually in the categories of fiction, playwriting/ screenwriting, and poetry to encourage the creative development of professional Rhode Island artists by enabling them to set aside time to pursue their work and achieve specific career goals. One fellowship of $5,000 and one runner-up prize of $1,000 are awarded in each category.

Available to: Rhode Island residents at least eighteen years old who are not full-time undergraduate or graduate students
Deadline: April 1
Apply to: Fellowships, above address

**Richard Free Library**
**58 North Main Street**
**Newport, NH 03773**
**E-mail: rfl@newport.lib.nh.us**
**Fax: 603-863-3022**

IN The *Sarah Josepha Hale Award* of $500 annually recognizes a distinguished body of literary work by a writer who was born or resides in New England or whose work is primarily associated with New England. There is no application process. *By Internal Nomination Only.*

**Mary Roberts Rinehart Fund**
**George Mason University**
**English Department**
**MSN 3E4**
**4400 University Drive**
**Fairfax, VA 22030-4444**
**E-mail: bgompert@gmu.edu**
**Web site: www.gmu.edu/departments/writing/rinehart.htm**

Ⓜ The *Mary Roberts Rinehart Fund* awards three $2,000 grants to writers who have not yet published a book, to complete previously unpublished works of fiction, poetry, biography, autobiography, or history with a strong narrative quality. Candidates must be nominated by a sponsoring writer, agent, or editor. Inquire for details.

Available to: See above
Deadline: November 30
Apply to: Above address

**River City**
**Department of English**
**University of Memphis**
**Memphis, TN 38152**
**Phone: 901-678-4591**
**E-mail: rivercity@memphis.edu**
**Web site: www.people.memphis.edu/~rivercity**
**Fax: 901-678-2226**

Ⓕ Three *River City Writing Awards in Fiction* are given annually for unpublished short stories of up to 7,500 words. First prize is $2,000, second is $500, and third is $300. All winning stories are published in *River City*. There is a $10 entry fee, which will be applied toward a subscription to *River City*. Manuscripts will not be returned.

Available to: No restrictions
Deadline: March 1
Apply to: Thomas Russell, Editor, River City Writing Awards, above address

(P) Three *River City Writing Awards in Poetry* are given annually for unpublished poems of up to two pages. *River City* will publish the prize-winning poems. There is a $5 entry fee.

Available to: No restrictions
Deadline: March 1
Apply to: Thomas Russell, Editor, River City Writing Awards, above address

**River Oak Review**
**PO Box 3127**
**Oak Park, IL 60303**
**Web site: www.riveroakarts.org**

(F) The *River Oak Review Short Story Contest* annually awards $500 and publication in *River Oak Review* to an unpublished short story of no more than 5,000 words. A $15 reading fee covers a one-year subscription to the *Review*. Send SASE or see the Web site for complete guidelines.

Available to: No restrictions
Deadline: June 1
Apply to: Short Story Contest, above address

(P) The *River Oak Review Poetry Contest* annually awards $500 and publication in the *Review* for an unpublished poem or group of poems. Poets may submit up to four poems of no more than 500 lines total. A $15 reading fee covers a one-year subscription to the *Review*. Send SASE for guidelines.

Available to: No restrictions
Deadline: December 1
Apply to: Poetry Contest, above address

**River Styx**
**634 North Grand Boulevard, 12th floor**
**St. Louis, MO 63103**

(P) *River Styx*, a triquarterly journal of poetry, fiction, and art, sponsors an *International Poetry Contest* for a short body of work—no more than three poems or 14 pages. First prize is $1,000 and publication. Second- and third-place winners will also be published. The $20 entry fee covers the cost of a one-year subscription to *River Styx*. Send SASE for guidelines.

Available to: No restrictions
Deadline: May 31
Apply to: International Poetry Contest, above address

**Robinson Jeffers Tor House Foundation**
**PO Box 223240**
**Carmel, CA 93922**
**Phone: 831-624-1813**
**E-mail: ihf@torhouse.org**
**Web site: http://www.torhouse.org**
**Fax: 831-624-3699**

(P) The *Robinson Jeffers Tor House Prize for Poetry* awards $1,000 for a single, unpublished poem. An Honorable Mention, carrying a $200 stipend, is also offered. Poets may submit up to three poems, no more than 3 pages each, with a $10 reading fee, or up to six poems with a $15 reading fee; the fee for each additional poem is $2.50. Send SASE, e-mail, or see the Web site for guidelines.

Available to: No restrictions
Deadline: March 15
Apply to: Poetry Prize, above address

**Rockefeller Foundation**
**Bellagio Study and Conference Center**
**420 Fifth Avenue**
**New York, NY 10018-2702**
**E-mail: bellagio@rockfound.org**
**Web site: http://www.rockfound.org/bellagio**

® Four-week residences in the Italian Alps from approximately February 1 to December 15 are offered to artists and scholars. Writers must have at least one major book publication to their credit to be eligible. Room is available for spouses. Residents must pay for their own travel. Write, e-mail, or see the Web site for additional information. E-mail applications are accepted only from outside the U. S.

Available to: No restrictions
Deadline: January 10, May 10, and August 26; apply ten to twelve months in advance of desired residence dates
Apply to: Above address

**Rocky Mountain National Park**
**Estes Park, CO 80517**
**Phone: 970-586-1206**

® The *Artist-in-Residence Program* offers professional writers and other artists the opportunity to pursue their particular art form surrounded by the inspiring landscape of Rocky Mountain National Park. The Park offers each chosen participant use of the historic William Allen White cabin for two weeks from early June to late September. No additional stipend is available. In return, residents donate to the Park's collection a piece of work representative of their style and their stay (with the National Park Service holding the copyright of the donated work), and participate in two public presentations. Write for additional information.

Available to: No restrictions
Deadline: Inquire
Apply to: Artist-in-Residence Program, above address

**Rocky Mountain Student Theater Project**
**Box 1724**
**Telluride, CO 80901**
**E-mail: owenperk@aol.com**
**Web site: http://members.aol.com/PlayFest/RMSTP.html**

Ⓓ The *Roy Barker Playwriting Prize* annually awards a first prize of $500, a second of $250, and a third of $100, as well as a full production for each, for a full-length play, one-act, translation, adaptation, play for young audience, or solo piece by a high school student. One-act plays 30 to 45 minutes long are preferred. There is a $5 entry fee. Write, e-mail, or see the Web site for contest rules.

Available to: High school students
Deadline: May 1
Apply to: The Roy Barker Playwriting Prize, above address

**Rocky Mountain Women's Institute**
**1836 Logan Street**
**Denver, CO 80203**
**Phone: 303-830-1818**
**E-mail: erbraden@yahoo.com**

® The RMWI's goal is to promote the intellectual and artistic accomplishments of women by creating a community of artists, writers, and scholars. The Institute annually selects seven to ten talented individuals to be associates; they compete on the basis of their work. Associates are given a stipend of $1,250 and services to support them in the completion of a creative project. Their year ends with public performances, exhibitions, and readings. Contact the Institute for guidelines.

Available to: No restrictions
Deadline: Inquire
Apply to: Above address

**Rome Art and Community Center**
**308 West Bloomfield Street**
**Rome, NY 13440**
**Web site: www.borg.com/**

(P)  The *Milton Dorfman Poetry Prize* of $500 is awarded annually for original, previously unpublished poems. A second prize of $200 and a third of $100 are also given. There is no limit to the numbers of submissions; a reading fee of $5 per poem is required. The winning poem will be published and read by the contest judge at the Center's open house. Write for further information.

Available to: No restrictions
Deadline: November 1
Apply to: Milton Dorfman Poetry Prize, above address

**The Rotary Foundation**
**One Rotary Center**
**1560 Sherman Avenue**
**Evanston, IL 60201-3698**
**Phone: 847-866-3000**
**E-mail: scholarshipinquiries@rotaryintl.org**
**Web site: www.rotary.org**
**Fax: 847-328-8554**

In the effort to promote international understanding and relations among people of different nations, The Rotary Foundation offers *Ambassadorial Scholarships* to sponsor "ambassadors of goodwill" to study in another country. Students of disciplines including writing who receive a scholarship should use it at a specific foreign institution and are expected to apply directly to the institution. Scholarship recipients will not be assigned to study in areas of a country where they have previously lived for more than six months. Foreign students seeking funding to continue studies at their current university are not eligible. For applications and further guidelines, consult www.rotary.org/programs/amb_scho/index.html.

Available to: See above
Deadline: March-July for the following year (see Web site for exact dates)
Apply to: Above address

*Rotary Grants for University Teachers* provide funding to faculty willing to share their expertise in many fields, including writing, with students in developing nations. Availability of grants is determined locally. Consult the Web site for more information.

Available to: No restrictions
Deadline: Inquire
Apply to: Above address

Seventy *Rotary Center Scholarships for International Studies in Peace and Conflict Resolution* are offered annually for two-year master's-level degree programs in international relations, peace studies, and conflict resolution at Rotary Centers. For more information and application materials see www.rotary.org/programs/amb_scho/centers.

Available to: See above
Deadline: Inquire
Apply to: Above address

**Runes, A Review of Poetry**
**Arctos Press**
**PO Box 401**
**Sausalito, CA 94966-0401**
**E-mail: runesrev@aol.com**
**Web site: members.aol.com/runes**

(P)   The *Runes Award* offers $1,000 plus publication in *Runes, A Review Of Poetry* for an original, unpublished poem of 100 lines or less on a specified theme; the theme for the 2002 contest was "Mystery." The entry fee of $10 for three poems covers a one-year subscription to *Runes*. Send SASE or e-mail for guidelines.

Available to: No restrictions
Deadline: Submissions accepted in April and May
Apply to: Above address

**St. Martin's Press**
**175 Fifth Avenue**
**New York, NY 10010**
**Web site: http://www.minotaurbooks.com/minotaur/faq.html**

(F)   The *Best First Private Eye Novel Contest*, co-sponsored by Private Eye Writers of America, and the *Malice Domestic Best First Novel Contest*, for traditional mystery novels, each annually award $10,000 (as an advance against royalties) and publication. Send SASE or consult the Web site for contest rules before submitting a manuscript. Authors must be unpublished in the mystery genre and must have no novels under contract for publication in the genre.

Available to: No restrictions
Deadline: August 1 for Private Eye; October 15 for Malice Domestic
Apply to: Private Eye Contest, above address, or Malice Domestic Contest, Thomas Dunne Books, above address

**Salmon Run Press**
**PO Box 672130**
**Chugiak, AK 99567-2130**
**Web site: http://www.oregonstatepoetryassoc.org/SalmonRunPress.html**

(P)   The *Salmon Run National Poetry Book Award* offers $1,000 and publication for a poetry manuscript of 68 to 96 pages. The winning book will be published in an edition of 500 or 1,000 copies, and will be advertised nationally. There is a $10 reading fee. Send SASE for guidelines.

Available to: No restrictions
Deadline: February 20
Apply to: Poetry Book Award, above address

**Constance Saltonstall Foundation for the Arts**
**PO Box 6607**
**Ithaca, NY 44851-6607**
**Phone: 607-277-4933**
**Web site: http://www.saltonstall.org**

(R)   The Foundation awards one-month summer residences at the Saltonstall Arts Colony to visual artists, poets, and fiction and creative prose writers who live in New York state. The Foundation also awards grants of up to $5,000 to writers and visual artists living in central and western New York counties. See the Web site for guidelines and application.

Available to: Residents of certain New York state counties; see above
Deadline: January 15
Apply to: Above address

**San Francisco Chronicle**
**901 Mission Street**
**San Francisco, CA 94103-2988**
**Web site: http://www.sfgate.com/chronicle/internships**

Ⓙ The *San Francisco Chronicle* offers two types of newsroom internships. A summer internship, a twelve-week training program, begins in mid-June, and is intended for college students and recent graduates. A two-year program offers newsroom training to new college graduates. Interns are paid approximately $540 a week; two-year interns are eligible for comprehensive health benefits after three months. Write or consult the Web site for additional information and application procedures.

Available to: See above
Deadline: Applications must be postmarked October 1-November 15
Apply to: Leslie Guevarra, Newsroom Hiring and Staff Development, above address (specify Summer or Two-Year Internship Program)

**San Jose Center for Poetry and Literature**
**110 South Market Street**
**San Jose, CA 95113**
**Web site: www.sjcpl.com**

Ⓟ The Center's *Poetry Prize* annually awards $500 and publication in *Cæsura*, the Center's journal, for an unpublished poem of any length. Poems must not have been awarded a prize in any other competition. Poets may submit up to three poems with a $10 reading fee; the fee for additional poems is $3 each. Write for guidelines. No prize will be given in 2002; inquire for 2003.

Available to: No restrictions
Deadline: October 15
Apply to: Poetry Prize, above address

**Sarabande Books**
**2234 Dundee Road, Suite 200**
**Louisville, KY 40205**
**Web site: http://www.sarabandebooks.org**

Ⓕ The *Mary McCarthy Prize in Short Fiction* awards $2,000 and publication by Sarabande for a collection of short stories or novellas, or a short novel (under 250 pages). Winners receive a standard royalty contract. Send SASE or consult the Web site for guidelines and entry form.

Available to: U. S. resident citizens
Deadline: Submissions accepted January 1-February 15
Apply to: Mary McCarthy Prize in Short Fiction, above address

Ⓟ The *Kathryn A. Morton Prize in Poetry* awards $2,000 and publication by Sarabande for a full-length volume of poetry. Winners receive a standard royalty contract. Send SASE or consult the Web site for guidelines and entry form.

Available to: U. S. resident citizens
Deadline: Submissions accepted January 1-February 15
Apply to: Kathryn A. Morton Prize in Poetry, above address

**Scholastic**
**555 Broadway**
**New York, NY 10012**
**E-mail: a&wgeneralinfo@scholastic.com**
**Web site: http://www.scholastic.com/artandwriting**

The *Scholastic Writing Awards* offer junior and senior high school students (grades 7 through 12) cash prizes from $100 to $5,000 in eight categories. Several scholarship grants and publishing opportunities are also available. Write or see the Web site for further information and application procedures.

Available to: Students grades 7 through 12

Deadline: Varies by geographic region (inquire)
Apply to: Scholastic Writing Awards, above address

**Schomburg Center for Research in Black Culture**
**515 Malcolm X Boulevard**
**New York, NY 10037-1801**
**Phone: 212-491-2200**

The *Scholars-in-Residence Program* at the Schomburg Center is designed to encourage research and writing in black history and culture. Fellows spend six months or a year in residence, with access to resources at the Schomburg Center and the New York Public Library; they receive a maximum stipend of $15,000 for six months and up to $30,000 for twelve. The program is open to scholars studying black history and culture from a humanistic perspective and to professionals in fields related to the Center's collections. Studies in social sciences, the arts, science and technology, psychology, education, and religion are eligible if they use a humanistic approach and contribute to humanistic knowledge. Write or call for additional information and application materials.

Available to: U. S. citizens or foreign nationals resident in the United States at least three years immediately before application
Deadline: January 15
Apply to: Scholars-in-Residence Program, above address

**Schoolcraft College**
**18600 Haggerty Road**
**Livonia, MI 48152**
**E-mail: macguffin@schoolcraft.cc.mi.us**

(P) The *MacGuffin National Poet Hunt* awards a $500 first prize, a $250 second prize, and a $100 third prize for an unpublished poem. All winning entries will appear in *The MacGuffin*, a magazine published three times a year by Schoolcraft College. Poets may submit up to five poems, with a $15 entry fee. Send SASE for guidelines.

Available to: No restrictions
Deadline: Submissions accepted April 1-May 31
Apply to: MacGuffin National Poet Hunt, above address

**Kurt Schork Memorial Fund**
**1333 H Street, NW — Reuters**
**Washington, DC 20005**
**Phone: 202-354-5812**
**E-mail: ksmf1@juno.com**
**Web site: www.ksmfund.org**
**Fax: 202-898-8448**

(J) The *Kurt Schork Memorial Prize* of $10,000 annually recognizes exceptional news reporting by freelance journalists and journalists from the developing world. The award honors the work and the legacy of the exceptional journalist Kurt Schork, who was killed in Sierra Leone in 2000 while on assignment for Reuters. See the Web site for more information.

Available to: No restrictions
Deadline: Inquire
Apply to: Kurt Schork Memorial Prize, above address

(J) Two *Kurt Schork Memorial Scholarships* are given annually to deserving students at the Columbia University Graduate School of Journalism to encourage future reporters to strive for the high standards of journalism that Kurt Schork embodied. Each scholarship consists of $5,000. See the Web site for more information.

Available to: Students at the Columbia University Graduate School of Journalism
Deadline: Inquire
Apply to: Kurt Schork Memorial Scholarships, above address

Scripps Howard Foundation
312 Walnut Street, 28th floor
Cincinnati, OH 45202-5380
E-mail: cottingham@scripps.com
Web site: http://www.scripps.com/foundation
Fax: 513-977-3800

ⓙ The *Business/Economic Reporting/William Brewster Styles Award* of $2,500 is given for outstanding business and/or economics reporting published during the preceding calendar year. There is a $25 entry fee. Write, e-mail, or see the Web site for guidelines and entry form.

Available to: Daily newspaper journalists in the U. S. and its territories
Deadline: January 31
Apply to: Business/Economic Reporting Award, above address

ⓙ The *Commentary Award* of $2,500 honors outstanding commentary by a columnist whose signed work appeared regularly in a daily newspaper in the United States or its territories during the preceding calendar year. There is a $25 entry fee. Write, e-mail, or see the Web site for guidelines and entry form.

Available to: Daily newspaper journalists in the U. S. and its territories
Deadline: January 31
Apply to: Commentary Award, above address

ⓙ The *Editorial Writing/Walker Stone Award* of $2,500 annually honors outstanding achievement in editorial writing. Submitted material must have been published in a newspaper in the preceding calendar year; work published in magazines is not eligible. There is a $25 entry fee. Write, e-mail, or visit the Web site for guidelines and entry form.

Available to: Daily newspaper journalists in the U. S. and its territories
Deadline: January 31
Apply to: Editorial Writing Award, above address

ⓙ The *Environmental Reporting/Edward J. Meeman Awards* recognize outstanding environmental reporting published in daily newspapers during the preceding calendar year. A $2,500 prize is given in each of two categories: newspapers with a circulation over 100,000, and newspapers with a circulation under 100,000. The awards encourage journalists to help educate the public and public officials toward better understanding of the environment and environmental protection. There is a $25 entry fee. Write, e-mail, or see the Web site for guidelines and entry form.

Available to: Daily newspaper journalists in the U. S. and its territories
Deadline: January 31
Apply to: Environmental Reporting Awards, above address

ⓙ The *Human Interest/Ernie Pyle Writing Award* of $2,500 is given annually to an individual whose newspaper writing "most exemplifies the style and craftsmanship of the late Ernie Pyle [who wrote] movingly about everyday people with everyday dreams." Warmth, human interest, and storytelling ability rank high in the judging. Submitted material must have been published in a newspaper in the preceding calendar year. There is a $25 entry fee. Write, e-mail, or see the Web site for guidelines and entry form.

Available to: Daily newspaper journalists in the U. S. and its territories
Deadline: January 31
Apply to: Human Interest Award, above address

ⓙ The *Roy W. Howard National Reporting Competition* encourages college students who aspire to the profession to which Howard dedicated his life. The competition is open to college freshmen, sophomores, and juniors. Entrants may submit one story or a series, published in a campus or professional newspaper, involving events, trends, or personalities. The winners receive a cash prize and an all-expenses-paid trip to Indiana University. Write to the address listed below or see the Web site for additional information and application.

Available to: See above
Deadline: Inquire
Apply to: Trevor Brown, Dean, School of Journalism, Indiana University, Bloomington, IN 47405; 812-855-9249

(J) The *Public Service Reporting/Roy W. Howard Awards* recognize outstanding public service and/ or investigative reporting published in daily newspapers during the preceding calendar year. A $2,500 prize is given in each of two categories: newspapers with a circulation over 100,000, and newspapers with a circulation under 100,000. There is a $25 entry fee. Write, e-mail, or see the Web site for guidelines and entry form.

Available to: Daily newspaper journalists in the U. S. and its territories
Deadline: January 31
Apply to: Public Service Reporting Awards, above address

(J) The Scripps Howard Foundation awards internships to journalism students. Selected students at participating schools receive grants allowing them to work in a professional site agreeable to them and approved by the school. Professional organizations offer meaningful work and instructive supervision, and the schools monitor, evaluate, and counsel the students. Check with your school for additional information.

Available to: Journalism students at participating schools
Deadline: Inquire
Apply to: See above

**Seattle Arts Commission**
**312 First Avenue North**
**Seattle, WA 98109**
**Phone: 206-684-7310**
**Web site: www.cityofseattle.net**

(M) The *Seattle Artist Program* funds the development of new works and works-in-progress by Seattle artists in a variety of disciplines, including poetry, prose/fiction, scriptwriting, screenwriting, and critical writing/creative nonfiction. Write for further information. Art forms to be awarded vary by year; literature grants are awarded in even-numbered years. Write or see the Web site for further information.

Available to: Seattle artists
Deadline: November of year prior to that of funding
Apply to: Irene Gomez, above address

**Seattle Post-Intelligencer**
**101 Elliot Avenue, West**
**Seattle, WA 98119**
**E-mail: janetgrimly@Seattle-PI.com**
**Web site: www.washington.edu/students/ugrad/scholar/special/mccallum.html**

(J) The *Bobbi McCallum Memorial Scholarship* of $1,000 is given to women college students attending a Washington state college or university who are interested in pursuing a newspaper career. Selection is based on need, academic achievement, and motivation. Application must include five samples of work, published or unpublished, a financial statement, and two letters of recommendation.

Available to: Women journalism majors entering their junior or senior year in college in Washington state
Deadline: April 1
Apply to: Janet Grimly, Assistant Managing Editor, above address

**The Seattle Times**
**1120 John Street**
**Seattle, WA 98109**
**Phone: 206-464-2414**
**E-mail: dlesch@seattletimes.com**

(J) *Summer Newsroom Internships* at the Pulitzer Prize-winning *Seattle Times* are offered annually to ten to twelve outstanding students pursuing a career in journalism. Most of the positions are for general assignment reporters working at the metro desk and in suburban bureaus. Applicants must be sophomores, juniors, or seniors attending a four-year college or university, or graduate students, and must be majoring in journalism or have demonstrated a commitment to journalism. Previous experience is required. Selected interns are placed in full-time, paid twelve-week positions. Write for additional information and application procedures.

Available to: See above
Deadline: November 1
Apply to: Newsroom Intern Coordinator, above address

(J) The *Seattle Times Three-Year Internship* is designed for beginning journalists with some daily newspaper experience whose goal is to develop high-quality professional skills. Most reporting interns rotate among features, business news, and suburban and metro assignments; the rotation is made once a year. Opportunities are available for sports and copyediting interns as well. Some newspaper experience is required, through an internship at metropolitan dailies, or a year or two at smaller dailies. Positions are filled as vacancies arise.

Available to: See above
Deadline: Ongoing
Apply to: Above address

## Serpentine
**1761 Edgewood Road**
**Redwood City, CA 94062**
**E-mail: contest@serpentinia.com**
**Web site: http://www.serpentinia.com**

(F) The *Serpentine Annual Short Story Contest* offers a first prize of $1,000, a second of $200, a third of $100, and four honorable mentions of $50 for short stories no longer than 10,000 words. Winners must supply story text in common electronic format to qualify and be published in a special on-line edition. The reading fee is $18 per manuscript. E-mail or see the Web site for guidelines.

Available to: No restrictions
Deadline: December 31
Apply to: Above address

## Seventeen Magazine
**1440 Broadway, 13th floor**
**New York, NY 10018**

(F) The *Seventeen Magazine Fiction Contest* is open to anyone between thirteen and twenty-one years of age. Each entry should be an unpublished (except in school publications) short story not exceeding 4,000 words. The winning writer receives $1,000 and publication in *Seventeen*; the second-place winner receives $500, third-place $250, and five honorable mentions $50 each. Send SASE for rules.

Available to: See above
Deadline: April 30
Apply to: Fiction Contest, above address

## The Sewanee Review
**University of the South**
**735 University Avenue**
**Sewanee, TN 37383-1000**

[IN] The *Aiken Taylor Award for Modern American Poetry* of $10,000 is given annually to a poet who has had a substantial and distinguished career. *By Internal Nomination Only.*

**Sewanee Writers' Conference**
**310 St. Luke's Hall**
**735 University Avenue**
**Sewanee, TN 37383-1000**
**Web site: www.sewaneewriters.org**

®　Numerous fellowships and scholarships are available for the annual twelve-day summer Sewanee Writers' Conference. Fellows receive full tuition plus room and board; most scholarships cover two-thirds of Conference expenses. Fellowship applicants in poetry and fiction must have a book published or in press at a major university or commercial publisher; candidates in playwriting should send details of work that has seen amateur or professional production. Scholarship applicants should have a number of publications in major academic or popular magazines. Applications are reviewed as they are received; early applications are encouraged. Send SASE for additional information and application.

Available to: See above
Deadline: Applications accepted from February 1, until spaces are filled
Apply to: Cheri Peters, Creative Writing Program Manager, above address

**Shenandoah**
**Washington and Lee University**
**Troubadour Theater, 2nd floor**
**Lexington, VA 24450**
**E-mail: lleech@wlu.edu**
**Web site: http://shenandoah.wlu.edu**
**Fax: 540-463-8461**

Ⓜ　The following annual awards are given to work published in *Shenandoah* during the calendar year: the *James Boatwright III Prize for Poetry* of $1,000, to the author of the best poetry; the *Thomas H. Carter Prize for the Essay* of $500, to the author of the best essay; the *Jeanne Charpiot Goodheart Prize for Fiction* of $1,000, to the author of the best story. Manuscripts are read between September 1 and May 30; manuscripts received during June, July, and August will be returned unread. Send SASE for general guidelines.

Available to: *Shenandoah* contributors
Deadline: See above
Apply to: Above address

**Shenandoah International Playwrights**
**Pennyroyal Farm**
**717 Quicks Mill Road**
**Staunton, VA 24401**
**E-mail: theatre@shenanarts.org**
**Web site: www.shenanarts.org**

Ⓓ Ⓢ　Ten to twelve playwrights and screenwriters are offered a four-week retreat in the Shenandoah Valley of Virginia in August and September. The retreat includes writers from around the world who collaborate with a multicultural company of professional theater artists in the translation, development, and adaptation of new plays and screenplays. Writers receive fellowships that provide roundtrip transportation, room and board, and the services of the professional company. Write for additional information.

Available to: No restrictions
Deadline: February 1
Apply to: Above address

**Joan Shorenstein Center on the Press, Politics, and Public Policy**
**Harvard University**
**John F. Kennedy School of Government**
**79 Kennedy Street, 2nd floor Taubman**
**Cambridge, MA 02138**
**E-mail: alison_kommer@harvard.edu (for Goldsmith Prizes); edith_holway@harvard.edu**
**(for Shorenstein Fellowships)**
**Web site: http://www.ksg.harvard.edu/presspol/**
**Fax: 617-495-8696**

Ⓝ  The *Goldsmith Book Prizes* offer $2,500 to each of the authors of distinguished English-language books, in two categories (academic—theoretical, research-oriented books—and trade— popular books targeted at a wide audience), that aim to improve the quality of government or politics by examining the press and government or the intersection of press and politics in the formation of public policy. Publication must have been within twelve months preceding the submission deadline. Edited volumes are not accepted. Write, e-mail, or see the Web site for guidelines and application.

Available to: No restrictions
Deadline: December 31
Apply to: Goldsmith Book Prize, above address

Ⓙ  The *Goldsmith Prize for Investigative Reporting* annually awards $25,000 to the journalist or journalists whose investigative reporting in a story or series best promotes more effective and ethical conduct of government, the making of public policy, or the practice of politics. The subject may relate to foreign policy, but only insofar as it has an impact on U. S. public policy. Five finalists will be awarded $2,000 each. Publication must have been within twelve months preceding the submission deadline. Print and broadcast submissions are accepted. Write, e-mail, or see the Web site for guidelines and application.

Available to: Journalists with U. S. news organizations
Deadline: December 31
Apply to: Goldsmith Prize for Investigative Reporting, above address

A limited number of *Joan Shorenstein Fellowships on the Press, Politics, and Public Policy* are available at the Center for established scholars, journalists, and policymakers interested in the relationship between the press and politics. Fellowships are for one academic semester (September through December, or February through May), during which participants are expected to conduct research and write a 40-page paper on a press/ politics topic. Fellows participate in informal weekly seminars with visiting journalists, scholars, and policymakers, and in other activities sponsored by the Center. There is a stipend of $15,000 for the semester; travel and living expenses are not covered. Office space and a computer and printer are provided. Write or see the Web site for additional information.

Available to: See above
Deadline: February 1
Apply to: Fellowship Program, above address

**Short Story Journal**
**1817 Marengo Street**
**New Orleans, LA 70115**
**Web site: http://shortstoryjournal.tripod.com/Contest/Contest.htm**

Ⓕ  The *Short Story Contest* annually offers a first prize of $500 and a second of $100 for a short story. The winners are published in *Short Story* and invited to read at the International Conference on the Short Story, to be held in New Orleans. There is a $15 entry fee. Send SASE for guidelines.

Available to: No restrictions
Deadline: Inquire
Apply to: Short Story Contest, above address

**Siena College**
**Department of Creative Arts, Theatre Program**
**515 Loudon Road**
**Loudonville, NY 12211-1462**
**Web site: http://www.siena.edu/theatre/playwrights.htm**

Ⓓ The *Siena College International Playwrights' Competition* biennially awards a $2,000 honorarium, full production, and up to $1,000 for travel, housing, and board during a four-to-six-week production residence for full-length, unpublished, unproduced, nonmusical plays. Scripts with roles suitable for college-age performers, small casts, and simple sets are encouraged. Send SASE or see the Web site for guidelines before submitting.

Available to: No restrictions
Deadline: February 1-June 30 in even-numbered years
Apply to: International Playwrights' Competition, above address

**Silverfish Review Press**
**PO Box 3541**
**Eugene, OR 97403**
**E-mail: SFRpress@aol.com**
**Web site: http://www.qspeed.com/silverfish**

Ⓟ The *Gerald Cable Book Award* annually offers $1,000 and publication by the Press for a book-length manuscript of original poetry by an author who has not published a full-length collection. Translations are not eligible. There is a $20 reading fee. Send SASE or e-mail for guidelines.

Available to: See above
Deadline: November 1
Apply to: Gerald Cable Book Award, above address

**Sitka Center for Art and Ecology**
**Neskowin Coast Foundation**
**PO Box 65**
**Otis, OR 97368**
**E-mail: info@sitkacenter.org**
**Web site: http://www.sitkacenter.org**

Ⓡ Residences of up to four months are offered to writers, naturalists, and artists at Cascade Head Ranch, located within the Cascade Head National Scenic Research Area. The residences are in three categories: emerging artist/naturalist, mid-career artist/naturalist, and artist/naturalist on sabbatical. Each resident is provided with living and studio space and is asked to provide community service on behalf of the Sitka Center. Residents must provide their own food. Write, e-mail, or visit the Web site for additional information and application.

Available to: No restrictions
Deadline: April 15
Apply to: Above address

**Slipstream**
**PO Box 2071**
**New Market Station**
**Niagara Falls, NY 14301**
**Web site: http://www.slipstreampress.org**

Ⓟ The *Slipstream Annual Poetry Chapbook Contest* awards $1,000, publication of a chapbook for the winning manuscript, and 50 copies of the book. All other entrants receive a copy of the book, as well as one issue of *Slipstream*. Send up to 40 pages of poetry, a $10 reading fee, and SASE with sufficient postage for return of manuscript.

Available to: No restrictions
Deadline: December 1
Apply to: Above address

**Gibbs Smith, Publisher**
PO Box 667
Layton, UT 84041
E-mail: info@gibbs-smith.com
Web site: http://www.gibbs-smith.com
Fax: 801-544-5582

(P)    The *Peregrine Smith Poetry Competition* awards a $1,000 prize plus publication by Gibbs Smith
for a book-length manuscript of poems, 48 to 64 typewritten pages. Submissions, which
must be accompanied by a $20 reading fee, will not be returned. Send SASE, e-mail, or
see the Web site for guidelines.

Available to: No restrictions
Deadline: Submissions accepted in April only
Apply to: Peregrine Smith Poetry Competition, above address

**Smithsonian American Art Museum**
**Research and Scholars Center**
**Washington, D.C. 20560-0970**
E-mail: eldredge@saam.si.edu
Web site: http://hmaa-ryder.si.edu/study/opportunities-eldredge.html
Fax: 202-786-2583

(N)    The *Charles C. Eldredge Prize* is awarded annually for outstanding scholarship in the field of
American art. An award of $2,000 is given to the author of a recent book-length publication
that provides new insight into works of American art, the artists who made them, or
aspects of history and theory that enrich understanding of the artistic heritage. Single-
author book-length publications—including monographs, exhibition catalogues,
catalogues raisonnées, and collected essays—in the field of American art history appearing
within the three calendar years before the application deadline are eligible. Write for
additional information and nomination procedures.

Available to: No restrictions
Deadline: December 1
Apply to: Charles C. Eldredge Prize, above address

**The Smithsonian Institution**
**Office of Fellowships**
**950 9th Street, NW, Suite 9300**
**Washington, DC 20560-0902**
E-mail: siofg@ofg.si.edu
Web site: http://www.si.edu/research+study

The Smithsonian Institution offers fellowships to graduate students, predoctoral students,
and postdoctoral and senior investigators, for opportunities to conduct research in
association with members of the Smithsonian professional research staff and to use
Smithsonian resources. Graduate student fellows are appointed for ten weeks with a
stipend of $3,700. Predoctoral, postdoctoral, and senior fellows are appointed for three
to twelve months with a stipend of $17,000 per year for predoctoral and $30,000 per
year for postdoctoral and senior fellows. A travel allowance and an allowance for
research-related expenses, up to $2,000, are possible. Write for additional information
and application.

Available to: No restrictions
Deadline: January 15
Apply to: Above address

**Snake Nation Press**
**110 West Force Street**
**Valdosta, GA 31601**
Web site: http://www.snakenationpress.org

(P)    The *Violet Reed Haas Poetry Prize* offers $500 and publication by Snake Nation Press for a 50-

to-75-page manuscript of poems. There is a $10 entry fee, which covers a copy of the winning book. Write for further information.

Available to: No restrictions
Deadline: May 1
Apply to: Violet Reed Haas Poetry Prize, above address

Ⓕ The *Mighty Withlacoochee Award for Fiction* offers $1,000 and publication of a novella or short story collection. Write for further information.

Available to: No restrictions
Deadline: Inquire
Apply to: Mighty Withlacoochee Award for Fiction, above address

**Soapstone, A Writing Retreat for Women**
**622 SE 29 Avenue**
**Portland, OR 97214**
**Phone: 503-233-3936**
**E-mail: mail@soapstone.org**
**Web site: www.soapstone.org**
**Fax: 503-233-0774**

Ⓡ Residences of one to four weeks are given to between twenty-four and thirty-six women writers, who will be selected to come in pairs. Soapstone is in the Coast Range of Oregon, approximately nine miles from the ocean, on twenty-two acres of land along the banks of Soapstone Creek. When writers apply in pairs, each must be accepted individually on the merit of her work; single writers will be paired. Applicants are judged on the strength of their writing, with attention given to promoting diversity and to assisting women of limited economic means who may never have had such an opportunity. Residents are provided with blankets, pillows, and limited kitchen equipment. There is a $20 application fee. Consult the Web site for application.

Available to: Women writers
Deadline: August 15
Apply to: Above address

**Social Science Research Council**
**810 Seventh Avenue**
**New York, NY 10019**
**E-mail: srfp@ssrc.org**
**Web site: http://www.ssrc.org**
**Fax: 212-377-2727**

The Social Science Research Council is an autonomous, nongovernmental, not-for-profit international association devoted to advancing interdisciplinary research in the social sciences. It pursues this goal through a wide variety of fellowship and grant programs for training and research. Stipends vary according to geographic region and type of grant. Write for complete information.

Available to: Restrictions vary by program; inquire
Deadline: Varies by program; inquire
Apply to: Above address

**Society for Historians of American Foreign Relations**
**Ohio University**
**Contemporary History Institute**
**Athens, Ohio 45701**
**Web site: http://www.ohiou.edu/shafr/prizes.htm**

Ⓝ The *Myrna Bernath Book Award* of $2,500 is given in odd-numbered years for a book on diplomatic affairs written by a woman. Books must have been published during the two years preceding the award year. Five copies of each book must be submitted with the nomination and sent to Carol Adams, Salt Lake Community College, 4600 Redwood Road, Salt Lake City, UT 84130.

Available to: Women
Deadline: November 15
Apply to: See above

(N) The *Stuart L. Bernath Book Prize* of $2,000 is given for a first book, which must be a history of international relations; biographies of statesmen and diplomats are eligible, but general surveys, autobiographies, editions of essays and documents, and works representative of social science disciplines other than history are not. One award is available annually for books published the preceding year. Five copies of each book must be submitted with the nomination and sent to Garry Clifford, Department of Political Science, 341 Mansfield Road, University of Connecticut, Storrs, CT 06269.

Available to: No restrictions
Deadline: February 1
Apply to: See above

In addition to the above prizes, the Society offers a number of scholarships and fellowships as part of the Stuart L. Bernath Memorial Prize program. Consult the Web site for detailed information.

**Society for the History of Technology**
**John Hopkins University**
**Department of the History of Technology**
**216B Ames Hall**
**Baltimore, MD 21218**
**Phone: 410-516-8349**
**E-mail: shot@jhu.edu**
**Web site: http://shot.press.jhu.edu**
**Fax: 410-516-7502**

(N) The *Edelstein Prize* (formerly known as the Dexter Prize) of $3,500 is awarded to the author of an outstanding scholarly book in the history of technology published during the previous two years. Books originally written in languages other than English are eligible for three years after the date of their English translation. Publishers and authors are invited to nominate titles, by sending one copy to each of the committee members listed on the Web site.

Available to: No restrictions
Deadline: April 1
Apply to: Professor Stuart Leslie, Secretary, above address

(N) The *Sally Hacker Popular Book Prize* of $2,000 is given for the best popular book on the history of technology directed to a broad audience, including students and the interested public. The nominated book must have been written in the three years preceding the award. The book should assume that the reader has no prior knowledge of the subject or its method of treatment, and should explain technological change in history with a minimum of technical or academic prose. Send SASE or visit the Web site for nomination and submission procedures.

Available to: No restrictions
Deadline: April 1
Apply to: Above address

(N) The *Brooke Hindle Post-Doctoral Fellowship in the History of Technology*, which honors the contribution of Brooke Hindle to the work of the Society and is made possible thanks to the generosity of his family, offers a stipend of $10,000, This may be used for any purpose connected with research or writing about the history of technology, for a period of no less than four months between September and August of the year of the award. Applicants must hold a doctorate in the history of technology or a related field, or expect to have graduated by August 1 of the year of the award.

Available to: See above
Deadline: May 1 previous to year of fellowship
Apply to: Chair, Fellowship Committee, above address

(N) The *Samuel Eleazar and Rose Tartakow Levinson Annual Prize* of $400 recognizes an original essay in the history of technology that examines a technology or technological device / process within the framework of social or intellectual history. Any single-authored, unpublished paper written by a graduate student is eligible. Manuscripts already published or accepted for publication will not be considered. Manuscripts should be in English and of a length suitable for publication as a journal article. Three copies should be sent to Stuart W. Leslie, Secretary, Department of History of Science, 216B Ames Hall, Johns Hopkins University, 3400 North Charles Street, Baltimore, MD 21218.

Available to: See above
Deadline: May 1
Apply to: See above

(N) The *Joan Cahalin Robinson Prize*, of $350 and a certificate, is awarded annually for the best paper presented by a graduate student giving his or her first paper at a meeting of the Society. Candidates are judged on the quality of the historical research and scholarship of the paper; special attention is paid to the effectiveness of the oral presentation. Young scholars who have received their Ph.D. no more than one year before the award are also eligible.

Available to: See above
Deadline: May 1
Apply to: Members of the Prize Committee (consult Web site for names and addresses)

(N) The *Abbott Payson Usher Prize* of $400 encourages the publication of original research of the highest standard, and is awarded annually to the author of the best scholarly work published during the preceding three years under the auspices of the Society. Consult the Web site for application details.

Available to: No restrictions
Deadline: Inquire
Apply to: Above address

**Society for the Study of Social Problems**
**University of Tennessee**
**906 McClung Tower**
**Knoxville, TN 37996-0490**
**E-mail: mkoontz3@utk.edu**
**Web site: http://www.it.utk.edu/sssp**
**Fax: 865-974-7013**

(N) The *C. Wright Mills Award* of $500 is given annually for the book that best exemplifies social science scholarship, critically addresses an issue of contemporary public importance, and contains implications for courses of action. The book should be published during the calendar year preceding that in which the award is made.

Available to: No restrictions
Deadline: January 15
Apply to: Michele Smith Koontz, Administrative Officer, above address

**Society of American Historians**
**Columbia University**
**603 Fayerweather**
**New York, NY 10027**
**E-mail: es28@columbia.edu**
**Web site: http://www.theaha.org/affiliates/soc_am_hisn.htm**
**Fax: 212-222-4902**

(IN) The *Bruce Catton Prize* of $5,000 is awarded for lifetime achievement in historical writing. *By Internal Nomination Only.*

(F) The *James Fenimore Cooper Prize for Historical Fiction* of $2,500 is awarded in odd-numbered years for a work of literary fiction that significantly advances the historical imagination. The winning entry is chosen for its literary quality and historical scholarship. For the next prize, books must be copyrighted in 2001 or 2002. Publishers should submit one copy of each eligible book to each selection committee member. Write for competition guidelines, including names and addresses of committee members.

Available to: No restrictions
Deadline: January 31
Apply to: Above address

(N) The *Allan Nevins Prize*, for the best Ph.D. dissertation on a significant theme in American history, is open to graduates of any Ph.D.-granting department in the U. S. One award of $1,000 is made each year. The winning manuscript is normally published by one of the distinguished houses that currently support the prize; the published work will be considered for selection by the History Book Club. Manuscripts must be submitted by the chairman of the department awarding the degree or by the sponsor of the dissertation. Those who hold a Ph.D. or are defending a Ph.D. dissertation in 2002 are eligible. The published work will be considered for selection by the History Book Club.

Available to: See above
Deadline: January 31
Apply to: Above address

(N) The *Francis Parkman Prize* is awarded for the best nonfiction book, including biography, on any aspect of the history of what is now the U. S., copyrighted in the previous calendar year. One award of $2,500, a certificate, and an engraved bronze medal, is given annually. The Parkman winner automatically becomes a selection of the History Book Club. Publishers should submit one copy of each nominated title to each of the selection committee members. Write for competition guidelines, including names and addresses of committee members.

Available to: No restrictions
Deadline: January 31
Apply to: Above address

**Society of American Travel Writers Foundation**
**c/o Mary Lu Abbott, President**
**2222 Westerland Dr. #121**
**Houston, TX 77063**
**E-mail: maryluabbott@aol.com**
**Web site: http://www.satw.org/public/lowell4.htm**
**Fax: 713-532-6461**

(J) The SATW Foundation *Lowell Thomas Travel Journalist Competition* awards nearly $20,000 in prizes to North American journalists for outstanding work in print and electronic media. The Grand Award, for the best collection of three to nine entries, honors the Travel Journalist of the Year with $1,500 and gives additional awards of $750 and $500. A total of nineteen awards, of $500, $250, and $150, are given in the following categories: newspaper article on U. S./Canada travel; magazine article on U. S./Canada travel; newspaper article on foreign travel; magazine article on foreign travel; newspaper photo illustration of travel article; magazine photo illustration of travel article; special package/project; self-illustrated article; article on each of the following: land travel, marine travel, adventure travel, environmental tourism, and cultural tourism; travel news/investigative reporting/service-oriented consumer article; personal comment; travel book; guidebook; and Internet travel article. Write or visit the Web site for further information.

Available to: No restrictions
Deadline: May 1
Apply to: SATW Foundation Competition, c/o Professor Ted Spiker, University of Florida, Department of Journalism, 2070 Weimer Hall, Gainesville, FL 32611

**Society of Children's Book Writers**
8271 Beverly Boulevard
Los Angeles, CA 90048
E-mail: membership@scbwi.org
Web site: http://www.scbwi.org
Fax: 323-782-1892

©   Four *Work-in-Progress Grants*, one for a contemporary novel for young people, one for a work whose author has never had a book published, one for a general work-in-progress, and one for a nonfiction research project, will be awarded annually. Each grant is $1,000, and each category offers a runner-up award of $500. Write, e-mail, or visit the Web site for additional information.

> Available to: Full and associate members of the Society of Children's Book Writers
> Deadline: Applications accepted February 1-March 1
> Apply to: Above address

©   The *Barbara Karlin Grant* recognizes and encourages the work of aspiring picture-book writers who have never had a picture book published. One grant of $1,000 is awarded annually. Write, e-mail, or visit the Web site for additional information.

> Available to: Full and associate members of the Society of Children's Book Writers
> Deadline: Applications accepted April 1-May 15
> Apply to: Barbara Karlin Grant, above address

**Sons of the Republic of Texas**
1717 8th Street
Bay City, TX 77414
E-mail: srttexas@srttexas.org
Web site: http://www.srttexas.org
Fax: 409-245-6644

The *Presidio La Bahia Award* is given for writing that promotes research into and preservation of Spanish colonial influence on Texas culture. A total of $2,000 is available annually as an award or awards (depending on number and quality of entries), with a minimum first prize of $1,200. Send SASE for additional information and guidelines.

> Available to: No restrictions
> Deadline: September 30
> Apply to: Above address

Ⓜ   The *Summerfield G. Roberts Award* of $2,500 is given annually for the best book or manuscript of biography, essay, nonfiction, fiction (novel or short story), or poetry that describes or represents the Republic of Texas, 1836-1846. The manuscript must be written or published during the calendar year for which the award is given. Send SASE for additional information and guidelines.

> Available to: U. S. citizens
> Deadline: January 15
> Apply to: Above address

Ⓝ   The *Texas History Essay Contest* offers a first prize of $3,000, a second of $2,000, and a third of $1,000 to graduating high school seniors for an essay on a particular topic related to Texas history. Essays must be between 1,500 and 2,000 words. Send SASE, e-mail, or see the Web site for guidelines.

> Available to: Graduating high school seniors
> Deadline: February 1
> Apply to: Texas History Essay Contest, above address

**Paul and Daisy Soros Fellowships for New Americans**
**400 West 59th Street**
**New York, NY 10019**
**Phone: 212-547-6926**
**E-mail: pdsoros_fellows@sorosny.org**
**Web site: www.pdsoros.org**
**Fax: 212-548-4623**

The *Paul and Daisy Soros Fellowships for New Americans* support thirty individuals a year for up to two years' graduate study at any accredited university in the U. S. Fellowships provide $20,000 maintenance and half-tuition wherever the fellow attends. Students already in graduate study are eligible, though not past their second year. Candidates must be either Green Card holders, naturalized U. S. citizens, or children of two naturalized U. S. citizens.

Available to: See above
Deadline: November 30
Apply to: Above address

**Source Theatre Company**
**1835 14th Street, NW**
**Washington, DC 20009**
**E-mail: source_theatre@hotmail.com**
**Web site: www.sourcetheatre.org**

(D) The *Source Theatre Company Literary Prize* annually offers $250 and workshop production at the Washington Theatre Festival for a professionally unproduced play. Send SASE for additional information and guidelines.

Available to: No restrictions
Deadline: January 15
Apply to: Keith Parker, Literary Manager, above address

**South Carolina Arts Commission**
**1800 Gervais Street**
**Columbia, SC 29201**
**Phone: 803-734-8698**
**Web site: http://www.state.sc.us/arts**
**Fax: 803-734-8526**

(M) *Individual Artist Fellowships in Literature*, $7,500 each, are given to poets, playwrights, and fiction or creative-nonfiction writers of exceptional promise or proven professional ability, to set aside time, purchase materials, or otherwise advance their careers. Full-time undergraduate students are not eligible.

Available to: South Carolina residents
Deadline: Inquire
Apply to: Fellowships Program, above address

*Individual Artist Project Grants*, up to $5,000, are offered to writers with specific projects.

Available to: South Carolina residents
Deadline: April 1
Apply to: Project Grants, above address

(F) The *South Carolina Fiction Project*, co-sponsored by the South Carolina Arts Commission and the Charleston *Post and Courier*, offers a short story competition. Up to twelve previously unpublished stories of 2,500 words maximum, are selected by a panel of professional writers; the winners each receive $500 and publication in the *Post and Courier*.

Available to: South Carolina residents
Deadline: January 15
Apply to: South Carolina Fiction Project, above address

**South Coast Repertory**
PO Box 2197
Costa Mesa, CA 92628-2197
Web site: www.scr.org
Fax: 714-545-0391

Ⓓ The *Hispanic Playwrights Project* selects full-length plays by Hispanic-American playwrights for workshops at South Coast Repertory, at which the playwrights work with directors and casts of professional actors. New, unproduced plays are preferred; previously produced plays that would benefit from further development may also be considered. Musicals are not accepted, nor are plays written fully in Spanish. Manuscripts should be submitted with a synopsis and a biography of the playwright.

   Available to: Hispanic-American playwrights
   Deadline: January
   Apply to: Juliette Carrillo, Director, Hispanic Playwrights Project, above address

**South Dakota Arts Council**
800 Governors Drive
Pierre, SD 57501-2294
E-mail: sdac@stlib.state.sd.us
Web site: http://www.sdarts.org
Fax: 605-773-6962

Ⓜ *Artist Grants* of $3,000 each are available annually to South Dakota residents of at least two years, in general writing, fiction, and nonfiction. Write for guidelines and application.

   Available to: See above
   Deadline: March 1
   Apply to: Dennis Holub, Executive Director, above address

Ⓜ Forty to fifty *Artists-in-Schools Grants* of approximately $800 per week are available annually in general writing, fiction, and nonfiction. Write for guidelines and application.

   Available to: Practicing professional artists living in neighboring states who wish to work in residence in South Dakota, at all grade levels
   Deadline: October 1
   Apply to: Michael Pangburn, above address

Ⓜ Some thirty-six opportunities in the *Touring Arts Program* (about one-half fee paid to presenter) are available annually in general writing, fiction, and nonfiction. Write for guidelines and application.

   Available to: Practicing artists who wish to tour South Dakota cities
   Deadline: October 1
   Apply to: Michael Pangburn, above address

**Southeastern Theatre Conference**
Box 9868
Greensboro, NC 27429-0868
Phone: 336-272-3645
Web site: http://www.setc.org
Fax: 336-272-8810

Ⓓ The *Charles M. Getchell New Play Award* offers $1,000, a staged reading, paid travel, and room and board to attend the convention, and consideration for publication in *Southern Theatre* magazine, for an unproduced, full-length play or program of two related one-acts by a resident of the states in the Southeastern Theatre Conference region. Send SASE for guidelines before submitting.

   Available to: Residents of Alabama, Florida, Georgia, Kentucky, Mississippi, North Carolina, South Carolina, Tennessee, Virginia, West Virginia
   Deadline: Submissions accepted March 1-June 1
   Apply to: Susan Sharp, Director of Theatre, Jackson State Community College, 2046 North Parkway, Jackson, TN 38301

**Southern Appalachian Repertory Theatre**
**Box 1720**
**Mars Hill, NC 28754-1720**

Ⓓ The *Southern Appalachian Playwrights' Conference* selects up to five playwrights to participate in a three-day conference in March or April at which one work by each writer is given an informal reading and critiqued by a panel of theater professionals. One work may be selected each year for production in the theater's summer season. Playwrights receive room and board, and the writer of the work selected for production receives a $500 honorarium. Film or TV scripts are not accepted; musicals should be submitted accompanied by an audiocassette with at least four songs. Send SASE for guidelines.

Available to: No restrictions
Deadline: October 31
Apply to: Southern Appalachian Playwrights' Conference, above address

**Southern Environmental Law Center**
**201 West Main Street, Suite 14**
**Charlottesville, VA 22902-5065**
**E-mail: selcva@selcva.org**
**Web site: http://www.southernenvironment.org**
**Fax: 804-977-1483**

Ⓙ Ⓝ The *Phillip D. Reed Memorial Award for Outstanding Writing on the Southern Environment* is given for work that relates to the natural environment in any or all of the states of Alabama, Georgia, North Carolina, South Carolina, Tennessee, and Virginia. A prize of $1,000 is offered in journalistic nonfiction, such as a newspaper series or magazine article, and in literary nonfiction, such as a book or essay. Submissions must be at least 3,000 words and must have been published during the calendar year preceding the award deadline. Write, e-mail, or see the Web site for guidelines.

Available to: No restrictions
Deadline: March 1
Apply to: Cathryn McCue, above address

**Southern Historical Association**
**Department of History**
**University of Georgia**
**Athens, GA 30602**
**E-mail: gsdavis@arches.uga.edu**
**Web site: http://www.uga.edu/~sha**
**Fax: 706-542-2455**

Ⓝ The *Frank Lawrence and Harriet Chappell Owsley Award*, given in odd-numbered years for a book published in even-numbered years, honors a distinguished work in southern history. The *H. L. Mitchell Award*, given in even-numbered years for a book published in the two preceding years, honors a distinguished work about the history of the southern working class, including but not limited to industrial laborers and / or small farmers and agricultural laborers. The *Francis Butler Simkins Award*, given in odd-numbered years for a book published in the preceding two years, honors the best first book by an author in southern history. The *Charles S. Sydnor Prize*, given in even-numbered years for a book published in odd-numbered years, honors a distinguished work in southern history. The *Bennett H. Wall Award*, given in even-numbered years for a book published in the preceding two years, honors the best book published in southern business or economic history. All awards carry a cash prize.

Available to: U. S. citizens
Deadline: Inquire
Apply to: Above address

Southern Oregon University
Extended Campus Programs
1250 Siskiyou Boulevard
Ashland, OR 97250
E-mail: friendly@sou.edu
Web site: www.sou.edu/ecp/arts/walden

® The *Walden Residency Program* offers residences of six weeks for writers of drama, fiction, poetry, and creative nonfiction. Send #10 SASE for application form or print from the Web site.

Available to: Oregon residents
Deadline: Last working day in November
Apply to: Brooke Friendly, above address

The Southern Poetry Review
Advancement Studies Department
Central Piedmont Community College
Charlotte, NC 28235
Fax: 704-330-6455

℗ The *Guy Owen Poetry Prize* of $500 is given annually for the best poem selected by an outside judge. A maximum of five poems may be submitted with an $8 entry fee, which covers a one-year subscription to *The Southern Poetry Review*. *(PEN was unable to confirm the information for this edition, but has reason to believe it is still current. Inquire before applying.)*

Available to: No restrictions
Deadline: April 30
Apply to: Guy Owen Poetry Prize, above address

The Southern Review
Louisiana State University
43 Allen Hall
Baton Rouge, LA 70803
E-mail: bmacon@unix1.sncc.LSU.edu
Web site: http://www.LSU.edu/guests/wwwtsm
Fax: 504-388-5098

Ⓕ The *Southern Review/Louisiana State University Short Fiction Award* offers $500 to the best first collection of short stories by a U. S. writer published in the country in the preceding year. Publishers or authors should send two copies of qualifying books for consideration.

Available to: U. S. citizens
Deadline: January 31
Apply to: Above address

The Southerner
University of Tennessee
Box 8820
Knoxville, TN 37996
Web site: http://www.southerner.net/warrenprize.html

Ⓕ The *Robert Penn Warren Prize for Fiction* offers a first prize of $1,000, a second of $500, and a third of $250 for published writers, and a first prize of $500, a second of $250, and a third of $100 for unpublished writers of short stories with southern themes, characters, or settings. Submissions should not exceed 5,000 words. For the purposes of this contest, only published novelists and short story authors are considered published writers; published poets and nonfiction writers, including journalists, should apply as unpublished writers. There is a $10 entry fee. Send SASE or see the Web site for contest rules.

Available to: See above
Deadline: November 1
Apply to: Robert Penn Warren Prize, above address

**Southwest Review**
PO Box 750374
Dallas, TX 75275-0374
E-mail: SWR@mail.smu.edu
Web site: southwestreview.org
Fax: 214-768-1408

Ⓕ Ⓝ The *John H. McGinnis Memorial Awards* of $1,000 are given annually for the best essay and best story appearing in *Southwest Review* during the preceding year.

Available to: *Southwest Review* contributors

Ⓟ The *Morton Marr Poetry Prize* offers an annual cash award of $1,000 and publication in *Southwest Review* for a poem by a writer who has not yet published a first book. Poets may submit no more than six poems in a traditional form (e.g., sonnet, sestina, villanelle, rhymed stanzas, blank verse) and should mail their submissions, along with the $5 entry fee, to the address above.

Available to: Young writers who have not published a first book
Deadline: November 30
Apply to: Above address

Ⓟ The *Elizabeth Matchett Stover Memorial Award* of $200 is awarded annually for the best poem or group of poems published in *Southwest Review* during the preceding year.

Available to: *Southwest Review* contributors

**Sow's Ear Poetry Review**
19535 Pleasant View Drive
Abingdon, VA 24211-6827
E-mail: richman@preferred.com

Ⓟ The *Sow's Ear Chapbook Competition* offers a first prize of $1,000, publication, and 25 copies of the chapbook (and distribution to subscribers); a second prize of $200; and a third of $100 for the best collection of poems, 22 to 26 pages total. Multiple submissions are accepted. There is a $10 entry fee, which covers a copy of the winning chapbook, if specified. Send SASE or e-mail for guidelines.

Available to: No restrictions
Deadline: Submissions accepted March-April
Apply to: Chapbook Competition, above address

Ⓟ The *Sow's Ear Poetry Competition* offers a first prize of $1,000, a second of $250, and a third of $100 for the best unpublished poems. Winners as well as some fifteen to twenty finalists are published in *Sow's Ear*. Multiple submissions are accepted. There is a reading fee of $2 per poem; submission of five poems or more entitles entrant to a subscription to the review. Send SASE or e-mail for guidelines.

Available to: No restrictions
Deadline: Submissions accepted September-October
Apply to: Poetry Competition, above address

**SPAIN**
**Cultural Office**
**Embassy of Spain**
2375 Pennsylvania Avenue, NW
Washington, DC 20037
Web site: www.spainemb.org

Ⓜ Several organizations and foundations in Spain offer sizable literary prizes to authors of all nationalities for unpublished work (fiction, poetry, nonfiction) written in Castilian. Information may be obtained from the Cultural Office of the embassy.

Available to: Authors writing in Spanish
Deadline: Inquire
Apply to: Above address

**Spoon River Poetry Review**
**4241 Department of English**
**Publication Unit**
**Illinois State University**
**Normal, IL 61790-4241**

(P) The *Editor's Prize* awards $1,000 and publication in *Spoon River* for an unpublished poem. Two second-place prizes of $100 each are also awarded. All submissions are considered for publication. Poets may submit up to three poems, of no more than 10 pages total, in duplicate, with the poet's name on one copy only. A reading fee of $16 covers a one-year subscription to the review. Send SASE for guidelines.

Available to: No restrictions
Deadline: April 15
Apply to: Editor's Prize, above address

**SQUARE Magazine**
**99 Park Avenue, Suite 387**
**New York, NY 10016**
**E-mail: squaremag@aol.com**
**Web site: http://www.squaremagazine.com**

(S) The *SQUARE Magazine Screenwriting Award* offers a first prize of $500 and production company consideration for an original feature-length film or TV screenplay in any genre. The amount of the entry fee depends on the date of submission (see below). Visit the Web site for guidelines and entry form.

Available to: No restrictions
Deadline: Early submission, May 18 ($40 entry fee); regular submission, June 22 ($50 entry fee); late submission, July 27 ($60 entry fee)
Apply to: Screenwriting Award, above address

**St. Louis Poetry Center**
**567 North and South Road #8**
**St. Louis, MO 63130**
**Phone: 660-543-8106**
**E-mail: kdp810@cmsu2.cmsu.edu**

(P) The *St. Louis Poetry Center and Pleiades Poetry Contest* offers annual prizes of $2,000 plus publication, $250, and $100 for the best unpublished poems. Submissions of up to three poems, limited to 60 lines each, are considered for publication by *Pleiades: A Journal of New Writing*. There is a $15 application fee. Send SASE for more information.

Available to: No restrictions
Deadline: May 15
Apply to: Above address

**Stanford University**
**Creative Writing Center**
**Department of English**
**Stanford, CA 94305-2087**
**E-mail: Gay.pierce@forsythe.stanford.edu**
**Web site: http://www.stanford.edu/dept/english/cw**
**Fax: 415-723-3679**

(F) (P) Ten *Wallace E. Stegner Fellowships* are offered to five promising fiction writers and five poets who can benefit from residence at the university and from the instruction and criticism of the staff of the writing program. The two-year fellowships provide a stipend of $20,000 each year, plus the required tuition (about $6,000). Previous publication is not essential.

Available to: No restrictions
Deadline: December 1
Apply to: Program Coordinator, Wallace E. Stegner Fellowships, above address

**Stanford University**
**John S. Knight Fellowship**
**Building 120, Room 424**
**Stanford, CA 94305-2050**
**Phone: 650-723-4937**
**E-mail: knightfellow@forsythe.stanford.edu**
**Web site: http://knight.stanford.edu**
**Fax: 650-725-6154**

Ⓙ  The *John S. Knight Fellowships* are offered each year to twelve U. S. mid-career journalists and up to eight international mid-career journalists who have demonstrated uncommon excellence in their work and who have the potential of reaching the top ranks in their specialties. The fellowships are awarded for an academic year, from mid-September to mid-June. Fellows receive a stipend of $55,000, plus housing and child care supplements and a book allowance. The program pays university tuition for all fellows. U. S. applicants must have at least seven years' full-time professional experience; international applicants at least five. Write, e-mail, or fax for additional information and application, or check the Web site.

Available to: Professional journalists
Deadline: February 1 for U. S. applicants; March 1 for international
Apply to: John S. Knight Fellowships, above address

**State Historical Society of Iowa**
**402 Iowa Avenue**
**Iowa City, IA 52240-1806**
**E-mail: mbergman@blue.weeg.uiowa.edu**
**Web site: www.iowahistory.org/grants/shsi_grants/research_grants.html**

Ⓝ  The Society's grant program awards eight stipends, of $1,000 each, to support original research and interpretive writing about the history of Iowa and the Midwest. Preference is given to applicants pursuing previously neglected topics or new interpretations of more familiar topics. Grantees are expected to produce an annotated manuscript for *The Annals of Iowa*, the Society's scholarly journal. See the Web site for guidelines and application.

Available to: No restrictions
Deadline: April 15
Apply to: Research Grants, Iowa Department of Cultural Affairs, above address

**STORYQUARTERLY**
**431 Sheridan Road**
**Kenilworth, IL 60043**
**Web site: www.storyquarterly.com**

Ⓕ  The *Robie Macauley Fiction Award* offers $500 for the best story chosen by independent judges. The winner is selected on the basis of originality of voice, absence of jargon, author control, sense of humor, and a new insight. Send SASE or see the Web site for more details.

Available to: No restrictions
Deadline: Inquire
Apply to: Above address

**Story Line Press**
**Three Oaks Farm**
**PO Box 1240**
**Ashland, OR 97520-0055**
**E-mail: mail@storylinepress.com**
**Web site: http://www.storylinepress.com**
**Fax: 541-512-8793**

Ⓟ  The *Nicholas Roerich Poetry Prize* awards $1,000, publication by Story Line, and a reading at the Nicholas Roerich Museum in New York City to the author of a first book-length poetry manuscript. Submissions should be accompanied by SASE, a $20 reading fee, and a brief biography. The runner-up receives a full scholarship as the Nicholas Roerich/Story Line Press fellow at the Wesleyan Writers' Conference. Send SASE or see the Web site for guidelines.

Available to: Poets who have not published a book-length volume of poetry
Deadline: October 31
Apply to: Nicholas Roerich Poetry Prize, above address

Ⓕ   The *Three Oaks Prize for Fiction* awards $1,500 and publication by Story Line for a novel, novella, or book-length collection of short stories. There is a $25 entry fee. Send SASE or see the Web site for guidelines.

Available to: Writers who have not published a work of fiction except in literary journals or anthologies
Deadline: April 30
Apply to: Three Oaks Prize, above address

**STUDIO for Creative Inquiry**
**Carnegie Mellon University**
**College of Fine Arts**
**Pittsburgh, PA 15213-3890**
**E-mail: info-studio@andrew.cmu.edu**
**Web site: http://www.cmu.edu/studio**
**Fax: 412-268-2829**

Ⓡ   The STUDIO fellowship program connects established artists to the robust science-technology resources at Carnegie Mellon through two concurrent yearlong residences. The broad mission of the STUDIO is to facilitate work in two major areas: artistic creation and development of educational tools. Artists receive a salary and have access to the resources of the university. Assistance is offered in finding housing in the community. E-mail or see the Web site for additional information.

Available to: No restrictions
Deadline: Inquire
Apply to: Above address

**Sundance Institute**
**Sundance Theatre Laboratory**
**8857 West Olympic Boulevard**
**Beverly Hills, CA 90211**
**Phone: 310-360-1981**
**Web site: http://www.sundance.org**
**Fax: 310-360-1975**

Ⓓ Ⓢ   The *Sundance Institute Screenwriters Lab*, a five-day workshop held in January and June offers participating writers one-on-one problem-solving sessions with distinguished veteran screenwriters. The *June Filmmakers Lab*, a three-week workshop, offers directors hands-on experience rehearsing, shooting, and editing scenes, with an ensemble of professional actors, and the support of outstanding creative advisors. The *Sundance Playwrights Retreat at the Ucross Foundation* provides a three-week playwriting residency in Wyoming (this program by invitation only). Send SASE for guidelines, application form and entry fee, or consult the Web site.

Available to: No restrictions
Deadline: Inquire
Apply to: Above address

Ⓓ   The *Sundance Theatre Laboratory*, a three-week workshop, offers playwrights and other theater artists the opportunity to develop new plays or explore new approaches to existing scripts. Up to eight projects are selected for the Laboratory, held at Sundance in Utah in July. The program provides professional actors, dramaturgs, rehearsal space, stage management, roundtrip air transportation, accommodations, and food for the team working on each project. Applications may be submitted by individual playwrights, though playwright/

directors teams are preferred. There is a $25 entry fee. Write or consult the Web site for guidelines and application.

Available to: No restrictions
Deadline: December 15
Apply to: Sundance Theatre Laboratory, above address

**Sunset Center**
**Box 1950**
**Carmel, CA 93921**

Ⓓ The *Festival of Firsts Playwriting Competition* offers up to $1,000 and possible production for previously unproduced full-length plays. Musicals and operas are not eligible. There is a $15 entry fee. Send SASE for guidelines and entry form.

Available to: No restrictions
Deadline: Submissions accepted June 15-August 31
Apply to: Brian Donoghue, Director, above address

**SWEDEN**
**Swedish Information Service**
**Bicentennial Fund**
**One Dag Hammarskjöld Plaza, 45th floor**
**New York, NY 10017-2201**
**Web site: http://www.swedeninfo.com**
**Fax: 212-752-4789**

The Swedish Bicentennial Fund, which fosters the exchange of qualified persons between the U. S. and Sweden, provides opportunity for study and contact for two-to-four-week periods, for individuals in a position to influence public opinion and contribute to the development of their society. Several grants, usually equal to 25,000 Swedish kronor each, are awarded annually; they are intended for transportation and living expenses. Study projects must be carefully defined, and should include a detailed plan for achieving specific goals. Applicants who have visited Sweden many times will be considered only in exceptional cases. Two letters of recommendation are required. Send SASE or see the Web site for guidelines and application.

Available to: U. S. citizens or permanent residents
Deadline: February (inquire for exact date)
Apply to: Above address

**SWITZERLAND**
**Château de Lavigny International Writers' Colony**
**Fondation Ledig-Rowohlt**
**Montbenon 2**
**CH-1003 Lausanne**
**Switzerland**

Ⓡ Residences are offered in June through August, for three-week stays, to published writers. A private room and all meals are provided (breakfast and lunch are self-service; dinner is prepared and served). The château features shared common areas and gardens. Writers arrange their own transportation to and from Switzerland; they will be met at the Geneva airport or the Lausanne or Morges train station. Write for additional information and guidelines.

Available to: No restrictions; fluency in French or English required
Deadline: March 1
Apply to: Anna Bourgeois, Program Director, above address

Syracuse University
Department of English
401 Hall of Languages
Syracuse, NY 13244-1170
Phone: 315-443-2173
E-mail: tazollo@syr.edu
Web site: http://sumweb.syr.edu/english

The Syracuse Department of English offers five one-year fellowships to applicants for the
MFA degree in creative writing: the *Elise G. Mead Fellowship* (poetry), the *Cornelia Carhart
Ward Fellowship* (fiction), and three *Creative Writing Fellowships*. These include an
academic-year award stipend and a full-tuition scholarship for 24 credits for the
academic year (12 credit hours per semester). Normally, these are awarded to new
students and are not renewable. Contact the Creative Writing Program at the above
address for more details.

Available to: Syracuse Creative Writing applicants
Deadline: January 1
Apply to: Director, Creative Writing Program, above address


Tanne Foundation
c/o Grants Management Associates
77 Summer Street
Boston, MA 02110-1006
E-mail: mjenney@grantsmanagement.com
Web site: http://www.grantsmanagement.com
Fax: 617-426-7172

The Tanne Foundation offers one-time fellowship awards intended to recognize prior
achievement and enrich the recipient's artistic life. Awards are made to individual artists
who have demonstrated exceptional talent and creativity. The Foundation supports artistic
endeavors in culturally underserved communities and underappreciated forms of artistic
expression. Write for additional information.

Available to: inquire
Deadline: Inquire
Apply to: Michelle Jenney, Administrator, above address


Mark Taper Forum
Center Theatre Group/New Work Festival
601 West Temple Street
Los Angeles, CA 90012

Ⓓ  The Taper encourages playwrights to send submission queries, with a short description of a
play and 5 to 10 sample pages, so that the Taper can determine whether to request the
entire manuscript for possible production or development. Allow six to eight weeks for a
response. One-act plays are not eligible. Unsolicited scripts will not be read. Cover letter
should mention whether the play is to be considered for the New Work Festival: plays
given a festival workshop or reading must be unproduced and unpublished. For all
submissions, include SASE for a response and, if needed, the return of submitted materials.

Available to: No restrictions
Deadline: None for general submissions; New Work Festival submissions accepted January
1-April 1
Apply to: Pier Carlo Talenti, Literary Manager, above address


Loren Taylor Memorial Playwriting Competition
Jackson County Stage Co.
PO Box 463
Carbondale, IL 62901

Ⓓ  The *Loren Taylor Memorial Playwriting Competition* awards the best original, previously
unproduced play for young audiences where subject is Mark Twain or characters created

by him, with a $500 cash prize and a full stage production at the Jackson County Stage, plus travel and maximum twelve characters. Musicals are not eligible. Send SASE for more details.

Available to: U. S. nationals or permanent residents
Deadline: December 1
Apply to: Above address

**Dora Teitelboim Center for Yiddish Culture**
**PO Box 14-0820**
**Coral Gables, FL 33114-0820**
**Web site: www.yiddishculture.org**

Ⓕ Ⓝ The *Dora Teitelboim Center for Yiddish Culture Writing Contest* offers prizes ranging from $300 to $1,000, plus publication in a national Jewish magazine, to the best fiction or nonfiction, in English or Yiddish, on the subject "Bestowing Jewish Culture on the Next Generation". Send SASE for application and guidelines.

Available to: No restrictions
Deadline: March 31
Apply to: Writing Contest, above address

**Tennessee Arts Commission**
**401 Charlotte Avenue**
**Nashville, TN 37243-0780**
**Phone: 615-741-1701**
**E-mail: dennis.adkins@state.tn.us**
**Web site: http://www.arts.state.tn.us**
**Fax: 615-741-8559**

Ⓜ The Tennessee Arts Commission offers a writing fellowship of $5,000, to writers of poetry in even-numbered years and of prose in odd-numbered years. Write for additional information and guidelines.

Available to: Tennessee residents
Deadline: January (inquire for exact date)
Apply to: Above address

**Tennessee Writers Alliance**
**PO Box 120396**
**Nashville, TN 37212**
**Web site: http://momsmoney.com/contest.htm**

Ⓕ Ⓟ The *Tennessee Writers Alliance Literary Awards* offer prizes of $500, $250, and $100 in the categories of short fiction and poetry. The entry fee is $10 for Alliance members and $15 for nonmembers. Consult the Web site for submission guidelines.

Available to: No restrictions
Deadline: July 15
Apply to: Literary Awards, above address

**Texas Institute of Letters**
**Center for the Study of the Southwest**
**Flowers Hall 327**
**Southwest Texas State University**
**San Marcos, TX 78666**
**E-mail: mb13@swt.edu**
**Web site: http://www.stedwards.edu/newc/marks/til/index.htm**

The Texas Institute of Letters gives the following literary awards every March for books by Texas authors or on Texas subjects published during the preceding calendar year. Send SASE for guidelines and names/addresses of judges before submitting.

Ⓟ The *Best Book of Poetry Award* of $5,000.

The *John Bloom Humor Award* of $1,000 for the "goldang funniest Texas book."

Ⓕ    The *Brazos Bookstore Short Story Award* of $750 for the best short story.

Ⓝ    The *Carr P. Collins Award* of $5,000 for the best book of nonfiction (generally for belletristic work).

Ⓣ    The *Sourette Diehl Fraser Translation Award* of $1,000 for the best translation of a book into English.

Ⓒ    The *Friends of the Austin Public Library Awards* of $500 each for the best children's book and the best young-adult book.

Ⓝ    The *Friends of the Dallas Public Library Award* of $1,000 for the book that contributes most significantly to knowledge (generally for scholarly work).

Ⓙ Ⓝ    The *O. Henry Award* of $1,000 for the best nonfiction writing in a magazine or Sunday newspaper supplement.

Ⓕ    The *Jesse H. Jones Award* of $6,000 for the best book of fiction.

Ⓟ    The *Natalie Ornish Poetry Award* of $1,000 for an outstanding book of poetry.

Ⓕ    The *Steven Turner Award* of $1,000 for the best first book of fiction.

Ⓙ    The *Stanley Walker Award* of $1,000 for the best work of journalism appearing in a daily newspaper; the emphasis is on literary merit.

     Available to: Texas authors or books on a Texas subject
     Deadline: First working day in January
     Apply to: Mark Busby, Secretary-Treasurer, above address

**Theatre Communications Group**
**355 Lexington Avenue, 4th floor**
**New York, NY 10017**
**Phone: 212-697-5230**
**E-mail: grants@tcg.org**
**Web site: www.tcg.org**
**Fax: 212-983-4847**

Ⓓ    *Extended Collaboration Grants* are designed to enable writers to collaborate with other artists for a period beyond a sponsoring theater's normal preproduction and rehearsal schedule. Grants of $5,000 each are awarded to support playwrights working with directors, designers, composers, actors, and other artists, to develop projects proposed by the sponsoring theater. Artistic directors of TCG constituent theaters must apply on behalf of the artists. Write, e-mail, or see the Web site for guidelines and application materials.

     Available to: See above
     Deadline: Inquire
     Apply to: Extended Collaboration Grants, above address

Ⓓ    The *National Theatre Artist Residency Program* awards some ten to fourteen grants of $50,000 or $100,000 to accomplished theater artists who have created a significant body of work and the theaters with high artistic standards and the organizational capacity to provide substantial support services to artists. Funds are to be used for compensation and residence expenses for one or two artists, working singly or in collaboration, during discrete periods devoted exclusively to residence-related activities and totaling at least six full months over a two-year period. Proposals must be developed jointly by playwrights and institutions. Write, e-mail, or see the Web site for guidelines and application.

     Available to: No restrictions
     Deadline: December 1 for intent-to-apply cards; December 15 for applications
     Apply to: National Theatre Artist Residency Program, above address

Ⓓ The *NEA/TCG Theatre Residency Program for Playwrights* awards $25,000 to each of twelve playwrights to create new works while in residence at a not-for-profit professional theater. Host theaters receive the $5,500 Vivendi/Universal Residency Award to help them support the resident playwright's work. Playwrights must have had at least one play published or produced within the last five years; theaters must have high artistic standards, a history of developing new works, and a minimum operating budget of $150,000 in the most recently completed fiscal year. A total of six months (not necessarily consecutive) must be dedicated to the development of a new work with the host theater. Write, e-mail, or see the Web site for guidelines and application materials.

Available to: U. S. citizens or permanent residents
Deadline: May 31 for intent-to-apply cards; June 14 for applications
Apply to: Michael Francis, Artistic Programs Assistant, above address

**Theatre Conspiracy**
**10091 McGregor Boulevard**
**Fort Myers, FL 33919**
**Phone: 941-936-3239**
**E-mail: info@theatreconspiracy.org**
**Web site: www.theatreconspiracy.org**
**Fax: 941-936-0510**

Ⓓ The *Theatre Conspiracy Annual New Play Contest* awards $600 and full production for an unproduced full-length play with simple production demands and a cast limit of six (no musicals). There is a $5 entry fee , which is waived for members of the Dramatists Guild of America. Send SASE or e-mail for guidelines.

Available to: No restrictions
Deadline: November 30
Apply to: New Play Contest, above address

**Thorngate Road**
**Department of English and Humanities**
**Pratt Institute**
**200 Willoughby Avenue**
**Brooklyn, NY 11205**
**Phone: 718-636-3790**
**E-mail: jelledge@pratt.edu**
**Fax: 718-636-3573**

Ⓟ The *Frank O'Hara Award Chapbook Competition* offers $500, publication, and 25 copies of the finished book for poetry, prose poems, and cross-genre texts by gay, lesbian, bisexual, and transgendered authors. Submissions are limited to 16 single- or double-spaced pages of text. There is a $15 reading fee per entry. Send SASE for guidelines.

Available to: Gay, lesbian, bisexual, and transgendered authors
Deadline: February 1
Apply to: Jim Elledge, Frank O'Hara Award Chapbook Competition, above address

**Thunderbird Films**
**214 Riverside Drive #112**
**New York, NY 10025**
**E-mail: estannard@dekker.com**
**Web site: http://home.att.net/~thunderbirdfilms**

Ⓢ The *Thunderbird Films Annual Screenplay Competition* offers $1,000 and a possible production option for a feature-length screenplay. There is a $40 entry fee. Send SASE, e-mail, or see the Web site for details.

Available to: No restrictions
Deadline: March 30
Apply to: Screenplay Competition, above address

**James Thurber Residency Program**
**Thurber House**
**77 Jefferson Avenue**
**Columbus, OH 42315**
**Web site: http://www.thurberhouse.org**

The *James Thurber Residency Program* selects journalists, creative writers (fiction, nonfiction, poetry), and playwrights to spend a season living, writing, and teaching at Thurber House. Each writer will receive a stipend and accommodations in Thurber's boyhood home. The majority of the writer's time is reserved for the writer's own work, but there are responsibilities, as described below.

Ⓙ The *James Thurber Journalist-in-Residence* will teach a writing course at the Ohio State University School of Journalism, give a public reading, and conduct a workshop in the community. Candidates should have experience in reporting, feature writing, reviewing, or other areas of journalism, as well as significant publications; experience as a teacher or writing coach is helpful. The residence is available next in summer 2003. The stipend is $6,000 per quarter.

Ⓙ The *James Thurber Newsroom Journalist-in-Residence* will work as a writing coach with a select group of general newsroom and city desk reporters at the *Columbus Dispatch* twenty hours a week for four weeks (shorter residencies may be negotiated). Candidates who currently work or have worked at a significant daily newspaper are invited to bring their depth of newsroom experience to this assignment at the newspaper where Thurber began his journalism career. The residence is available next in fall 2002, winter or spring 2003. The stipend is $4,000.

Ⓓ The *James Thurber Playwright-in-Residence* will teach a playwriting class at the OSI Theatre Department two afternoons a week and will be involved with either a staged reading or a full production of his or her own work. Candidates should have had at least one play published and/or produced by a significant company and should show aptitude for teaching. The residence is available next in winter or spring 2003. The stipend is $6,000.

The *James Thurber Writer-in-Residence* will teach a class in creative writing, a graduate-level intensive workshop/seminar in the Creative Writing Program at OSU; participate in a writing residency with a community agency; and offer a public reading. Candidates should have national visibility in poetry, fiction, or creative nonfiction, substantial book publications, and teaching experience. The residence is available next in winter or spring 2003. The stipend is $6,000. For application, send a vita and a letter of interest.

Available to: See above
Deadline: Inquire
Apply to: Michael J. Rosen, Literary Director, above address

**tnr—the new renaissance**
**26 Heath Road #11**
**Arlington, MA 02174-3645**

Ⓕ Ⓟ *the new renaissance* has two award programs, each covering work published in a three-issue volume of the magazine (about every eighteen to twenty-two months). The *Louise E. Reynolds Memorial Fiction Award* offers a first prize of $500, a second of $250, and a third of $100. The *tnr Poetry Award* offers a first prize of $250, a second of $125, and a third of $50. There is also an honorable mention with a cash prize of $50. The $16.50 entry fee for nonsubscribers pays for either two back issues of the magazine or a current issue (writer's choice); the entry fee for subscribers is $11.50. Send SASE for guidelines.

Available to: No restrictions
Deadline: Fiction submissions accepted January 1-June 30 and September 1-October 31; no poetry submissions after July 1
Apply to: Above address

Towson University
College of Liberal Arts
8000 York Road
Towson, MD 21252-0001
Web site: www.towson.edu

Ⓜ The *Towson University Prize for Literature* of $1,000 is offered annually for a single book or
book-length manuscript of fiction, poetry, drama, or creative nonfiction by a Maryland
writer. The prize, supported by a grant from the Alice & Franklin Cooley Endowment, is
given on the basis of aesthetic excellence. If published, the book must have appeared
within three years before the year of nomination. If unpublished, the work must have
been accepted by a publisher. Nomination forms are required.

Available to: Maryland writers
Deadline: June 15
Apply to: Dean, College of Liberal Arts, above address


Harry S. Truman Library Institute
Harry S. Truman Library
500 West U. S. Highway 24
Independence, MO 64050-1798

Ⓝ The Institute offers several awards and research grants to scholars and graduate students to
encourage study of the history of the Truman administration and the public career of
Harry Truman and to promote the use of the Library as a national center for historical
scholarship. Prospective applicants should write to the Grants Administrator at the above
address for current information.

Ⓝ The *Harry S. Truman Book Award* of $1,000 is given biennially for the best book written within
the previous two years dealing primarily and substantially with an aspect of U. S. history
between April 12, 1945, and January 20, 1953, or with the public career of Harry Truman.
Five copies of each book should be submitted to the Book Award Administrator.

Available to: No restrictions
Deadline: January 20 in even-numbered years
Apply to: Book Award Administrator, above address


Truman State University Press
100 East Normal Street
Kirksville, MO 63501-4221
E-mail: tsup@truman.edu
Web site: http://tsup.truman.edu
Fax: 660-785-4480

Ⓟ The *T. S. Eliot Prize* annually awards $2,000 and publication by the Press for the best collection
of contemporary poetry in English. Manuscripts should be 60 to 100 pages of original
poetry. There is a reading fee of $25. Send SASE or e-mail for guidelines, or consult the
Web site.

Available to: No restrictions
Deadline: October 31
Apply to: T. S. Eliot Prize, above address


Trustus Theatre
Box 11721
Columbia, SC 29211
E-mail: Trustus88@aol.com
Web site: http://www.trustus.org
Fax: 803-771-9153

Ⓓ The *Trustus Playwrights' Festival* awards $750 ($250 upon selection/staged reading, $500 upon
production after one-year development period), plus paid travel and accommodations,
for a full-length play. Cast limit is eight. Submissions must not have been produced

professionally. Send SASE for guidelines and application.

Available to: No restrictions
Deadline: Submissions accepted December 1, 2002-February 1, 2003
Apply to: Trustus Playwrights' Festival, above address

**Tulsa Library Trust**
**400 Civic Center**
**Tulsa, OK 74103**
**Web site: http://www.tulsalibrary.org/PHAward.htm**

[IN]   The *Peggy V. Helmerich Distinguished Author Award* of $25,000 is given to a nationally acclaimed writer for a body of work. There is no application process. *By Internal Nomination Only.*

**Tupelo Press**
**PO Box 539**
**Dorset, VT 05251**
**Phone: 802-366-8185**
**E-mail: editors@tupelopress.org**
**Web site: http://www.tupelopress.org**
**Phone: 802-366-8185**

(F)   The *Tupelo Press Award for the Best Novel-Length Fiction* offers $3,000, publication under a standard royalty contract, and an invitation to read at the Great River Arts Institute, for a fiction manuscript of at least 50,000 words. There is a $20 entry fee. Send SASE, e-mail, or see the Web site for further information and entry form.

Available to: U. S. citizens
Deadlines: Inquire
Apply to: Fiction Award, above address

(P)   The *Tupelo Press Poetry Awards* offer a judge's prize of $3,000 and an editor's prize of $1,000 for an unpublished, full-length collection of poetry by poets who have not yet published a collection, excluding translations, self-published books, and chapbooks of 48 to 80 pages. Both prizewinners will be published by Tupelo Press and invited to read at the Great River Arts Institute. There is a $25 entry fee. Send SASE for guidelines.

Available to: U. S. citizens
Deadline: Entries accepted January 1-April 15
Apply to: Poetry Award, above address

(P)   The *Annual Chapbook Contest* awards $1,000 and possible publication, with 50 copies for the author, for the best poetry manuscript of 20 to 30 pages, with no more than one poem per page. Previously published poems with proper acknowledgment are acceptable; translations and previously self-published books are not. The contest is open to any poet writing in English who is a U. S. citizen and who has not published a full-length book. There is a $15 reading fee. Send SASE for more information.

Eligibility: See above
Deadline: October 31
Apply to: Tupelo Press Chapbook Awards, above address

**Ucross Foundation**
**30 Big Red Lane**
**Clearmont, WY 82834**
**Phone: 307-737-2291**
**E-mail: ucross@wyoming.com**
**Web site: www.ucrossfoundation.org**
**Fax: 307-737-2322**

(R)   The Ucross Foundation, located in the foothills of the Big Horn Mountains, offers residences of two weeks to two months (average stay six weeks) to writers and other creative artists. There is no charge for room, board, or studio space.

Available to: No restrictions
Deadlines: March 1 for fall; October 1 for spring
Apply to: Residency Program, above address

**Ukiah Players Theatre**
**1041 Low Gap Road**
**Ukiah, CA 95482**
**E-mail: players@pacific.net**
**Web site: www.ukiahplayerstheatre.org**

(D) The *New American Comedy Festival* selects two entries from an open competition to receive staged readings in the spring. Of those two plays, one will be chosen for a workshop and given full production the following season. The workshop consists of seven days of developmental script work with a professional dramaturg, director, and local cast. Playwright's travel, lodging, and daily expenses are covered by the theater during this time. Write for guidelines and application.

Available to: No restrictions
Deadline: Inquire
Apply to: New American Comedy Festival, above address

**Unicorn Theatre**
**3828 Main Street**
**Kansas City, MO 64111**
**Phone: 816-531-7529, ext. 18**

(D) The *New Play Development Program* develops and produces nonmusical, issue-oriented, thought-provoking new plays set in contemporary times (post-1950) with a cast limit of ten. The playwright whose script is selected receives a royalty of $1,000, and the play is produced as part of the Unicorn's regular season. Call for more information.

Available to: No restrictions
Deadline: Ongoing; response time may be from four to eight months
Apply to: Herman Wilson, Literary Assistance, above address

**Unitarian Universalist Association**
**25 Beacon Street**
**Boston, MA 02108**
**E-mail: nlawrence@uua.org**
**Web site: http://www.uua.org**
**Fax: 617-367-3237**

(M) The *Frederic G. Melcher Book Award* consists of $2,000 and a citation for a book of fiction, nonfiction, drama, or poetry, published in the year preceding the award, that has contributed significantly to religious liberalism. Books must be nominated by the Melcher Book Award Committee or the publisher.

Available to: No restrictions
Deadline: January 31
Apply to: Nancy Lawrence, UUA Staff Liaison, above address

**United Daughters of the Confederacy**
**328 North Boulevard**
**Richmond, VA 23220-4057**

(N) The *Mrs. Simon Baruch University Award* is offered as a grant-in-aid for publication of an unpublished book or monograph dealing with southern history in or near the period of the Confederacy. One award of $2,000 and one of $500 are given biennially.

Available to: Graduate students or recipients of master's, doctoral, or other advanced degree within the last fifteen years
Deadline: May 1 of even-numbered years
Apply to: Chairman of the Committee, Mrs. Simon Baruch University Award, above address

**UNITED KINGDOM**
**Boardman Tasker Charitable Trust**
**c/o Maggie Body**
**Pound House**
**Llangennith**
**Swansea, West Glamorgan SA3 1JQ**
**England**
**E-mail: margaretbody@lineone.net**
**Web site: http://www.boardmantasker.com/**
**Fax: 44-01792-386215**

Ⓜ The *Boardman Tasker Prize* of £2,000 is awarded annually to "a book which has made an outstanding contribution to mountain literature." Eligible books must have been published or distributed in the United Kingdom for the first time between the November 1 preceding the prize year and October 31 of the prize year and must be submitted by publishers. Entries may be fiction, nonfiction, poetry, or drama concerned with a mountain environment and must be written in English, either initially or in translation. Publishers only may submit four copies of each eligible book, or page proofs if necessary, with a required entry form for each title. Write for additional information and forms.

Available to: No restrictions
Deadline: August 1
Apply to: Maggie Body, Secretary, Boardman Tasker Charitable Trust, above address

**UNITED KINGDOM**
**British Centre for Literary Translation**
**University of East Anglia**
**Norwich NR4 7TJ**
**England**
**E-mail: transcomp@uea.ac.uk**
**Web site: www.bcla.org/trancomp.htm**
**Fax: 44-01603-592737**

Ⓣ The BCLT, in conjunction with the British Comparative Literature Association, awards a first prize of £350, a second prize of £200, and a third prize of £100 for the best literary translation from any language into English. Poetry, fiction, or literary prose, from any period, is eligible. Write for complete rules and entry form.

Available to: No restrictions
Deadline: January 31
Apply to: BCLT/BCLA Translation Competition, above address

**UNITED KINGDOM**
**Forward Publishing**
**c/o Colman Getty Public Relations**
**17 & 18 Margaret Street**
**London W1W 8RP**
**England**
**E-mail: pr@colmangettypr.co.uk**
**Fax: 44-020-7631-2699**

Ⓟ The *Forward Poetry Prizes* are awarded annually for the best poetry published in the United Kingdom or the Republic of Ireland. A £10,000 prize recognizes the best collection of poetry published in the preceding year; £5,000 the best first collection of poetry; and £1,000 the best individual poem to appear in a newspaper, periodical, or magazine. The winning individual poem and selected poems from the winning collections will be published in *The Forward Book of Poetry*, an anthology of the year's best verse. Entries must be submitted by editors of books or periodicals published in the United Kingdom or the Republic of Ireland; entries from poets are not accepted. Editors may nominate up to four poems or collections. For the 2003 prize, collections must have been published between October 1, 2002, and September 30, 2003; individual poems between June 1, 2002, and April 30, 2003. Write for guidelines.

Available to: No restrictions

Deadline: May (inquire for exact date)
Apply to: Forward Poetry Prize Administrator, above address


**UNITED KINGDOM**
**International PEN**
**9/10 Charterhouse Buildings**
**Goswell Road**
**London EC1M 7AT**
**United Kingdom**
**E-mail: intpen@dircon.co.uk**
**Web site: www.oneworld.org/internatpen**

(F)    The *David T. K. Wong Short Story Award* awards £7,500 in odd-numbered years for a short story in English, between 2,500 and 6,000 words, on a theme which reflects one or more ideals of International PEN as expressed in the PEN charter. Stories should be submitted to the author's national PEN Center, or if that Center is not participating in the selection process, to the Irish PEN Centre. Individual participating PEN Centers may require an entry fee, to be determined by each Center. Manuscripts should not be sent to International PEN; the above Web site and e-mail address are for enquiries only.

Available to: No restrictions
Deadline: October 31 of year preceding award
Apply to: David T. K. Wong Short Story Award, c/o participating Centers of PEN, or to the Irish PEN Centre, 26 Rosslyn, Killarney Road, Bray, County Wicklow, Ireland; phone, 353-1-626-5178; e-mail, irishpen@ireland.com; fax, 353-1-296-2285


**UNITED KINGDOM**
**International Retreat for Writers at Hawthornden Castle**
**Lasswade**
**Midlothian EH18 1EG**
**Scotland**

(R)    The retreat offers residences of four weeks for five published creative writers (novelists, poets, playwrights) at a time. Residences, which include room and board, are scheduled in spring, summer, and fall. Write for further information and application.

Available to: Published writers
Deadline: September 30
Apply to: Above address


**UNITED KINGDOM**
**Orange Prize for Fiction**
**c/o Book Trust**
**45 East Hill**
**London SW18 2QZ**
**England**
**E-mail: lisagee@mac.com**
**Web site: www.orange.co.uk/about/sponsorship/culture/orange_prize/educational.html**

(F)    The *Orange Prize for Fiction* annually awards £30,000 for the best novel written in English by a woman of any nationality and published in the United Kingdom. Short story collections and/or novellas are not eligible. Entries must be published in the United Kingdom between the April 1 preceding the prize year and the March 31 of the prize year; they may have been previously published elsewhere. Publishers only may submit up to three full-length novels per bona fide imprint; publishers may submit a list of up to five other titles which must be accompanied by a justification of not more than 250 words. Books being published between the deadline and March 31 may be submitted as bound proofs.

Available to: Women writers
Deadline: Early January (inquire for exact date)
Apply to: Above address

**UNITED KINGDOM**
**Reuters Foundation**
**85 Fleet Street**
**London EC4P 4AJ**
**England**
**Web site: http://www.foundation.reuters.com**

ⓙ   Reuters awards one annual *Fellowship in Medical Journalism,* tenable at Green College, Oxford University. to English-speaking mid-career journalists for research and study relating to medical matters. The award is for one term (mid-April to mid-July) within the Reuters Foundation Programme for International Journalists. The fellowship covers travel expenses, tuition fees, and a monthly living allowance. Write or see the Web site for further information and application.

   Available to: No restrictions
   Deadline: October 31
   Apply to: Director, above address

ⓙ   The *Reuters-IUCN Media Awards,* which recognize excellence in professional reporting on the environment and sustainable development, seek to enhance public awareness and foster a dialogue between journalists and environmental/development experts that will encourage high-quality reporting based on sound scientific data. Candidates may submit published articles on environmental management, environmental degradation, nature conservation, sustainable use of natural resources, public and private investment, and social, economic, and development topics relevant to the environment. Winners of the regional awards are invited to participate in a Reuters Foundation environmental journalism workshop. The global award winner receives a three-month Reuters Foundation Fellowship at Oxford. All awards cover travel, accommodations, and living costs for the duration of the respective course. Write or see the Web site for additional information.

   Available to: No restrictions
   Deadline: Inquire (generally August)
   Apply to: U. S. journalists: IUCN-U. S. Office, 1400 16th Street, NW, Suite 502, Washington, DC 20036; residents of other countries should contact Reuters, or IUCN, or consult the Web site for addresses of other regional offices

ⓙ   The *Reuters Oxford University Fellowships* provide a three-month study opportunity at the Reuters Foundation Programme at Green College, Oxford, for established U. S. journalists. The fellowship is open to American writers and broadcasters, including specialists in economic, environmental, medical, and scientific subjects. It covers travel expenses, tuition fees, and a monthly living allowance. Write or see the Web site for further information and application.

   Available to: U. S. journalists
   Deadline: February 28
   Apply to: Director, above address

**UNITED KINGDOM**
**Stand Magazine**
**179 Wingrove Road**
**Newcastle-upon-Tyne NE4 9DA**
**England**
**Web site: http://www.people.vcu.edu/~dlatane/stand.html**

Ⓕ Ⓟ *Stand Magazine's Short Story Competition* and *Poetry Competition* each offer first and second prizes of £1,500 and £500, respectively, for the best short stories and poems submitted. Send SASE to the U. S. address below for guidelines and entry form.

> Available to: No restrictions
> Deadline: Short story submissions accepted January 1 - June 30; poetry, July 1 - December 31
> Apply to: David Latane, English Department, Virginia Commonwealth University, Richmond, VA 23284-2005

**UNITED KINGDOM**
**Translators Association**
**84 Drayton Gardens**
**London SW10 9SB**
**England**
**E-mail: info@societyofauthors.org**
**Web site: http://www.societyofauthors.org**
**Fax: 44-020-7373-5768**

The following prizes are given for translations published in the United Kingdom by a British publisher, except for the Vondel Prize, given for a translation that may have been published in the U. S. Translators may be of any nationality. For each prize, publishers should submit three copies of the translation and three copies (photocopies allowed) of the original to Dorothy Sym at the above address. Entry forms are not required. There is no limit on the number of submissions. For further information, contact Dorothy Sym.

Ⓣ The *John Florio Prize* of £1,000, awarded biennially for the best translation of an Italian work of literary merit and general interest. The original must have been published in the last 100 years.

> Available to: No restrictions
> Deadline: December 20, 2003, for books published in 2002 and 2003
> Apply to: John Florio Prize, above address

Ⓣ The *Calouste Gulbenkian Prize* of £1,000, awarded triennially for the best translation into English of a Portuguese work by a Portuguese national. The original must have been published in the last 100 years.

> Available to: No restrictions
> Deadline: December 20, 2004, for books published 2002-2004
> Apply to: Calouste Gulbenkian Prize, above address

Ⓣ The *Scott Moncrieff Prize* of £1,000, awarded annually for the best translation of a full-length French work of literary merit and general interest. The original must have been published in the last 150 years.

> Available to: No restrictions
> Deadline: December 20 for books published that year
> Apply to: Scott Moncrieff Prize, above address

Ⓣ The *Sasakawa Prize* of £2,000, awarded every five years for the best translation of a full-length Japanese work of literary merit and general interest from any period.

> Available to: No restrictions
> Deadline: Inquire
> Apply to: Sasakawa Prize, above address

Ⓣ The *Schlegel-Tieck Prize* of £2,200, awarded annually for the best translation of a German work of literary merit and general interest. The original must have been published in the last 100 years.

Available to: No restrictions
Deadline: December 20 for books published that year
Apply to: Schlegel-Tieck Prize, above address

Ⓣ The *Bernard Shaw Prize* of £1,000, awarded triennially for the best translation into English of a Swedish work of literary merit in any genre.

Available to: No restrictions
Deadline: December 20, 2002, for books published 2000-2002
Apply to: Bernard Shaw Prize, above address

Ⓣ The *Premio Valle Inclan* of £1,000, awarded annually for the best translation of a Spanish work of literary merit and general interest from any period and from anywhere in the world.

Available to: No restrictions
Deadline: December 20 for books published that year
Apply to: Premio Valle Inclan, above address

Ⓣ The *Vondel Translation Prize* of £2,000, awarded biennially for a translation into English of a Dutch or Flemish work of literary merit and general interest. The translation must have been published first in the United Kingdom or the U. S.

Available to: No restrictions
Deadline: December 20, 2002, for books published in 2001 and 2002
Apply to: Vondel Translation Prize, above address

**UNITED KINGDOM**
**University of Cambridge**
**Corpus Christi College**
**Cambridge CB2 1RH**
**England**

Scholarships for research in all subjects are available annually to students of Corpus Christi College, of any nationality, who are not eligible for United Kingdom state grants and who hold a first-class honors degree or the equivalent. Excellent English is essential. Students must register for a postgraduate research degree (Ph.D.) at the university. Duration of the award is three years, subject to satisfactory progress. The value of the award in 1999-2000 was £6,252 per annum. Scholarships are normally awarded in collaboration with the Cambridge Overseas Trust and Cambridge Commonwealth Trust.

Available to: See above
Deadline: March 30
Apply to: Tutor for Advanced Students, above address

**UNITED KINGDOM**
**University of Edinburgh**
**South Bridge**
**Edinburgh EH8 9YL**
**Scotland**
**E-mail: A.McKelvie@ed.ac.uk**
**Fax: 44-131-650-2253**

Ⓕ Ⓝ The *James Tait Black Memorial Prizes*, of £3,000 each, are awarded annually to the best novel and the best biographical work published in Britain in the twelve-month period before the submission deadline. The awards are judged by the Professor of English Literature at the University. Books must originate with a British publisher, and must be submitted only by publishers; books by previous winners will not be considered. Winners are announced in December.

Available to: See above
Deadline: September 30
Apply to: University of Edinburgh, Department of English Literature, David Hume Tower, George Square, Edinburgh EH8 9JX, Scotland

UNITED KINGDOM
The Wiener Library
4 Devonshire Street
London W1N 2BH
England
Tel: 44-020-7636-7247
Fax: 44-020-7436-6428

Ⓝ The *Fraenkel Prize in Contemporary History* is given for outstanding unpublished works in the field of contemporary history written in English, French, or German, covering one of the traditional fields of interest to the Wiener Library, such as Central European and Jewish history in the twentieth century, World War II, fascism and totalitarianism, political violence, and racism. The work must be unpublished at the time of the submission deadline. Two distinct awards will be made:
    a. One of $6,000, in a competition open to all entrants; the work should be between 50,000 and 100,000 words.
    b. One of $4,000, in a competition open to entrants who have yet to publish a major work, which should be between 25,000 and 100,000 words.
Candidates should specify which of the awards they are competing for.

    Available to: See above
    Deadline: Generally May 10; inquire for 2003
    Apply to: Administrative Coordinator, above address


UNITED KINGDOM
Writing Out Award
The Finborough Theatre
118 Finborough Road
London SW10 9ED
England
E-mail: info@writingout.com
Web site: www.writingout.com

Ⓓ Ⓢ The *Writing Out Award,* sponsored by the London Borough of Newham, offers a first prize of £1,500 for an original dramatic work on lesbian or gay themes. The first prize includes a showcase production of the winning script at a prominent London theater. Two runners up receive £500 each. The competition is open to writers of any nationality, exploring gay or lesbian themes in a play for stage or radio, or a screenplay. Especially welcome are works reflecting the spectrum of ethnic communities in London's East End. Scripts submitted must not have had a professional production in any media.

    Available to: No restrictions
    Deadline: December 1
    Apply to: Administrator, Writing Out Award, above address


United Methodist Communications
Public Media Division
PO Box 320
Nashville, TN 37202
E-mail: scholarships@umcom.umc.org
Web site: http://www.umc.org
Fax: 615-742-5404

Ⓙ The $2,500 *Leonard M. Perryman Communications Scholarship for Ethnic Minority Students* is offered yearly in recognition of Perryman, a journalist for the United Methodist Church for nearly thirty years. The scholarship is intended to aid ethnic-minority college students (juniors or seniors) who intend to pursue a career in religious communication and are attending an accredited institution of higher education. The scholarship, which enables the recipient to continue media studies (audiovisual, electronic, or print), seeks to promote excellence in communications among minority students. Write for guidelines and application.

    Available to: U. S. ethnic-minority undergraduates
    Deadline: February 15
    Apply to: Scholarship Committee, above address

ⓙ Two *Stoody-West Fellowships in Religious Journalism,* each $6,000, are offered annually in memory of the professional competence and inspired service of Drs. Ralph Stoody and Arthur West. The grants assist Christians engaged in religious journalism (audiovisual, electronic, or print) or planning to enter graduate study in this field at an accredited school or department of journalism. Write for guidelines and application.

Available to: Christian journalists with an undergraduate degree
Deadline: March 15
Apply to: Scholarship Committee, above address

**United States Civil War Center**
**Louisiana State University**
**Raphael Semmes Drive**
**Baton Rouge, LA 70803**
**Phone: 225-578-3151**
**E-mail: lwood@lsu.edu**
**Web site: http://www.cwc.lsu.edu**
**Fax: 225-578-4876**

ⓕ The *Michael Shaara Award for Excellence in Civil War Fiction* offers an annual prize of $1,000 to the best Civil War novel or series of short stories published each year. Children's books are not accepted. Nominations should be made by the publisher; authors and critics may also nominate. Send five copies of the nominated work to the Center; copies become its property. Write, e-mail, or see the Web site for additional information.

Available to: No restrictions
Deadline: December 31
Apply to: Michael Shaara Award, above address

**United States Holocaust Memorial Museum**
**Center for Advanced Holocaust Studies**
**100 Raoul Wallenberg Place, SW**
**Washington, DC 20024-2150**
**E-mail: wlower@ushmm.org**
**Web site: http://www.ushmm.org**
**Fax: 202-479-9726**

The *Center for Advanced Holocaust Studies Fellowships* support research and writing projects for which the Museum's archival and other resources are critical. Awards are made in a variety of fields to qualified Ph.D. candidates preparing dissertations at accredited American universities, postdoctoral researchers with recent degrees from accredited American universities, and senior scholars from accredited academic and research institutions worldwide. A monthly stipend of $3,000 is offered for a semester or an academic year. Write, e-mail, or see the Web site for further information.

Available to: See above
Deadline: November 1
Apply to: Wendy Lower, Visiting Scholar Programs, above address

The *Miles Lerman Center for the Study of Jewish Resistance Research Fellowship* is designed to encourage exploration of aspects of Jewish resistance including, but not limited to, partisan activity, rebellions in camps and ghettos, sabotage and espionage, document forgery, underground hiding and rescue, and the impact of resistance. Applicants must be Ph.D. candidates preparing dissertations at accredited U. S. universities, postdoctoral researchers with recent degrees, or senior scholars from accredited academic and research institutions worldwide. Fellows receive a monthly stipend of $3,000 for a semester or a full academic year. Write, e-mail, or see the Web site for further information.

Available to: See above
Deadline: November 1
Apply to: Wendy Lower, Visiting Scholar Programs, above address

The *Pearl Resnick Postdoctoral Fellowship* offers promising young scholars who have received a Ph.D. or equivalent degree within the last ten years an academic year in residence at the

Center for Advanced Holocaust Studies. Fellows are provided with a monthly stipend of $4,000 plus up to $3,500 to cover travel expenses for them and accompanying family members (spouse and dependent children). Write, e-mail, or see the Web site for further information and application.

Available to: See above
Deadline: November 1
Apply to: Wendy Lower, Visiting Scholar Programs, above address

Approximately six *Charles H. Revson Foundation Fellowships for Archival Research* are offered each year to Ph.D. recipients or advanced Ph.D. candidates. Those with equivalent degrees or recognized professional status will also be considered. Proposals that use new archival acquisitions of the Museum (from, e.g., Ukraine, Croatia, France, Bulgaria, Italy, Romania, Spain, and the Netherlands) and proposals for research on the fate of Roma and Sinti (Gypsies), Jehovah's Witnesses, Poles, and other groups targeted by the Nazis and their allies and collaborators are of particular interest. Fellows receive a monthly stipend of $3,000 for a three-to-five-month residence. Write, e-mail, or see the Web site for further information and application.

Available to: See above
Deadline: November 1
Apply to: Wendy Lower, Visiting Scholar Programs, above address

The *Joyce and Arthur Schechter Fellowship* supports scholarly research in residence at the Museum. Applicants must hold a Ph.D. or be an advanced Ph.D. candidate by time of the application deadline. Candidates with equivalent degrees or recognized professional status will be considered. Fellows receive up to $5,000 for a six-week-to-three-month residence. Write, e-mail, or see the Web site for further information and application.

Available to: See above
Deadline: November 1
Apply to: Wendy Lower, Visiting Scholar Programs, above address

**United States Institute of Peace**
**1200 17th Street, NW, 2nd floor**
**Washington, DC 20036-3011**
**E-mail: jrprogram@usip.org**
**Web site: http://www.usip.org**

® The *Jennings Randolph Program for International Peace* offers fellowships to outstanding professionals and scholars who wish to "undertake research and other kinds of communication that will improve understanding and skills on the part of policymakers and the public regarding important problems of international peace and conflict management." Fellows work in residence at the Institute; they receive a stipend (amount keyed to income earned in the twelve months before the fellowship), health benefits if needed, and support for appropriate project costs. The program works closely with the Institute toward publishing the results of fellows' research. Write for further information and application.

Available to: No restrictions
Deadline: Inquire
Apply to: Jennings Randolph Program for International Peace, above address

**United States Naval Institute**
**291 Wood Road**
**Annapolis, MD 21402**
**E-mail: kclarke@usni.org**
**Web site: http://www.usni.org**

Ⓝ The *Armed Forces Joint Warfighting Essay Contest* annually offers prizes of $2,500, $2,000, and $1,000 for essays of 3,000 words on the subject of combat readiness. Winning essays are published in *Proceedings* magazine. Send SASE for rules.

Available to: No restrictions
Deadline: May 1
Apply to: Armed Forces Joint Warfighting Essay Contest, above address

(N) The *Vincent Astor Memorial Leadership Essay Contest* annually offers prizes of $1,500, $1,000 and two of $500 for essays of up to 3,500 words that address topics of leadership in the sea services. Winning essays are published in *Proceedings* magazine. Send SASE for rules.

> Available to: Junior officers and officer trainees of the U. S. Navy, Marine Corps, and Coast Guard
> Deadline: February 15
> Apply to: Vincent Astor Memorial Leadership Essay Contest, above address

(N) The *Arleigh Burke Essay Contest* annually offers prizes of $3,000, $2,000, and $1,000 for original, unpublished essays of up to 3,500 words that address "the advancement of professional, literary, and scientific knowledge in the naval and maritime services, and the advancement of the knowledge of sea power." Winning essays are published in *Proceedings*. Send SASE for rules.

> Available to: U. S. citizens
> Deadline: December 1
> Apply to: Arleigh Burke Essay Contest, above address

(N) The *Enlisted Essay Contest* annually offers prizes of $1,500, $1,000, and $500 for essays of up to 2,500 words that concern the mission of the U. S. Naval Institute: the advancement of professional, literary, and scientific knowledge in the naval and maritime services, and the advancement of the knowledge of sea power. Winning essays are published in *Proceedings* magazine. Send SASE for rules.

> Available to: Enlisted personnel, including active, reserve, and retired
> Deadline: September 1
> Apply to: Enlisted Essay Contest, above address

**United States Trotting Association**
**United States Harness Writers' Association**
**750 Michigan Avenue**
**Columbus, OH 43215**
**Phone: 614-224-2291, ext. 3232**
**E-mail: jpawlak@ustrotting.com**
**Web site: http://www.ustrotting.com**
**Fax: 614-228-1385**

(J) The *John Hervey Awards for Writing Excellence* and *Broadcasters Awards* are available to writers of stories and productions with harness racing as a focus. The contest is not limited to USHWA members. Awards of $500 and $100 are given in each of five categories: newspaper, magazine, television program, television feature, and photography.

> Available to: No restrictions
> Deadline: January (inquire for exact date)
> Apply to: John Pawlak, Hervey/Broadcasters Awards Administrator, above address

**University of Akron Press**
**374B Bierce Library**
**Akron, OH 44325-1703**
**E-mail: uapress@uakron.edu**
**Web site: http://www.uakron.edu/uapress/poetryprize.html**
**Fax: 330-972-0364**

(P) The *Akron Poetry Prize* awards $1,000 and publication by the Press for a collection of poems written in English, from 60 to 100 pages. Nonwinning manuscripts may be considered for publication in the series. There is a $25 reading fee. Send SASE, e-mail, or fax for guidelines, or see the Web site.

> Available to: No restrictions
> Deadline: Submissions accepted May 15-June 30
> Apply to: Akron Poetry Prize, above address

University of Alabama at Huntsville
Department of English
Huntsville, AL 35899
E-mail: maryh71997@ad.com
Web site: www.uah.edu/colleges/liberal/english/whatnewcontest.html

Ⓕ    The *H. E. Francis Award*, co-sponsored by the University and the Ruth Hindman Foundation,
      offers $1,000 to the best unpublished short story, not exceeding 5,000 words. Two honorable
      mentions receive publication only. There is a $15 submission fee. Write for guidelines or
      consult the Web site.

      Available to: No restrictions
      Deadline: December 31
      Apply to: Above address


University of Alaska Southeast
11120 Glacier Highway
Juneau, AK 99801-8761
E-mail: art.petersen@uas.alaska.edu
Web site: www.geocities.com/artpetersen

Ⓕ Ⓟ   The *Explorations Awards for Literature* annually give a first prize of $1,000 for poetry or short
      fiction, a second prize of $500, and two third prizes of $100 each, plus publication in
      *Explorations*, the university's literary magazine. Submissions require a reader/entry fee
      of $6 for one or two poems and $3 for each additional poem (up to any number, maximum
      60 lines each), and $6 per short story (any number, maximum 3,000 words each). Send
      SASE or consult the Web site for complete guidelines.

      Available to: No restrictions
      Deadline: May 15
      Apply to: Art Petersen, Editor, Explorations, above address


University of Arizona
Poetry Center
1216 North Cherry Avenue
Tucson, AZ 85719
Phone: 520-626-3765
E-mail: poetry@u.arizona.edu
Web site: http://www.coh.arizona.edu/poetry/default.html
Fax: 520-621-5566

Ⓡ    The Poetry Center provides a writer with a one-month summer residence (between June 1
      and August 31) in a quiet neighborhood of Tucson. The guesthouse is a historic adobe
      located two houses from the acclaimed collections of the University of Arizona Center,
      and two blocks from campus. A $500 stipend is included. Applicants should submit no
      more than 10 pages of poetry or 20 pages of fiction or literary nonfiction, along with a
      one-page résumé. There is a $10 reading fee. Send SASE, e-mail, or fax for guidelines.

      Available to: Writers who have not published more than one full-length work
      Deadline: Submissions accepted February 15-March 15
      Apply to: Residency Program, above address


University of Arkansas Press
McIlroy House
201 Ozark Avenue
Fayetteville, AR 72701
E-mail: uaprinfo@cavern.uark.edu
Web site: www.uark.edu/~uaprinfo
Fax: 501-575-6044

Ⓣ    The *Arabic Translation Awards* are given to two book-length translations from Arabic of poetry,
      fiction, or nonfiction. Translations must be previously unpublished in book form, and all
      translation rights must be cleared for University of Arkansas Press publication. For each

award, the original author (if still holding rights) receives $7,500 in lieu of royalties; the translator also receives $7,500. Winning manuscripts are published the following season by the Press. Send SASE for more information.

Available to: No restrictions
Deadline: April 15
Apply to: Archie Schaffer, above address

**University of California at Irvine**
**Department of Spanish and Portuguese**
**322 Humanities Hall**
**Irvine, CA 92697-5275**

Ⓜ  The *Chicano/Latino Literary Contest* offers a $1,000 first prize plus publication by the University of California Press for a book-length manuscript by a Chicano or Latino writer in the genre specified for the year (drama in 2002, the novel in 2003). A second prize of $500 and a third of $250 are also offered. The first-prize winner receives paid transportation to Irvine to receive the award. Submissions may be in English or Spanish. Send SASE for guidelines.

Available to: U. S. citizens or permanent residents
Deadline: Submission must be postmarked by June 1
Apply to: Chicano/Latino Literary Contest, above address

**University of California, Los Angeles**
**William Andrews Clark Memorial Library**
**2520 Cimarron Street**
**Los Angeles, CA 90018**
**E-mail: clarkfel@humnet.ucla.edu**
**Web site: http://www.humnet.ucla.edu/humnet/c1718cs**
**Fax: 310-206-8577**

The Clark Library and the Center for Seventeenth- & Eighteenth-Century Studies offer a limited number of resident fellowships to postdoctoral scholars with research projects that require work in any area of the Clark's collections. Awards are for periods of one to three months in residence. Write or consult the Web site for additional information and application.

Available to: See above
Deadline: February 1
Apply to: Fellowship Coordinator, Center for Seventeenth- & Eighteenth-Century Studies, 310 Royce Hall, UCLA, 405 Hilgard Avenue, Los Angeles, CA 90095-1404

The *Ahmanson-Getty Postdoctoral Fellowships* are part of a theme-based resident fellowship program, established with the support of the Ahmanson Foundation of Los Angeles and the J. Paul Getty Trust, designed to encourage the participation of junior scholars in the core programs of the Center for Seventeenth- & Eighteenth-Century Studies. The major theme for a given year is announced the preceding fall (in 2000-2001, the theme was "Culture and Authority in the Baroque"). Scholars who have received their Ph.D. in the last six years and are engaged in research pertaining to the announced theme are eligible. Fellows are expected to make a substantive contribution to the Center's workshops and seminars. Awards are for two consecutive academic quarters in residence at the Clark Library. The stipend is $18,400 for two quarters. Write or consult the Web site for additional information and application.

Available to: See above
Deadline: February 1
Apply to: Fellowship Coordinator, Center for Seventeenth- & Eighteenth-Century Studies, 310 Royce Hall, UCLA, 405 Hilgard Avenue, Los Angeles, CA 90095-1404

**University of Chicago**
**Harriet Monroe Poetry Award**
**Division of Humanities**
**1050 East 59th Street**
**Chicago, IL 60637**
**Web site: www-news.uchicago.edu**

[IN]    The *Harriet Monroe Poetry Award* of $1,000 is awarded periodically to U. S. poets of notable achievement and special promise. The president of the university regularly chooses poets from various sections of the U. S. to sit on the selection committee, which gives preference to poets of progressive rather than academic tendencies. *By Internal Nomination Only.*

**University of Evansville**
**Department of English**
**1800 Lincoln Avenue**
**Evansville, IN 47722**
**Phone: 812-479-2963**

(P)    The *Richard Wilbur Award* offers $1,000 and publication by the University of Evansville Press for a poetry manuscript, 50 to 100 pages in length. There is a $20 entry fee. Send SASE for guidelines.

Available to: U. S. poets
Deadline: December (inquire for exact date)
Apply to: Richard Wilbur Award, above address

**University of Georgia Press**
**330 Research Drive, Suite B-100**
**Athens, GA 30602-4901**
**Web site: www.uga.edu/ugapress**
**Fax: 706-369-6131**

(F)    The *Flannery O'Connor Award for Short Fiction* offers $1,000 plus publication under a standard book contract for collections of original short fiction in English, by published or unpublished writers. Two winners are selected annually. Stories that have been published in magazines or anthologies may be included; stories that have been published in a book-length collection written solely by the author may not. Submissions should be accompanied by a $15 handling fee. Manuscripts are not returned. Send SASE for guidelines.

Available to: No restrictions
Deadline: Submissions accepted April 1-May 31
Apply to: Flannery O'Connor Award for Short Fiction, above address

**University of Hawaii at Manoa**
**Kumu Kahua Theatre**
**46 Merchant Street**
**Honolulu, HI 96813**
**Fax: 808-536-4226**

(D)    The *Kumu Kahua Playwriting Contest* annually awards $500 for a full-length play set in Hawaii and dealing with some aspect of the Hawaii experience. The contest also awards $400 for a full-length play set in or dealing with Hawaii, the Pacific islands, the Pacific Rim, or the Pacific/Asian experience. An award of $200 is offered for plays on any topic of any length by a Hawaii resident. Reading and/or production is possible for winning submissions. Write for guidelines before submitting.

Available to: See above
Deadline: January 1
Apply to: Kumu Kahua Playwriting Contest, above address

**University of Iowa Press**
**University of Iowa**
**119 West Park Road**
**100 Kuhl House**
**Iowa City, IA 52242-1000**
**Fax: 319-335-2055**

(P) Two *Iowa Poetry Prizes* are given annually for unpublished poetry manuscripts by new as well as established poets. The Press publishes the two prizewinning books every year. Previous winning writers are not eligible. Write for guidelines before submitting.

Available to: See above
Deadline: Submissions accepted during May
Apply to: Iowa Poetry Prizes, above address

(F) The *Iowa Short Fiction Award* and the *John Simmons Short Fiction Award* are offered for book-length collections of short fiction by writers who have not published a book of prose. The Press publishes the two prizewinning books every year.

Available to: No restrictions
Deadline: Submissions accepted August 1-September 30
Apply to: Iowa Short Fiction Awards, Iowa Writers' Workshop, 102 Dey House, Iowa City, IA 52242

**University of Kansas**
**University Theatre**
**1530 Naismith Drive**
**Lawrence, KS 66045**
**Phone: 785-864-3381**

(D) The *Great Plains Play Contest* annually awards a first prize of $2,000, production, and $500 for travel and housing costs, for a full-length play, musical, or opera for adult and young audiences that deals with a historical or contemporary aspect of the Great Plains. Second prize is $500. Submissions must not have been produced professionally.

Available to: No restrictions
Deadline: September 1
Apply to: Great Plains Play Contest, above address

**University of Massachusetts**
**Department of Theater**
**112 Fine Arts Center**
**Amherst, MA 01003**

(D) *New Works for a New World* offers four playwrights a two-week development residence with actors, director, and dramaturg, culminating in a staged reading. Special interest is given to work by writers of color and work that reflects "the diversity of American culture." Selected playwrights receive an honorarium of $1,500, plus paid travel and housing. Send SASE for guidelines.

Available to: See above
Deadline: Inquire
Apply to: New Works for a New World, above address

**University of Massachusetts Press**
**PO Box 429**
**Amherst, MA 01004**
**Web site: http://www.umass.edu/umpress**
**Fax: 413-545-1226**

(P) The *Juniper Prize* is granted for an original manuscript of poems, in odd-numbered years for a first book collection and in even-numbered years for a subsequent collection. In the first-book category, manuscripts are accepted from writers whose poems may have appeared in literary journals or anthologies but have not been published or accepted for publication in book form (with the exception of chapbooks under 45 pages). In the subsequent-book category, manuscripts are considered only from authors who have had at least one full-length book or chapbook of poetry published or accepted for publication (chapbooks must be at least 30 pages; self-published work is not eligible. In both categories, the winning manuscript will be published by University of Massachusetts Press and the poet awarded $1,000. There is an entry fee of $15. For additional information, write to the above address or consult the Web site.

Available to: Anyone except University of Massachusetts employees and students, and previous prize recipients
Deadline: September 30
Apply to: Juniper Prize, University of Massachusetts Press, Amherst, MA 01003

**University of Michigan**
**Wallace House**
**620 Oxford Road**
**Ann Arbor, MI 48104-2635**
**Phone: 734-998-7666**
**Web site: mjfellows.org/**

(J) The *Livingston Awards for Young Journalists* offer three $10,000 prizes for the best local, national, and international reporting in any print or broadcast medium.

Available to: Journalists under thirty-five
Deadline: February 1
Apply to: Livingston Awards, above address

(J) The *Mike Wallace Fellowship in Investigative Reporting*, the *Burton R. Benjamin Fellowship in Broadcast Journalism*, the *Knight Fellowships in Specialty Reporting*, the *Sports Reporting Fellowship*, the *Public Policy Journalism Fellowships*, the *Daniel B. Burke Fellowship*, the *Time-Warner Fellowship*, and the *Ford Transportation Technology Fellowship* are available to full-time employees (freelancers included) of any print or broadcast medium who have at least five years' experience. Each fellowship carries a $40,000 stipend plus tuition.

Available to: See above
Deadline: February 1
Apply to: Charles Eisendrath, Director, Michigan Journalism Fellows, above address, for information

**University of Michigan Press**
**PO Box 1104**
**Ann Arbor, MI 48106-1104**

[IN] The *University of Michigan Press Book Award* of $1,000 is given annually for the work, written or edited by a member of the University of Michigan teaching and research staff, including emeritus members, that has most distinguished the Press's list. *By Internal Nomination Only.*

**University of Missouri**
**Missouri Lifestyle Journalism Awards**
**181 Gannett Hall**
**School of Journalism**
**Columbia, MO 65211**
**Web site: http://www.missouri.edu/~jschool/lifestylejournalism.html**

(J) The *Missouri Lifestyle Journalism Awards* (formerly the J. C. Penney Missouri Newspaper Awards) are available to writers, editors, and reporters for daily and weekly newspapers. Winners are chosen in the following categories: single story and series; consumer affairs; fashion and design; multiculturalism; arts/entertainment; food/nutrition; health/fitness; and feature. Fifteen $1,000 awards are given annually. The entry fee is $155. Consult the Web site for further information and application.

Available to: See above
Deadline: February 22
Apply to: Director, Missouri Lifestyle Journalism Awards, above address

**University of Nebraska Press**
**233 North 8th Street**
**Lincoln, NE 68588-0255**
**Fax: 402-472-0308**

(N)  The *North American Indian Prose Award* offers a cash advance of $1,000 and publication by the University of Nebraska Press for a book-length work of biography, autobiography, history, literary criticism, or essays by an author of North American Indian descent. Send SASE for guidelines.

Available to: North American Indian writers
Deadline: July 1
Apply to: North American Indian Prose Award, above address

**University of Nevada**
**Department of Theatre**
**4505 Maryland Parkway**
**Box 455036**
**Las Vegas, NV 89154-5036**
**Web site: www.unlv.edu/colleges/fine_arts/theater/**

(D)  The *Morton R. Sarett Memorial Award* biennially offers $3,000 and production for an original, innovative full-length play in English or a musical that has not been produced. The winning playwright will be provided with travel and housing to attend rehearsals and the opening performance. Send SASE for guidelines and application.

Available to: No restrictions
Deadline: December (inquire for exact date)
Apply to: Morton R. Sarett Memorial Award, above address

**University of New Hampshire**
**Department of Theatre and Dance/TRY**
**Paul Creative Arts Center**
**30 College Road**
**Durham, NH 03824-3538**
**Phone: 603-862-2919**
**E-mail: cgagnon@cisunix.unh.edu**
**Web site: http://www.unh.edu/theatre-dance**
**Fax: 603-862-0298**

(C) (D)  The *Anna Zornio Memorial Children's Theatre Playwriting Award* every four years offers up to $1,000 plus production for an unpublished play or musical for young audiences that has not been produced professionally. Plays, preferably with a single or unit set, should be not more than one hour long. Write for guidelines.

Available to: U. S. or Canadian resident
Deadline: September 1
Apply to: Anna Zornio Playwriting Award, above address

**University of New Mexico**
**English Department**
**Humanities Building**
**Albuquerque, NM 87131**

(F)  The *Premio Aztlán* of $2,000 is given annually to honor a book of fiction by a Chicano or Chicana writer who has published no more than two books. The prize includes an invitation to give a reading at the University of New Mexico. Writers or publishers should submit five copies of a work published during the calendar year. Send SASE for guidelines.

Available to: Chicano or Chicana fiction writers
Deadline: December 1
Apply to: Rudolfo Anaya, above address

**University of North Texas Press**
PO Box 311336
Denton, TX 76203-1336
Phone: 940-656-2142
Web site: http://www.unt.edu/untpress
Fax: 940-565-4590

Ⓟ The *Vassar Miller Prize in Poetry* consists of $1,000 and publication by University of North Texas Press of an original poetry manuscript of 50 to 80 pages. There is a $20 handling fee, payable to the Press. Send SASE for guidelines.

Available to: No restrictions
Deadline: November 30
Apply to: Scott Cairns, Series Editor, Vassar Miller Prize in Poetry, c/o English Department, Tate Hall 107, University of Missouri, Columbia, MO 65211


**University of Notre Dame**
**Department of English**
**Notre Dame, IN 46556**
E-mail: english.righter.1@nd.edu
Web site: http://www.nd.edu/~english/creatwrit/writinfo.html

Ⓕ Ⓟ The *Ernest Sandeen Prize in Poetry* and the *Richard Sullivan Prize in Fiction* each award $1,000 and publication by the University of Notre Dame Press of a book-length manuscript of, respectively, poetry and short fiction. Entrants must have published at least one book of poetry or short fiction. The Sandeen Prize is offered in odd-numbered years, the Sullivan Prize in even-numbered years. Send SASE for guidelines.

Available to: No restrictions
Deadline: August 31, 2003, for the Sandeen; August 31, 2004, for the Sullivan
Apply to: Sullivan Prize or Sandeen Prize, Director of Creative Writing, Department of English, University of Notre Dame, Notre Dame, IN 46556


**University of Pittsburgh Press**
**Eureka Building**
**3400 Forbes Avenue, 5th floor**
**Pittsburgh, PA 15260**
E-mail: mes5@pitt.edu
Web site: http://www.pitt.edu/~press

Ⓕ The *Drue Heinz Literature Prize,* given annually, consists of a cash award of $15,000 and publication of a collection of short fiction by University of Pittsburgh Press under a standard royalty contract. Send SASE or see the Web site for guidelines before submitting.

Available to: Writers who have published a book-length collection of short fiction or a minimum of three short stories or novellas in commercial magazines or literary journals of national distribution
Deadline: Submissions must be postmarked May 1-June 30
Apply to: Drue Heinz Literature Prize, above address

Ⓟ The *Agnes Lynch Starrett Poetry Prize,* given annually, consists of a cash award of $5,000 and publication of a first book of poetry by University of Pittsburgh Press under a standard royalty contract. There is a $20 reading fee. Send SASE or see the Web site for guidelines before submitting.

Available to: Anyone who has not published a full-length book of poetry
Deadline: Submissions must be postmarked March 1-April 30
Apply to: Agnes Lynch Starrett Prize, above address

**University of Rochester**
**Susan B. Anthony Institute for Gender and Women's Studies**
**Lattimore Hall, Room 538**
**Rochester, NY 14627-0434**
**Web site: http://www.rochester.edu/college/wst**

(F) The *Janet Heidinger Kafka Prize* is awarded annually to a woman U. S. citizen for the best published book-length work of prose fiction (novel, short story collection, experimental writing). Works submitted must have been published within the previous twelve months; collections of short stories must have been assembled for the first time, or at least one-third of the material must have been previously unpublished. The prize consists of a cash award, which varies according to funding. Entries may be submitted only by publishers, who should write for guidelines.

Available to: See above
Deadline: February 28
Apply to: Janet Heidinger Kafka Prize, above address

**University of Southern California**
**Professional Writing Program**
**WPH 404**
**Los Angeles, CA 90089-4034**

(P) The *Ann Stanford Poetry Prize* awards $1,000, $200, and $100 for previously unpublished poems. Poets may submit up to five poems, with a $10 reading fee. Winning entries are published in *Southern California Anthology*. Send SASE for contest rules. All entrants will receive an issue of the anthology.

Available to: No restrictions
Deadline: April 15
Apply to: Ann Stanford Poetry Prize, above address

**University of Virginia**
**Creative Writing Program**
**English Department**
**219 Bryan Hall**
**PO Box 400121**
**Charlottesville, VA 22904-4121**
**E-mail: LRS9E@virginia.edu**
**Web site: http://www.engl.virginia.edu/**

Several *Henry Hoyns* and *Poe/Faulkner Fellowships* are offered to first-year students enrolled as candidates for the MFA degree. Write for further information and application guidelines.

Available to: See above
Deadline: January 1
Apply to: Above address

**University of Wisconsin Press**
**1930 Monroe Street, 3rd floor**
**Madison, WI 53711-2059**
**Phone: 608-263-1110**
**Web site: www.wisc.edu/wisconsinpress/poetryguide.html**
**Fax: 608-263-1132**

(P) The *Brittingham Prize in Poetry* and the *Felix Pollak Prize in Poetry*, each consisting of a cash award of $1,000 and publication by University of Wisconsin Press, are awarded annually to the best book-length manuscripts of original poetry (50 to 80 pages). A $20 reading fee must accompany each manuscript. Send SASE for guidelines.

Available to: No restrictions
Deadline: Submissions must be postmarked during September
Apply to: Ronald Wallace, Series Editor, above address

**Unterberg Poetry Center of the 92nd Street Y**
**1395 Lexington Avenue**
**New York, NY 10128**
**Phone: 212-415-5500**

(P) The *"Discovery"/The Nation Poetry Contest: Joan Leiman Jacobson Poetry Prizes* are offered to four poets who have not published a book of poems (chapbooks and self-published books included). Each award consists of a $300 cash prize, a reading at the Poetry Center, and publication in *The Nation*. Four identical sets of a stapled, numbered 10-page manuscript should be submitted. Poems must be original and in English (no translations), and the manuscript should not exceed 500 lines. Personal identification must appear only in a single, separate cover letter, not on the poems; the cover letter must include name, address, and day and evening telephone numbers. Biographical information is not necessary. There is a $5 entry fee. Send SASE for complete guidelines.

Available to: See above
Deadline: January 18
Apply to: "Discovery"/The Nation Poetry Contest, above address


**Urban Stages/Playwrights Preview Productions**
**17 East 47th Street**
**New York, NY 10017**
**E-mail: tlreilly@urbanstages.org**
**Web site: http://www.urbanstages.org**
**Fax: 212-421-1387**

(D) The *Emerging Playwright Award* offers $500, production, and paid travel to attend rehearsals for full-length plays and one-acts that have not been produced in New York City. Submissions by minority playwrights and plays with ethnically diverse casts are encouraged. Write for guidelines.

Available to: No restrictions
Deadline: Ongoing
Apply to: Emerging Playwright Award, above address


**Utah Arts Council**
**617 East South Temple Street**
**Salt Lake City, UT 84102**
**Phone: 801-236-7555**
**E-mail: glebeda@arts.state.ut.us**
**Web site: http://www.dced.state.ut.us/arts**
**Fax: 801-236-7556**

(M) The *Utah Original Writing Competition* offers a $5,000 prize that will assist a publisher in the publication and promotion of a book by a Utah writer. The winner is selected from among four book-length works in categories alternating yearly: novel, short fiction or poetry collection, biography/autobiography or general nonfiction, and juvenile or young-adult book. The Council also offers prizes of up to $1,000 for novels, book-length collections of poems, individual poems, and short stories by Utah residents. Write for further information and guidelines.

Available to: Utah residents
Deadline: Last Friday in June
Apply to: Literary Competition Division, above address


**Utah State University Press**
**Logan, UT 84322-7800**
**Web site: http://www.usu.edu/usupress**

(P) The *May Swenson Poetry Award* offers $1,000, publication by Utah State University Press, and royalties for a poetry collection. Poets may submit manuscripts of 50 to 100 pages, along with a $25 reading fee, which covers a copy of the winning book. Send SASE or consult the Web site for complete guidelines.

Available to: No restrictions
Deadline: September 30
Apply to: May Swenson Poetry Award, above address

**The Valley Players**
**Box 441**
**Waitsfield, VT 05673-0441**
**Web site: www.valleyplayers.com/playwrights.html**

Ⓓ The *Vermont Playwrights Award* annually offers $1,000 and probable production for an unproduced, unpublished full-length play by a resident of Maine, New Hampshire, or Vermont. Plays should be suitable for a community group and have moderate production demands. Send SASE for guidelines.

Available to: Maine, New Hampshire or Vermont playwrights
Deadline: February 1
Apply to: Vermont Playwrights Award, above address

**Vermont Arts Council**
**136 State Street, Drawer 33**
**Montpelier, VT 05633-6001**
**Phone: 802-828-3291**
**E-mail: info@arts.vca.state.vt.us**
**Web site: http://www.state.vt.us/vermont-arts**
**Fax: 802-828-3363**

Ⓜ The *Opportunity Grants Program* makes funds available to individual Vermont artists for the creation of new work and artistic development. Grant amounts for new work range from $750 to $7,000; for development from $250 to $750. Write, e-mail, or see the Web site for additional information and application materials.

Available to: Vermont residents
Deadline: Inquire
Apply to: Opportunity Grants, above address

**Vermont Studio Center**
**Box 613**
**Johnson, VT 05656**
**Phone: 802-635-2727**
**E-mail: VSCVT@pwshift.com**
**Web site: http://www.vermontstudiocenter.com**
**Fax: 802-635-2730**

Ⓡ The Vermont Studio Center offers four-to-twelve-week residences year-round for writers and artists. Each of the twelve one-month periods features two visiting writers whose work falls into one of three genres: poetry, fiction, or nonfiction. Each writer gives a reading and a literary craft talk, and is available for conferences with residents in his or her genre. A number of full fellowships based on merit are awarded each year and cover all residence fees. In addition, *Vermont Studio Center Grants*, which include *Residency Grants* and *Work-Exchange Grants*, are awarded to those able to document financial need. VSC Grants cover part of the cost of the residence. There is a $25 application fee. Write, e-mail, or consult the Web site for additional information and application.

Available to: Emerging and mid-career writers
Deadline: October 1, February 15, and June 15 for full fellowships; ongoing for VSC Grants
Apply to: VSC Writers Program, Admissions Committee, above address

**Verse Press**
**Eastworks Building**
**116 Pleasant Street, Suite 20**
**Easthampton, MA 01027**
**Web site: http://www.versemag.org; or www.versepress.org**

(P) The *Verse Prize* awards $1,000 plus publication by Verse Press for a book of poetry by a published or unpublished poet writing in English. There is a $20 entry fee. Send SASE or consult the Web site for guidelines.

Available to: No restrictions
Deadline: February 28
Apply to: Verse Prize, above address


**Very Special Arts**
**1300 Connecticut Avenue, NW, Suite 700**
**Washington, DC 20036**
**E-mail: playwright@vsarts.org**
**Web site: http://www.vsarts.org**

(D) The *Playwright Discovery Award* is given to students in grades 6 through 12 for original one-act plays of up to 40 pages that address an aspect of disability. The script is selected for professional production at the John F. Kennedy Center for the Performing Arts. The first- and second-place winners receive $750 and $500, respectively, and an expenses-paid trip to Washington to see the production or staged reading. Third- and fourth-place winners receive $200 and travel to Washington to participate in a playwriting workshop. Write, e-mail, or consult the Web site for guidelines and application.

Available to: Students in grades 6 through 12, who are U. S. citizens or permanent residents
Deadline: April 15
Apply to: Above address


**Veterans of Foreign Wars National Headquarters**
**Voice of Democracy Program**
**406 West 34th Street**
**Kansas City, MO 64111**
**E-mail: kharmer@vfw.org**
**Web site: www.vfw.org**

(N) The annual *Voice of Democracy Audio Essay Competition* awards fifty-six national scholarships, totaling more than $100,000, to students in grades 9 through 12 for tape-recorded essays, 3 to 5 minutes, on an announced theme. For more information, consult a school counselor or a local VFW post.

Available to: See above
Deadline: November 1
Apply to: School counselor or local VFW post

(C) The *Youth Essay Competition* offers one high school student a grand prize of a $10,000 U. S. savings bond for the best essay of 300 to 400 words, on an aspect of democracy. (Specific themes change yearly.) The winner of the grand prize also receives an all-expenses-paid trip to VFW's annual Community Service Conference. Additional smaller prizes, also in the form of U. S. savings bonds, are available.

Available to: See above
Deadline: December 1
Apply to: See VFW Web site

**Villa Montalvo**
PO Box 158
Saratoga, CA 95071
Phone: 408-961-5818
Web site: http://www.villamontalvo.org
Fax: 408-961-5850

®   The *Artist Residency Program* awards artists, composers, and writers one-to-three-month
    residences at the 1912 Villa Montalvo in the foothills of the Santa Cruz Mountains.
    Writers are given fully equipped apartments with private kitchens; residents must
    provide their own food, supplies, and funds for living expenses. The program aims for
    "an ethnically diverse and international community of arts which will broaden artistic
    perspectives and catalyze dialogue." *Note: Residences are temporarily suspended till
    completion of the new complex in 2003.*

    Available to: No restrictions
    Deadlines: Selection process begins spring 2003
    Apply to: Peggy Urquhart, above address

℗ ®   The *Villa Montalvo Biennial Poetry Competition* awards $1,000 and a one-month residence at
    Villa Montalvo for unpublished original poems. A $500 second prize and $300 third prize
    are offered also. Send SASE for guidelines. *Note: Residences are temporarily suspended till
    completion of the new complex in 2003.*

    Available to: Residents of California, Nevada, Oregon, or Washington
    Deadline: Inquire
    Apply to: Biennial Poetry Competition, above address

**Virginia Center for the Creative Arts**
Box VCCA
Sweet Briar, VA 24595
E-mail: vcca@vcca.com
Web site: http://www.vcca.com
Fax: 804-946-7239

®   The Virginia Center for the Creative Arts accepts applications from professional writers, visual
    artists, and composers for residences ranging from two weeks to two months. The Center
    is located in Amherst County, one hour south of Charlottesville. A standard daily fee of
    $30 covers private studio, bedroom, and meals. Financial assistance is available for
    qualified applicants with demonstrated need. Write, e-mail, or see the Web site for more
    information.

    Available to: No restrictions
    Deadline: January 15 for June-September residences; May 15 for October-January;
        September 15 for February-May
    Apply to: Admissions, above address

**Virginia College Stores Association**
c/o Paul Clark
Volume Two Bookstore
801 University City Boulevard
Blacksburg, VA 24060
E-mail: paulc@bookstore.ct.edu

The *Virginia College Stores Association Book Award* annually offers $500 to an author residing in
    Virginia whose work possesses "outstanding literary, social, and intellectual merit." Books
    published within the calendar year may be submitted. Write or e-mail for guidelines
    prior to submitting.

    Available to: See above
    Deadline: January (inquire for exact date)
    Apply to: Book Award, above address

Virginia Commonwealth University
Department of English
PO Box 842005
Richmond, VA 23284-2005
E-mail: eng_grad@vcu.edu
Web site: http://www.has.vcu.edu/eng/grad/Levis_Prize.htm

(P) The *Levis Reading Prize* offers an honorarium of $1,000 and an expenses-paid trip to Richmond for the author of a first or second book of poetry published during the calendar year. Poet or publisher should submit one copy of a book at least 48 pages long. Send SASE, e-mail, or see the Web site for guidelines.

Available to: No restrictions
Deadline: January 15
Apply to: Levis Reading Prize, above address

Virginia Quarterly Review
One West Range, PO Box 400223
Charlottesville, VA 22904-4223
Web site: www.virginia.edu/vqr
Fax 434-924-1397

(F) (P) The *Emily Clark Balch Awards*, each $500, are given annually to the best short story and best poem published in *Virginia Quarterly Review* during the calendar year. The editors consider only stories and poems that have been accepted and published.

Available to: Authors of published submissions
Deadline: Submissions accepted year-round
Apply to: Above address or fax

Visiting Writers Program
Knapp Hall
State University of New York at Farmingdale
Farmingdale, NY 11735
E-mail: brownml@snyfarva.cc.farmingdale.edu
Web site:
    www.farmingdale.edu/campuspages/artssciences/englishhumanities/paward.html

(P) The *Paumanok Poetry Award* offers $1,000 plus expenses for a reading as part of the SUNY Farmingdale Visiting Writers Program series. Two runners-up receive $500 plus paid expenses for a reading in the series. To enter the competition, send five to seven poems (published or unpublished), a one-paragraph biography, a $12 reading fee, and SASE. Write for further information.

Available to: No restrictions
Deadline: September 15
Apply to: Above address

Wagner College
Department of Theatre and Speech
One Campus Road
Staten Island, NY 10301
E-mail: lsweet@wagner.edu
Fax: 718-390-3323

(D) The *Stanley Drama Award* of $2,000 is given for an original full-length play, musical, or one-act sequence that has not been produced professionally or received trade book publication. Only one submission per playwright will be considered. Plays entered previously in the competition may not be resubmitted; previous award winners may not reapply. Send SASE for required application form.

Available to: No restrictions
Deadline: October 1
Apply to: Stanley Drama Award, above address

**Edward Lewis Wallant Book Award**
**c/o Dr. and Mrs. Irving Waltman**
**3 Brighton Road**
**West Hartford, CT 06117**

Ⓕ The *Edward Lewis Wallant Book Award* is presented annually for a novel or collection of short stories significant to American Jews. The work must have been published during the calendar year. A $500 prize and a citation are awarded.

Available to: American writers
Deadline: December 31
Apply to: Above address

**Washington Center for Politics & Journalism**
**PO Box 15201**
**Washington, DC 20003-0201**
**Phone: 202-296-8455**
**E-mail: pol-jrn@wcpj.org**
**Web site: http://www.wcpj.org**
**Fax: 800-858-8365**

Ⓙ Each semester, the *Politics & Journalism Semester* invites about a dozen undergraduate or graduate journalists, whose career goal is political reporting, to Washington for one of two sixteen-week courses, from September to December and from February to May. Students receive a stipend of $2,500 to assist with the cost of relocating to and living in Washington for four months; in return, they must work full-time for the news bureaus to which they are assigned. Students may apply through their participating schools of journalism. Consult the Web site for additional information, application, and a list of participating institutions.

Available to: Undergraduates (at least second-term juniors), recent graduates (within one year), and graduate students
Deadline: Inquire
Apply to: Participating communication and journalism schools; or Politics & Journalism Semester, above address

**Washington Independent Writers**
**Legal and Educational Fund, Inc.**
**PO Box 70437**
**Washington, DC 20024-0437**
**Phone: 703-684-8686**
**E-mail: jamfull@aol.com**

Ⓒ The *Joan G. Sugarman Children's Book Award* of $1,000 is given to the author of a published work of fiction or nonfiction geared to children ages one through fifteen. Write for guidelines.

Available to: Residents of the District of Columbia, Maryland, or Virginia
Deadline: February 28
Apply to: Book Award, above address

**The Washington Post**
**News Department**
**1150 15th Street, NW**
**Washington, DC 20071-7301**
**Web site: www.washingtonpost.com/wp-srv/post/intern/intro.htm**
**Fax: 202-334-5231**

Ⓙ The *Washington Post Summer News Program* offers a paid twelve-week internship for college juniors or seniors and graduate students enrolled in a degree program who have some experience in journalism. Selected interns work full-time as reporters, copy editors, photographers, or artists. Write or consult the Web site for additional information and application.

Available to: See above
Deadline: November 1
Apply to: Summer News Program, above address

Washington State Arts Commission. *See* Artist Trust

**Water-Stone**
**Graduate Liberal Studies Program**
**Hamline University, Mail Stop A1730**
**1536 Hewitt Avenue**
**St. Paul, MN 55104-1284**
**Web site: www.hamline.edu/graduate/gls/1WaterStone.htm**

(P)     The *Jane Kenyon Poetry Prize* biennially offers prizes of $500, $300, and $200, plus publication in *Water-Stone*, for original, unpublished poems. Poets may submit up to three poems, 10 pages total. The $10 entry fee covers a one-year subscription to the review. Send SASE for guidelines.

Available to: No restrictions
Deadline: Inquire for 2003
Apply to: Poetry Prize, above address

(F) (N)     The *Brenda Ueland Prose Prize* biennially offers two prizes of $500 each, plus publication in *Water-Stone*, for original, unpublished fiction and creative nonfiction, maximum length of 5,000 words. Excerpts from longer works are eligible if they can stand on their own. There is a $10 entry fee, which covers a one-year subscription to the review. Send SASE for guidelines.

Available to: No restrictions
Deadline: Submissions accepted September 15-December 15, 2003
Apply to: Prose Prize, above address

**Frank Waters Foundation**
**PO Box 1127**
**Taos, NM 87571**
**E-mail: fwaters@laplaza.org**
**Web site: http://www.taoswolf.com/frankwaters**

(F)     The *Frank Waters Voices of the Southwest Writing Award* offers $2,000 for a novel whose focus is the "non-urban West," by a writer from Arizona, Colorado, Nevada, New Mexico, Texas, or Utah. Send SASE or e-mail for guidelines. The next award will be given in 2003.

Available to: See above
Deadline: December 1
Apply to: Voices of the Southwest, above address

**Thomas J. Watson Foundation**
**293 South Main Street**
**Providence, RI 02903**
**E-mail: WatsonFoundation@Brown.edu**
**Web site: http://www.WatsonFellowship.org**
**Fax: 401-274-1954**

The *Thomas J. Watson Fellowship Program* is designed to give exceptional graduates from fifty participating colleges the freedom to engage in a year of independent study and travel abroad. The Foundation provides fellows an opportunity for "a focused and disciplined *Wanderjahr* of their own devising—to thoroughly explore a particular interest, to test their aspirations and abilities, to view their lives and American society in greater perspective and, concomitantly, to develop a more informed sense of international concern." The fellowship provides a grant of $22,000 to each recipient; fellows whose spouse or dependent child(ren) will accompany them may be eligible for a grant of $31,000. The Program supplies, in addition to the stipend, an amount equal to twelve months' payment of outstanding federally guaranteed student loans (based on 120 months of repayment), to ease the financial burden of fellows during their fellowship year, and to provide encouragement for students to apply for fellowships. Fellows must maintain contact with the Foundation during their year abroad, send quarterly progress reports, and at fellowship's end, submit a report and an accounting of funds. Graduating seniors at participating institutions are eligible for nomination by their institution. Write or consult the Web site for additional information, including list of participating institutions, and application procedures.

Available to: See above
Deadline: November (inquire for exact date)
Apply to: Thomas J. Watson Fellowship Program, above address

**Wesleyan Writers Conference**
**Wesleyan University**
**Middletown, CT 06459-0094**
**Phone: 860-685-3604**
**E-mail: agreene@wesleyan.edu**
**Web site: http://www.wesleyan.edu/writing/conferen.html**
**Fax: 860-685-2441**

(M) The Wesleyan Writers Conference, staffed by award-winning writers, offers full and partial scholarships to participants. Scholarships include the *Joan and John Jakobson Scholarships*, open to writers of fiction, nonfiction, and poetry, and the *Jon Davidoff Scholarships for Journalists*. Teaching fellowships, including the *Barach Fellowship*, are also awarded. Write or consult the Web site for further information and guidelines.

Available to: No restrictions
Deadline: Inquire
Apply to: Fellowship and Scholarship Committee, above address

**West Coast Ensemble**
**Box 38728**
**Los Angeles, CA 90038**
**Web site: www.wcensemble.org**
**Fax: 323-876-8916**

(D) The *Full-Length Play Competition* awards $500 and production (and royalties on any performance beyond an eight-week run) for an unproduced, unpublished full-length play. The play must not have been produced previously in southern California; playwrights seeking a second production of a play produced elsewhere are welcome to submit.

(D) The *Musical Stairs Competition* selects five finalist musicals for presentation in a workshop staged-reading format, with the winner receiving a fully staged production and a prize of $500. Write for information.

Available to: No restrictions
Deadline: December 31 for full-length plays; June 30 for musicals
Apply to: Full-Length Play or Musical Stairs Competition, above address

**West Virginia Commission on the Arts**
**The Cultural Center**
**1900 Kanawha Boulevard East**
**Charleston, WV 25305-0300**
**Phone: 304-558-0220**
**E-mail: gordon.simmons@wvculture.org**
**Web site: www.wvculture.org**

(M) Fellowships of $3,500 are given in alternating years to West Virginia poets, playwrights, and fiction and nonfiction writers. Write, e-mail, or see the Web site for further information.

Available to: West Virginia residents
Deadline: September 1
Apply to: Above address

**Westchester Arts Council**
**31 Mamaroneck Avenue**
**White Plains, NY 10601**
**Phone: 914-428-4220, ext. 230**
**E-mail: council@watsarts.com**

Ⓓ   The *Westchester Prize for New Works* is designed to encourage the creation of new works for premiere in Westchester County. A total of $50,000 is awarded annually to emerging artists, including playwrights. Dramatic works that have been presented previously are not eligible. Applications should include a complete description of the work to be created, the nature of the intended collaboration with a Westchester cultural institution, and plans for installation or presentation, and community outreach. Call for more information.

>   Available to: Current or former residents of Westchester County, or individuals educated there
>   Deadline: June 29
>   Apply to: Joanne Mongelli, Director of Programs, above address

**Western History Association**
**University of New Mexico**
**1080 Mesa Vista Hall**
**Albuquerque, NM 87131-1181**
**E-mail: wha@unm.edu**
**Web site: http://www.unm.edu/~wha/**
**Fax: 505-277-5275**

Ⓝ   The *Robert G. Athearn Book Award* is offered in even-numbered years for a published book on the twentieth century American west that has a copyright date no more than two years old. The Association awards $500 to the author and $500 to the publisher. Write, e-mail, or see the Web site for list of award committee members.

>   Available to: No restrictions
>   Deadline: June 30
>   Apply to: Above address

Ⓝ   The *Caughey Western History Association Prize* annually offers $2,500 to the author of the most outstanding book on the history of the American West. Publishers should submit nominations for books published in the previous calendar year to each member of the award committee. Write, e-mail, or visit the Web site for list of committee members.

>   Available to: No restrictions
>   Deadline: June 30
>   Apply to: Above address

Ⓝ   The *Ewers Book Award* of $500 is given in even-numbered years for the best published book on North American (including Mexico) Indian ethnohistory. Books may be submitted by publishers, who should submit a letter of nomination and a copy of the book to each member of the award committee.

>   Available to: No restrictions
>   Deadline: June 30
>   Apply to: Above address

The *Huntington Library-Western History Association Martin Ridge Fellowship for Study in Western History Award* offers $2,000 and a one-month fellowship at the Huntington Library to Ph.D. recipients or doctoral students in history of the American west. Applicants should send a two-to-three-page description of their project, specifying the materials they plan to consult at the Huntington and indicating progress to date, as well as a brief curriculum vitae, to each member of the award committee. Fellowship recipients are expected to be in continuous residence at the Huntington for one month. Write, e-mail, or see the Web site for list of award committee members.

>   Available to: See above
>   Deadline: August 1
>   Apply to: Above address

The *Sara Jackson Award* offers $500 annually to support graduate student research in western U. S. history. Preference will be given to African-American and other minority students. Write for additional application information and list of award committee members.

Available to: Graduate students
Deadline: August 1
Apply to: Above address

Ⓝ The *W. Turrentine Jackson Award* awards $1,000 in odd-numbered years to a beginning professional historian for a first book on any aspect of the American West. Publishers should submit books published in the two years before the award deadline to each member of the award committee. Write, e-mail, or see the Web site for list of committee members.

Available to: No restrictions
Deadline: June 30
Apply to: Above address

The *Rundell Graduate Student Award* annually offers $1,000 to a doctoral candidate who has completed comprehensive Ph.D. examinations and is researching a dissertation topic in western U. S. history. Write, e-mail, or see the Web site for additional application information.

Available to: Doctoral candidates
Deadline: July 31
Apply to: Above address

The *Dwight L. Smith (ABC-CLIO) Award* of $500 ($300 to the author/editor and $200 to the publisher) is given in even-numbered years to the author/editor and the publisher of a significant bibliography or research tool—either a book or other publication, electronic or otherwise—on any aspect of the history of the American West. Publishers or authors/editors should send nominations and a copy of the work to each member of the award committee.

Available to: No restrictions
Deadline: June 30
Apply to: Above address

The Western History Association offers several other awards, some with lesser monetary stipends, for articles and research on western history. Write or consult the Web site for more information.

**Whetstone**
**Barrington Area Arts Council**
**PO Box 1266**
**Barrington, IL 60011**

Ⓜ The *Whetstone Prize* is given for the best poem, fiction, or creative nonfiction accepted for publication in *Whetstone*, an annual literary journal published by the Barrington Area Arts Council. Winning writers receive a cash award (usually $500 to a single author). Send $5 for a sample copy of the journal and guidelines.

Available to: No restrictions
Deadline: Submissions accepted year-round
Apply to: Whetstone Prize, above address

**White Eagle Coffee Store Press**
**PO Box 383**
**Fox River Grove, IL 60021-0383**
**E-mail: wecspress@aol.com**
**Web site: http://members.aol.com/wecspress**

Ⓕ The *A. E. Coppard Prize for Long Fiction* annually recognizes the author of a long story with $500, publication of a chapbook, and 25 copies of the published book. Fiction writers may submit unpublished stories, from 8,000 to 14,000 words, with a $15 entry fee; for additional manuscripts in the same envelope, $5 each. Writers from any country may apply, but all submitted work must be in English. All entrants receive a copy of the prizewinning chapbook. Send SASE for guidelines.

Available to: No restrictions
Deadline: December 15
Apply to: A. E. Coppard Prize for Long Fiction, above address

**White Pine Press**
**PO Box 236**
**Buffalo, NY 14201**
**E-mail: wpine@whitepine.org**
**Fax: 716-842-0158**

(P)   The *White Pine Press Poetry Prize* offers $1,000 and publication by the Press for a book-length collection of poems by a U. S. author. Poets may submit original typed manuscripts of up to 100 pages. Poems may have been published in periodicals or in limited-edition chapbooks. There is a $20 reading fee. Send SASE for notification of results; manuscripts will not be returned.

Available to: U. S. citizens
Deadline: Submissions accepted July 15-December 1
Apply to: White Pine Press Poetry Prize, above address

**Mrs. Giles Whiting Foundation**
**1133 Avenue of the Americas, 22nd floor**
**New York, NY 10036-6710**

[IN]   Ten *Whiting Writers' Awards,* of $30,000 each, are given in recognition of the quality of current and past writing and in anticipation of outstanding future work. The awards emphasize exceptionally promising emerging talent. *By Internal Nomination Only.*

**Wichita Falls Backdoor Players**
**Box 896**
**Wichita Falls, TX 76307**
**Web site: www.backdoortheatre.org**
**Fax: 940-322-8167**

(D)   The *Annual Backdoor Theatre New Play Project* offers a $500 honorarium, plus travel and housing for a five-week development program, for a full-length unproduced play. Children's plays and musicals are not eligible. See the Web site for additional information.

Available to: No restrictions; playwrights from Texas and surrounding region preferred
Deadline: March 15
Apply to: Artistic Director, New Play Project, above address

**Elie Wiesel Foundation for Humanity**
**529 Fifth Ave, Suite 1802**
**New York, NY 10017**
**E-mail: info@eliewieselfoundation.org**
**Web site: http://www.eliewieselfoundation.org**
**Fax: 212-490-6006**

(N)   The *Elie Wiesel Prize in Ethics Essay Contest* awards prizes of $5,000, $2,500, and $1,500, and two honorable mentions of $500 each, for essays of 3,000 to 4,000 words on one of three suggested topics, which change yearly. Registered full-time juniors or seniors at accredited four-year colleges or universities in the U. S. and Canada are eligible. Essays must be reviewed by a professor at the applicant's school and submitted with a faculty sponsor form. Write, e-mail, or see the Web site for additional information and application materials

Available to: See above
Deadline: December (inquire for exact date)
Apply to: Elie Wiesel Prize in Ethics, above address

**Tennessee Williams/New Orleans Literary Festival**
938 Lafayette Street, Suite 328
New Orleans, Louisiana 70113
E-mail: info@tennesseewilliams.net
Web site: http://www.tennesseewilliams.net/oneact.html
Fax: 504-523-3680

Ⓓ The *Tennessee Williams/New Orleans Literary Festival One-Act Play Competition* offers a cash
prize of $1,000, a reading of the winning play at the festival, and a full production during
the following year's festival. Only professionally unproduced, unpublished one-act plays
on an American subject are eligible. There is a $15 entry fee. Send SASE for information.

Available to: No restrictions
Deadline: December 15
Apply to: Tennessee Williams/New Orleans Literary Festival, One-Act Play Contest, c/o
Creative Writing Workshop, University of New Orleans-Lakefront, New Orleans,
LA 70148


**Woodrow Wilson International Center for Scholars**
One Woodrow Wilson Plaza
1300 Pennsylvania Avenue, N.W.
Washington, DC 20004-3027
Phone: 202/691-4170
E-mail: fellowships@wwic.si.edu
Web site: http://www.wwics.si.edu
Fax: 202-691-4001

The Woodrow Wilson Center awards some twenty to twenty-five fellowships annually in an
international competition. Successful applicants submit outstanding proposals in a broad
range of the social sciences and humanities on national and/or international issues—
topics that intersect with questions of public policy or provide the historical framework
to illuminate important contemporary policy issues. Fellows should be prepared to interact
with policymakers in Washington and with Wilson Center staff working on similar topics.
Applicants must hold a doctorate or have equivalent professional accomplishments.
Fellows are provided offices, access to the Library of Congress, computers or manuscript-
typing services, and research assistants. Fellowships are normally for an academic year,
though a few are available for shorter periods, minimum four months. Stipends normally
range from $20,000 to $60,000; in a few cases, they may reach up to $85,000. The Center
pays travel expenses and seventy-five percent of health insurance premiums for fellows
and immediate dependents. Write, e-mail, or see the Web site for additional information
and application materials.

Available to: See above
Deadline: October 1
Apply to: Scholar Selection and Services Office, above address


**Wind Magazine**
PO Box 24548
Lexington, KY 40524
Web site: http://www.wind.org/publications.htm

Ⓕ The *Wind Magazine Short Fiction Award* gives $500 and publication to a short story of up to
4,000 words. Finalists receive a one-year subscription to the magazine. The entry fee is
$10 per story.

Available to: No restrictions
Deadline: July 30
Apply to: Short Story Competition, above address

Ⓟ The *Joy Bale Boone Poetry Award* gives $500 and publication for a single unpublished poem of
up to 100 lines. The entry fee is $3 per poem.

Available to: No restrictions
Deadline: February 28
Apply to: Poetry Competition, above address

**Winning Writers**
**PO Box 8040**
**New York, NY 10116**
**E-mail: contest2002@winningwriters.com**
**Web site: www.winningwriters.com**

(P)  The *Winning Writers Poetry Contest* awards prizes of $1,000, $500, $250, and $50, plus publication on winningwriters.com, for the best poems on a given subject. (The subject for the 2002 contest was "War.") One to three poems, up to 500 lines, may be submitted. There is a $10 entry fee. See the Web site for more information.

Available to: No restrictions
Deadline: Inquire
Apply to: Poetry Contest, via e-mail or in writing, above address


**Wisconsin Arts Board**
**101 East Wilson Street, 1st floor**
**Madison, WI 53702**
**E-mail: artsboard@arts.state.wi.us**
**Web site: http://www.arts.state.wi.us**
**Fax: 608-267-0380**

(M)  The Wisconsin Arts Board offers fellowships of $8,000 each, to fiction, poetry, essay/criticism, and drama writers in even-numbered years, and to visual artists in odd-numbered years. All applicants should be Wisconsin residents. Full-time degree-credit students are not eligible. Write or see Web site for detailed guidelines and application form.

Available to: Wisconsin residents
Deadline: September 16
Apply to: Above address


**Wisconsin Historical Society**
**816 State Street**
**Madison, WI 53706-1488**
**Web site: http://www.shsw.wisc.edu/research/fellowships.html**
**Fax: 608-264-6404**

The *John C. Geilfuss, Amy Louise Hunter,* and *Alice E. Smith Fellowships* support research and writing for publication either in the *Wisconsin Magazine of History* or (in book form) by the Wisconsin Historical Society Press. Topics on any subject in Wisconsin history are eligible; all applications are automatically considered for all three awards. Grants vary in size, depending on the nature of the project, but usually are between $500 and $1,000 for an article-length work, and between $1,500 and $3,000 for a book-length work. The Press has the right of first refusal for any manuscripts developed with these awards. Full guidelines and downloadable application form can be found on the Web site.

Available to: No restrictions
Deadline: Applications accepted year-round; evaluated in January, April, July, and October
Apply to: Fellowship Program, Division of Public History, above address.

**Wisconsin Institute for Creative Writing**
**University of Wisconsin**
**Department of English**
**600 North Park Street**
**Madison, WI 53706**
**Web site: http://creativewriting.wisc.edu**

Ⓕ Ⓟ The *Carl Djerassi, Jay C. and Ruth Halls, Carol Houck Smith, Diane Middlebrook,* and *James McCreight Fellowships,* each $25,000, offer an academic year as artists-in-residence at the University of Wisconsin to six writers working on a first book of poetry or fiction. Fellows teach one introductory creative writing workshop per semester and give one public reading from their work in progress. Consult the Web site or send SASE for guidelines.

> Available to: Poets and fiction writers with an MA, MFA, or equivalent degree in creative writing who have not yet published a book
> Deadline: February (inquire for exact date)
> Apply to: Jesse Lee Kercheval, Director, above address

**The Thomas Wolfe Society**
**c/o Dr. James Clark, Jr.**
**807 Gardner Street**
**Raleigh, NC 27607**

Ⓝ The *Zelda & Paul Gitlin Literary Prize* awards $1,000 for the best scholarly article on Thomas Wolfe published during the preceding calendar year. Although it is the appointed Prize Committee that annually makes the decision pertaining to the winner, all the Society's members are encouraged to bring to the committee's chairman's attention any article on Thomas Wolfe that is of significant scholarly interest. Articles that have received the Thomas Wolfe Student Prize are not eligible. See the Web site for more information

> Available to: See above
> Deadline: Inquire
> Apply to: Chair of the Literary Prize Committee, above address

Ⓕ The *North Carolina Writers' Network Thomas Wolfe Fiction Prize* awards $1,000 and possible publication for a previously unpublished novel or short story. There is a $7 entry fee. See the Web site www.ncwriters.org/twfp.htm for more information.

> Available to: No restrictions
> Deadline: August 31
> Apply to: Thomas Wolfe Fiction Prize, North Carolina Writers' Network, 3501 Highway 54 West, Studio C, Chapel Hill, NC 27516

Ⓝ The *Thomas Wolfe Student Essay Prize* offers $500 to an undergraduate or graduate student for an essay related to Wolfe or his works. The winner will be invited to deliver the winning essay at the annual meeting of the Society. Submissions should be in English, 8 to 15 double-spaced, typed pages.

> Available to: No restrictions
> Deadline: January 15
> Apply to: Thomas Wolfe Student Essay Prize, above address

**Carter G. Woodson Institute for Afro-American and African Studies**
**University of Virginia**
**108 Minor Hall**
**Charlottesville, VA 22904-4162**
**Web site: http://www.virginia.edu/~woodson**
**Fax: 804-924-8820**

The *Carter G. Woodson Institute Predoctoral and Postdoctoral Residential Research Fellowships* are awarded to eligible scholars whose work focuses on race, ethnicity, and society in Africa and the Atlantic world (broadly defined as the African Diaspora). Predoctoral fellowships, covering two years, carry an annual stipend of $15,000. Postdoctoral fellowships, covering one year, carry a stipend of $25,000. Fellows must be in residence at the university for the duration of the award period and are expected to make periodic presentations of their work to the Woodson fellows and the larger academic community. Write or see the Web site for additional information.

Available to: No restrictions
Deadline: December 1
Apply to: Selection Committee, Residential Research Fellowships, above address

**Word Press**
**PO Box 541106**
**Cincinnati, OH 45254-1106**
**Web site: www.wordtechweb.com/wordpress**

Ⓟ The annual *Word Poetry Prize* offers $1,000 and publication of winning manuscripts by Word Press. There is a $25 reading fee (add $5 to receive a copy of the winning book). Consult the Web site for more information.

Available to: No restrictions
Deadline: Submissions accepted October 1-November 1
Apply to: Above address

**Word Works**
**Box 42164**
**Washington, DC 20015**
**E-mail: editor@wordworksdc.com**
**Web site: www.wordworksdc.org**

Ⓟ The *Washington Prize* awards $1,500 and publication by Word Works for an unpublished volume of original poetry of outstanding literary merit by a living American poet. Send SASE for guidelines and application procedures.

Available to: U. S. citizens
Deadline: Submissions accepted February 1-March 1
Apply to: Washington Prize, above address

**World Hunger Year**
**505 Eighth Avenue, 21st floor**
**New York, NY 10018-6582**
**Phone: 212-629-8850, ext. 122**
**E-mail: media@worldhungeryear.org**
**Web site: http://www.worldhungeryear.org**

Ⓙ The *Harry Chapin Media Awards* are given to "encourage better and more extensive reporting on issues broadly related to hunger and poverty." Awards of $2,500 each are given for the year's best journalism in the following categories: books, broadcast media, periodicals, newspapers, and photojournalism. Write, e-mail, or consult the Web site for further information and guidelines.

Available to: No restrictions
Deadline: January 18
Apply to: Harry Chapin Media Awards, above address

World Literature Today
University of Oklahoma
110 Monnet Hall
Norman, OK 73019-4033
Web site: http://www.ou.edu/worldlit/

[IN] The *Neustadt International Prize for Literature* is given to honor a life's work, or to direct attention to an outstanding writer whose literary career is still in progress. Political and geographic considerations do not enter into the selection, which is made by an international jury. One prize of $50,000 is given in even-numbered years. *By Internal Nomination Only.*

Writers Colony at Dairy Hollow
515 Spring Street
Eureka Springs, AR 72632
E-mail: director@writerscolony.org
Web site: http://www.writerscolony.org

® Residences of two to twelve weeks are available at Dairy Hollow, located in the Ozark Mountains. Residents are provided with private living/work space and meals (breakfast and lunch are self-service; dinner is served in an inn dining room five nights a week). The actual daily cost per resident is $125, and each resident is asked to contribute; however, demonstrable talent, self-discipline, and achievement are the only criteria for a residence. For every thirty days' residence, each writer is asked to contribute one day of community service within the region. There is a $35 application fee. Write, e-mail, or see the Web site for application.

Available to: No restrictions
Deadline: Inquire
Apply to: Above address or online@writerscolony.org

The Writers Community
YMCA of the USA
101 North Wacker Drive
Chicago, IL 60606
Phone: 800-872-9622 extension 515

The Writers Community of the YMCA National Writer's Voice funds semester-long residences at select YMCA Writer's Voice centers nationwide to established poets, fiction and nonfiction writers, playwrights, and children's book authors. Residents teach a master-level workshop and give a public reading. In recent years, writers received $5,500 each. Each center selects a local writer according to its own guidelines; centers should be contacted directly for application information.

Available to: Accomplished writers with experience and interest in teaching
Deadline: Inquire
Apply to: Above address for nationwide list of Writer's Voice centers

Writers' Conferences & Centers
c/o Associated Writing Programs
MSN 1E3
George Mason University
Fairfax, VA 22030
Web site: http://awpwriter.org/contests/

Writers' Conferences & Centers conducts an annual competition to provide scholarships for emerging writers who wish to attend a writers' conference. Two scholarships of $500 each will be awarded and applied to the fees of any of the member conferences of WC&C, an association of conferences, colonies, and festivals for writers. There is a $10 reading fee for each manuscript submitted. Send SASE or see the Web site for guidelines.

Available to: No restrictions
Deadline: Submissions must be postmarked in January or February
Apply to: WC&C Scholarship Program, PO Box 386, Amherst, MA 01004, Attn: Michael Pettit

**Writer's Digest**
**1507 Dana Avenue**
**Cincinnati, OH 45207**
**E-mail: competitions@fwpubs.com**
**Web site: http://www.writersdigest.com**

Ⓜ The *Writer's Digest Annual Writing Competition* offers more than $25,000 in prizes, to be awarded in ten categories, with one grand-prize-winner chosen from all entries. The grand prize package includes $1,500 and the winner's choice of a trip to New York City to meet with editors and agents, or a trip to the 2003 Maui Writers Conference. Original unpublished manuscripts may be entered in the following categories: personal essay/memoir, feature article, literary/mainstream short story, genre short story, rhyming poetry, nonrhyming poetry, stage play, television/movie script, children's fiction, and inspirational writing. There is a $10 entry fee for each manuscript except poetry: the fee for the first poem is $10, and $5 for each additional poem. See the Web site for rules and entry form.

Available to: No restrictions
Deadline: May 15
Apply to: Writing Competition, above address

**Writers Group of the Triad**
**4642 West Market Street**
**PMB 316**
**Greensboro, NC 27407-1285**
**Web site: www.people-places.com/triadwriters**

Ⓕ Ⓟ The *Greensboro Awards in Poetry and in Fiction* of $500 each are awarded for the best entry of five poems and for the best work of short fiction no longer than 4,000 words. There is a $10 entry fee for each entry. See the Web site for more details.

Available to: See above
Deadline: April 30
Apply to: Above address

**Writers at Work**
**PO Box 540370**
**North Salt Lake, UT 84054-0370**
**Phone: 801-292-9285**
**Web site: http://www.writersatwork.org**

Ⓜ Writers at Work sponsors a fellowship competition in fiction (short stories or novel excerpts), literary nonfiction, and poetry. The first prize in each category consists of $1,500, publication in *Quarterly West*, a featured reading, and tuition to the afternoon session at the Writers at Work summer conference in Park City, Utah. Second-place winners each receive $500 and tuition to the afternoon session at the conference. Eligible are writers who have not published a book-length volume of original work. Fiction and literary nonfiction submissions should not exceed 20 pages; poetry may be six poems not exceeding 10 pages total. Only unpublished work will be considered. A $15 reading fee and two SASEs are also requested. Send a copy of the manuscript with a cover letter including name, address, phone number, and title; title only should appear on the manuscript. Manuscripts are not returned. See the Web site for more information.

Available to: See above
Deadline: March 1
Apply to: Fellowship Competition (specify fiction, nonfiction, or poetry), above address

**WritersBlok**
**2201 Sherman St**
**Longmont, CO 80501**
**Web site: webster@writersblok.com**
**Fax: 970-461-0820**

Ⓕ The *WritersBlok Short Story Contest* offers prizes of $1,000, $250, and $75 for unpublished short stories of up to 15,000 words. Winners, whose work is published and featured on

BookLocker.com, collect eighty percent of sales profits. There is a $25 entry fee; additional entries are $5 each. Send SASE or e-mail for guidelines.

Available to: No restrictions
Deadline: Inquire
Apply to: Short Story Contest, above address


**Writers' League of Texas**
**1501 West 5th Street, Suite E-2**
**Austin, TX 78703**
**Phone: 512-499-8914**
**E-mail: awl@writersleague.org**
**Web site: http://www.writersleague.org**
**Fax: 512-499-0441**

The Writers' League of Texas (formerly known as Austin Writers' League) distributes state funds in literature for the Texas Commission on the Arts to foster growth and excellence of the literary arts in Texas. The League provides professional opportunities for Texas writers and supports projects that expand public participation in the literary arts. Grants may be given for projects (up to $3,000) or for operations (up to $6,000); funds must support activities based in Texas. Write or e-mail for guidelines.

Available to: Texas writers and Texas-based organizations
Deadline: December 10
Apply to: Above address

Ⓜ The *Violet Crown Book Awards* honor outstanding books published by Writers' League of Texas members. The awards offer a $1,000 stipend and a trophy in fiction, nonfiction, or literary work (poetry, essays, short stories). Books must have been published between July 1 preceding the award year and June 30 of the award year. A $10 entry fee is required. Membership in the League is $50 annually; writers may join when submitting their entry.

Available to: League members
Deadline: June 30
Apply to: Violet Crown Book Awards, above address

Ⓒ The *Teddy Book Award* honors an outstanding children's book published by a Writers' League of Texas member. The award consists of a $1,000 cash stipend and a trophy. Books may be fiction or nonfiction, picture book to young adult. A $10 entry fee is required. Membership in the League is $50 annually; writers may join when submitting their entry.

Available to: League members
Deadline: May 1
Apply to: Teddy Book Award, above address


**The Writers Workshop**
**387 Beaucatcher Road**
**Asheville, NC 28805**
**Phone: 828-254-8111**
**E-mail: writrwkshp@aol.com**

Ⓕ The *Mystery Contest* offers a cash award of $2,250 to the best mystery story of up to 10,000 words. Works must be unpublished. The author's name, address, and phone number should appear only on cover sheet, with the story title. The author may submit up to six stories. There is a $20 reading fee per story.

Available to: No restrictions
Deadline: October 31
Apply to: Above address

**Helene Wurlitzer Foundation of New Mexico**
**Box 1891**
**Taos, NM 87571**
**Phone: 505-758-2559**
**E-mail: hwf@taosnet.com**
**Fax: 505-758-2559**

® Residences in Taos, with free housing and utilities, are available from April through September, and on a limited basis from October through March. Residents must provide their own food and materials. Families are not accepted. Residences are booked well in advance; however, the Foundation does occasionally receive cancellations. Send SASE or fax request for application.

Available to: No restrictions
Deadline: January 18
Apply to: Michael A. Knight, Executive Director, above address

**Wyoming Arts Council**
**2320 Capitol Avenue**
**Cheyenne, WY 82002**
**Phone: 307-777-7742**
**E-mail: mshay@missc.state.wy.us**
**Web site: http://spacr.state.wy.us/cr/arts**
**Fax: 307-777-5499**

Ⓜ Up to four *Literary Fellowships* of $2,000 each are offered annually to writers who are legal residents of Wyoming, at least eighteen years old, and not full-time students.

Available to: See above
Deadline: July 15
Apply to: Above address

Ⓜ The *Neltje Blanchan Award*, given to a Wyoming writer whose work, in any genre, is inspired by nature, and the *Frank Nelson Doubleday Memorial Award*, given to a Wyoming woman writer in any creative genre, each carry a stipend of $1,000. Applicants must submit up to 25 pages of prose or 10 of poetry, published or unpublished. Write for guidelines.

Available to: Wyoming residents
Deadline: May 1
Apply to: Blanchan Award or Doubleday Award, above address

**Xeric Foundation**
**PMB 214**
**351 Pleasant Street**
**Northampton, MA 01060**
**E-mail: xericgrant@aol.com**
**Web site: www.xericfoundation.com**

Grants of up to $5,000 are offered to assist comic book creators with some of the costs of self-publishing (physical production and distribution, printing, color separation, solicitation, shipping). Grants are not intended to support an artist/writer fully through the process of self-publishing, but rather to encourage creators to learn from the experience of working toward such a goal. Write for additional information and application.

Available to: U. S. and Canadian residents
Deadline: January 31 and July 31
Apply to: Above address

**Yaddo**
**Box 395**
**Saratoga Springs, NY 12866**
**E-mail: chwait@yaddo.org**
**Fax: 518-584-1312**

® Invitations are extended to writers of any nationality who have published work of high artistic merit and are currently engaged in another project, and to unpublished writers working at professional levels in their fields, to spend two weeks to two months at Yaddo, a working community for writers, visual artists, composers, choreographers, performance artists, and film and video artists. Samples of work must be submitted, together with application form, letters of recommendation, and application fee of $20. Applicants are judged on their artistic merit and professional promise. Awards include room, board, and studio. Up to $1,000 in financial aid is available for writers who might otherwise be unable to accept an invitation to visit. There are no limitations on how the funds are used (child care, travel expenses, rent, etc.). Yaddo is open year-round, except for a short period in early September, and accommodates up to thirty-five artists at a time. Write for additional information and application form. Inquiries are accepted by e-mail but no forms will be transmitted or applications accepted by e-mail.

Available to: See above
Deadline: January 15 for residences starting mid-May of the same year through February of the following year; August 1 for residences starting late October of the same year through May of the following year
Apply to: Admissions Committee, above address

**Yale University Library**
**Beinecke Rare Book and Manuscript Library**
**PO Box 208240**
**New Haven, CT 06520**

[IN] The *Bollingen Prize* of $50,000 is awarded biennially to the American poet whose work represents the highest achievement in the field of American poetry, on the basis of a review of publications during the previous two years. The next award will be given in February 2003. *By Internal Nomination Only.*

**Yale University Press**
**PO Box 209040**
**New Haven, CT 06520-9040**
**Web site: http://www.yale.edu/yup/poetry.html**

(P) Yale University Press publishes one new book of poetry annually as part of the *Yale Series of Younger Poets*. Selection is made through a competition open to any U. S. citizen under age forty who has not previously published a volume of poetry. The author receives royalties. Manuscripts should be 48 to 64 pages in length. An application fee of $15 is required. Send SASE for submission guidelines.

Available to: See above
Deadline: Submissions accepted in January
Apply to: Editor, Yale Series of Younger Poets, above address

**Young Adult Library Services Association**
**American Library Association**
**50 East Huron Street**
**Chicago, IL 60611**
**E-mail: yalsa@ala.org**
**Web sites: http://www.ala.org/yalsa/edwards and www.ala.org/yalsa/printz**

(C) The *Margaret A. Edwards Award*, co-sponsored by *School Library Journal*, honors an author's lifetime achievement for writing books that have been popular with teenagers over a period of time. The award consists of a $2,000 prize and a citation presented at the ALA Annual Conference. Anyone may submit nominations. Write, e-mail, or see the Web site for nomination forms.

Available to: No restrictions
Deadline: June 1
Apply to: Margaret A. Edwards Award, above address

**Young Playwrights, Inc.**
**306 West 38th Street, Suite 300**
**New York, NY 10018**
**Phone: 212-307-1140**
**E-mail: writeaplay@aol.com**
**Web site: http://www.youngplaywrights.org**
**Fax: 212-307-1454**

Ⓓ The *Young Playwrights Festival National Playwriting Competition* annually involves playwrights age eighteen and under. Winners are brought to New York City for a weeklong conference, which culminates in staged readings of the winning plays. Some may be selected for professional production, for which royalties will be paid. There are no restrictions on style, subject, length, or number of submissions. Adaptations of works by others, screenplays, and musicals are not accepted. The e-mail address is for inquiries only.

Available to: See above
Deadline: December 1
Apply to: Young Playwrights Festival, above address

**Zoetrope: All-Story**
**1350 Avenue of the Americas, 24th floor**
**New York, NY 10019**
**E-mail: contests@all-story.com**
**Web site: http://www.zoetrope-stories.com**

Ⓕ The *Sam Adams Short Story Contest* annually awards a full scholarship, with roundtrip airfare, to the weeklong Zoetrope Short Story Writers Workshop at Francis Ford Coppola's Blancaneaux Lodge in Belize, to the writer of an unpublished short story of up to 5,000 words. Send SASE or see the Web site for guidelines.

Available to: No restrictions
Deadline: April 15
Apply to: Sam Adams Short Story Contest, above address

Ⓕ The *Zoetrope Short Fiction Contest* annually offers a first prize of $1,000, a second of $500, and a third of $250 for an unpublished short story of up to 5,000 words. Send SASE for guidelines. E-mail and fax submissions are not accepted.

Available to: No restrictions
Deadline: October 1
Apply to: Zoetrope Short Fiction Contest, above address

**Zone 3**
**Austin Peay State University**
**PO Box 4565**
**Clarksville, TN 37044**
**Phone: 931-221-7031**

Ⓟ The *Rainmaker Awards in Poetry* offer a first prize of $500 and publication in *Zone 3* for an original unpublished poem. A second prize of $300 and a third of $100 are also given. Poets may submit up to three poems. The entry fee of $8 covers a year's subscription to *Zone 3*.

Available to: No restrictions
Deadline: Ongoing
Apply to: Rainmaker Awards in Poetry, above address

# APPENDIX: STATE ARTS COUNCILS

Below, listed alphabetically by state, is relevant information for contacting state arts councils throughout the United States (as well as arts councils in the District of Columbia, Puerto Rico, and the U. S. Virgin Islands). Literature programs vary from state to state. To be eligible for funding, writers must be residents of the state or territory to whose arts council they are applying.

*Alabama State Council on the Arts*
Randy Shoults, Literature Program Manager
201 Monroe Street
Montgomery, AL 36130-1800
334-242-4076
E-mail: randy@arts.state.al.us
Web site: http://www.arts.state.al.us
Fax: 334-240-3269

*Alaska State Council on the Arts*
Kay Carlo, Grants Administrator
411 West 4th Avenue, Suite 1E
Anchorage, AK 99501-2343
907-269-6610
E-mail: aksa_info@eed.state.ak.us
Web site: http://www.aksca.org
Fax: 907-269-6601

*Arizona Commission on the Arts*
Paul Morris, Literature Director
417 West Roosevelt
Phoenix, AZ 85003
602-255-5882
E-mail: pmorros@ArizonaArts.org
Web site: http://www.arizonaarts.org
Fax: 602-256-0282

*Arkansas Arts Council*
George Mitchell, Executive Director
1500 Tower Building
323 Center Street
Little Rock, AR 72201
501-324-9766
E-mail: info@arkansasarts.com
Web site: http://www.arkansasarts.com
Fax: 501-324-9207

*California Arts Council*
Barry Hesserius, Director
1300 I Street, Suite 930
Sacramento, CA 95814
916-322-6555
E-mail: cac@cwo.com
Web site: http://www.cac.ca.gov
Fax: 916-322-6575

*Colorado Council on the Arts and Humanities*
Kelleen Zubick, Associate Director
750 Pennsylvania Street
Denver, CO 80203-3699
303-894-2617
E-mail: coloarts@artswire.org
Web site: http://www.coloarts.state.co.us
Fax: 303-894-2615

*Connecticut Commission on the Arts*
Douglas Evans, Executive Director
755 Main Street
1 Financial Plaza
Hartford, CT 06103
860-566-4770
E-mail: artsinfo@ctarts.org
Web site: http://www.ctarts.com
Fax: 860-566-6462

*Delaware Division of the Arts*
Peggy Amsterdam, Executive Director
Carvel State Office Building
820 North French Street
Wilmington, DE 19801
302-577-8278
E-mail: delarts@state.de.us
Web site: http://www.artsdel.org
Fax: 302-577-6561

*District of Columbia Commission on the Arts and Humanities*
Anthony Gittens, Executive Director
410 8th Street, NW, 5th floor
Washington, DC 20004
202-724-5613
E-mail: darts@dc.gov
Web site: http://www.dcarts.dc.gov
Fax: 202-727-4135

*Florida Division of Cultural Affairs*
JuDee L. Pettijohn, Executive Director
Florida Department of State
1001 DeSoto Park Drive
Tallahassee, FL 32399-0250
850-487-2980
E-mail: culturalaffairs@mail.dos.state.fl.us
Web site: http://www.dos.state.fl.us/dca
Fax: 850-922-5259

*Georgia Council for the Arts*
Betsy Baker, Executive Director
260 14th Street, Suite 401
Atlanta, GA 30318
404-685-2787
E-mail: info@arts-ga.com
Web site: http://www.gaarts.org
Fax: 404-651-7922

*Hawaii State Foundation on Culture and the Arts*
Ronald Yamakawa, Executive Director
250 South Hotel Street, 2nd floor
Honolulu, HI 96813
808-586-0300
E-mail: sfca@sfca.state.hi.us
Web site: http://www.state.hi.us/sfca
Fax: 808-586-0308

*Idaho Commission on the Arts*
Cort Conley, Literature Director
PO Box 83720
Boise, ID 83720-0008
208-334-2119
E-mail: cconley@ica.state.id.us
Web site: http://www.state.id.us/arts
Fax: 208-334-2488

*Illinois Arts Council*
Rhoda Pierce, Executive Director
James R. Thompson Center
100 West Randolph, Suite 10-500
Chicago, IL 60601
312-814-6750
E-mail: info@arts.state.il.us
Web site: http://www.state.il.us/agency/iac
Fax: 312-814-1471

*Indiana Arts Commission*
Bobbie Garver, Community Development
  Specialist
402 West Washington, Room W072
Indianapolis, IN 46204-2243
317-232-1268
E-mail: arts@state.in.us
Web site: http://www.state.in.us/iac
Fax: 317-232-5595

*Iowa Arts Council*
Anita Walker, Executive Director
Capitol Complex
600 East Locust
Des Moines, IA 50319-0290
515-281-6412
E-mail: kathy.davidson@dca.state.ia.us
Web site: http://www.dca.state.ia.us
Fax: 515-242-6498

*Kansas Arts Commission*
David Wilson, Executive Director
700 SW Jackson, Suite 1004
Topeka, KS 66603
785-296-3335
E-mail: kac@arts.state.ks.us
Web site: http://arts.state.ks.us/
  programs.html
Fax: 785-296-4989

*Kentucky Arts Council*
Gerri Combs, Executive Director
Old Capitol Annex
300 West Broadway
Frankfort, KY 40601
502-564-3757
E-mail: kyarts@mail.state.ky.us
Web site: http://www.kyarts.org
Fax: 502-564-2839

*Louisiana Division of the Arts*
Pam Breaux, Executive Director
PO Box 44247
Baton Rouge, LA 70804-4247
225-342-8180
E-mail: arts@crt.state.la.us
Web site: http://www.crt.state.la.us/arts
Fax: 225-342-8173

*Maine State Arts Commission*
Alden C. Wilson, Executive Director
193 State Street
25 State House Station
Augusta, ME 04333-0025
207-287-2724
E-mail: alden.wilson@state.me.us
Web site: http://www.mainearts.com
Fax: 207-287-2725

*Maryland State Arts Council*
Theresa Colvin, Executive Director
175 West Ostend Street, SE
Baltimore, MD 21230
410-767-6555
E-mail: pdunne@mdbusiness.state.md.us
Web site: http://www.msac.org
Fax: 410-333-1062

*Massachusetts Cultural Council*
Mary Kelley, Executive Director
10 St. James Avenue, 3rd floor
Boston, MA 02116-4600
617-727-3668
E-mail: mary.kelley@art.state.ma.us
Web site: http://www.massculturalcouncil.org
Fax: 617-727-0044

*Michigan Council for Arts and Cultural Affairs*
Betty Boone, Executive Director
525 West Ottawa
PO Box 30705
Lansing, MI 48909
517-241-4011
Web site: http://www.cis.state.mi.us/arts
Fax: 517-241-3979

Also:
*ArtServe Michigan*
George Orban, Program Director
17515 West Nine Mile Road, Suite 250
Southfield, MI 48075
248-557-8288
E-mail: advocacy@artservemichigan.org
Web site: http://www.artservemichigan.org
Fax: 248-557-8581

*Minnesota State Arts Board*
Robert C. Booker, Executive Director
Park Square Court
400 Sibley Street, Suite 200
Saint Paul, MN 55101-1928
651-215-1600
E-mail: msab@arts.state.mn.us
Web site: http://www.arts.state.mn.us
Fax: 651-215-1602

*Mississippi Arts Commission*
Tim Hedgepeth, Executive Director
239 North Lamar Street, Suite 207
Jackson, MS 39201
601-359-6030
E-mail: hedgepet@arts.state.ms.ud
Web site: http://www.arts.state.ms.us
Fax: 601-359-6008

*Missouri Arts Council*
Norree Boyd, Executive Director
Wainwright State Office Complex
111 North Seventh Street, Suite 105
Saint Louis, MO 63101-2188
314-340-6845
E-mail: moarts@mail.state.mo.us
Web site: http://www.missouriartscouncil.org
Fax: 314-340-7215

*Montana Arts Council*
Arlynn Fishbaugh, Executive Director
PO Box 202201
Helena, MT 59620-2201
406-444-6430
E-mail: mac@state.mt.us
Web site: http://www.mt.gov/art
Fax: 406-444-6548

*Nebraska Arts Council*
Suzanne Wise, Executive Director
St. Joslyn Carriage House
3838 Davenport
Omaha, NE 68131-2329
402-595-2122
E-mail: swise@nebraskaartscouncil.org
Web site: http://www.nebraskaartscouncil.org
Fax: 402-595-2334

*Nevada Arts Council*
Susan Boskoff, Executive Director
716 North Carson Street, Suite A
Carson City, NV 89703
775-687-6680
E-mail: seboskof@clan.lib.nv.us
Web site: http://dmla.clan.lib.nv.us/docs/arts
Fax: 702-687-6688

*New Hampshire State Council on the Arts*
Rebecca Lawrence, Director
40 North Main Street
Concord, NH 03301-4974
603-271-2789
E-mail: rlawrence@nharts.state.nh.us
Web site: http://www.state.nh.us/nharts
Fax: 603-271-3584

*New Jersey State Council on the Arts*
David Miller, Executive Director
20 West State Street
PO Box 306
Trenton, NJ 08625-0306
609-292-6130
E-mail: david@arts.sos.state.nj.us
Web site: http://www.njartscouncil.org
Fax: 609-989-1440

*New Mexico Arts*
Division of the Office of Cultural Affairs
Margaret Brommelsiek, Executive Director
PO Box 1450
Santa Fe, NM 87501-1450
505-827-6490
E-mail: NMAegrants@lvr.state.nm.us
Web site: http://www.nmarts.org
Fax: 505-827-6043

*New York State Council on the Arts*
Nicolette B. Clarke, Executive Director
175 Varick Street
New York, NY 10014
212-627-4455
E-mail: nclarke@nysca.org
Web site: http://www.nysca.org
Fax: 212-387-7164

Also:
*New York Foundation for the Arts*
Theodore S. Berger, Executive Director
155 Avenue of the Americas, 14th floor
New York, NY 10013-1507
212-366-6900
E-mail: nyfaweb@nyfa.org
Web site: http://www.nyfa.org
Fax: 212-366-1778

*North Carolina Arts Council*
Mary Regan, Executive Director
Department of Cultural Resources
Raleigh, NC 27699-4632
919-733-2111
E-mail: ncarts@ncmail.net
Web site: http://www.ncarts.org
Fax: 919-733-4834

*North Dakota Council on the Arts*
Jan Webb, Executive Director
418 East Broadway, Suite 70
Bismarck, ND 58501-4086
701-328-3954
E-mail: comserv@state.nd.us
Web site: http://www.state.nd.us/arts
Fax: 701-328-3963

*Ohio Arts Council*
Wayne Lawson, Executive Director
727 East Main Street
Columbus, OH 43205-1796
614-466-2613
E-mail: kemerick@oac.state.oh.us
Web site: http://www.oac.state.oh.us
Fax: 614-466-4494

*Oklahoma Arts Council*
Betty Price, Executive Director
PO Box 52001-2001
Oklahoma City, OK 73152-2001
405-521-2931
E-mail: okarts@arts.state.ok.us
Web site: http://www.state.ok.us/~arts
Fax: 405-521-6418

*Oregon Arts Commission*
Christine D'Arcy, Director
775 Summer Street, NE, Suite 200
Salem, OR 97301-1284
503-986-0082
E-mail: oregon.artscomm@state.or.us
Web site: http://art.econ.state.or.us
Fax: 503-986-0260

*Pennsylvania Council on the Arts*
Philip Horn, Executive Director
Finance Building, Room 216
Harrisburg, PA 17120
717-787-6883
E-mail: phorn@state.pa.us
Web site: http://artsnet.heinz.cmu.edu/pca
Fax: 717-783-2538

*Rhode Island State Council on the Arts*
Randall Rosenbaum, Executive Director
83 Park Street, 6th floor
Providence, RI 02903
401-222-3880
E-mail: info@risca.state.ri.us
Web site: http://www.risca.state.ri.us
Fax: 401-222-3018

*South Carolina Arts Commission*
Sara June Goldstein, Program Director for
  Literary Arts
1800 Gervais Street
Columbia, SC 29201
803-734-8696
E-mail: goldstsa@arts.state.sc.us
Web site: http://www.state.sc.us/arts
Fax: 803-734-8526

*South Dakota Arts Council*
Dennis Holub, Executive Director
800 Governors Drive
Pierre, SD 57501-2294
605-773-3131
E-mail: sdac@stlib.state.sd.us
Web site: http://www.state.sd.us/deca/
  sdarts/
Fax: 605-773-6962

*Tennessee Arts Commission*
Dennis Adkins, Director, Literary Arts
Citizens Plaza
401 Charlotte Avenue
Nashville, TN 37243-0780
615-741-1701
E-mail: dennis.adkins@state.tn.us
Web site: http://www.arts.state.tn.us
Fax: 615-741-8559

*Texas Commission on the Arts*
John Paul Batiste, Executive Director
PO Box 13406
Capitol Station
Austin, TX 78711-3406
512-463-5535
E-mail: jbatiste@arts.state.tx.us
Web site: http://www.arts.state.tx.us
Fax: 512-475-2699

*Utah Arts Council*
Guy Lebeda, Literary Coordinator
617 East South Temple Street
Salt Lake City, UT 84102-1177
801-236-7555
E-mail: glebeda@arts.state.ut.us
Web site: http://www.dced.state.ut.us/arts
Fax: 801-236-7556

*Vermont Arts Council*
Michele Bailey, Director of Artist Programs
136 State Street, Drawer 33
Montpelier, VT 05633-6001
802-828-3291
E-mail: info@vermontartscouncil.org
Web site: http://www.vermontartscouncil.org
Fax: 802-828-3363

*Virginia Commission for the Arts*
Peggy J. Baggett, Executive Director
Lewis House, 2nd floor
223 Governor Street
Richmond, VA 23219-2010
804-225-3132
E-mail: arts@state.va.us
Web site: http://www.arts.state.va.us
Fax: 804-255-4327

*Washington State Arts Commission*
Kris Tucker, Executive Director
PO Box 42675
234 East 8th Street
Olympia, WA 98504-2675
360-753-3860
E-mail: krist@wsac.wa.gov
Web site: http://www.wa.gov/art
Fax: 360-586-5351

*West Virginia Division of Culture and History*
Bob Eggleton, Director
The Cultural Center
1900 Kanawha Boulevard East
Charleston, WV 25305-0300
304-558-0220
E-mail: bob.eggleton@wvculture.org
Web site: http://www.wvlc.wvent.edu/
   culture/arts.html
Fax: 304-558-2779

*Wisconsin Arts Board*
Mark Fraire, Grant Programs and Services
   Specialist
101 East Wilson Street, 1st floor
Madison, WI 53702
608-266-0190
E-mail: artsboard@arts.state.wi.us
Web site: http://www.arts.state.wi.us
Fax: 608-267-0380

*Wyoming Arts Council*
John G. Coe, Executive Director
2320 Capitol Avenue
Cheyenne, WY 82002
307-777-7742
E-mail: jcoe@state.wy.us
Web site: http://wyoarts.state.wy.us
Fax: 307-777-5499

PUERTO RICO

*Institute of Puerto Rican Culture*
Teresa Tio, Executive Director
PO Box 9024184
San Juan, PR 00902-4184
787-725-5137
Web site: http://www.nasaa-arts.org/aoa/
   pr.html
Fax: 787-724-8393

U. S. VIRGIN ISLANDS

*Virgin Islands Council on the Arts*
John Jowers, Executive Director
PO Box 103
St. Thomas, VI 00802
340-774-5984
E-mail: vicouncil@islands.vi
Web site: http://www.nasaa-arts.org/aoa/
   vi.shtml
Fax: 340-774-6206

# INDEX OF AWARDS

# INDEX OF ORGANIZATIONS

# INDEX OF CATEGORIES

## POETRY/℗

## DRAMA / Ⓓ

## SCREENWRITING/Ⓢ

## MULTIPLE LISTING/Ⓜ

WRITERS' RESIDENCES / ®